Methods of
Experimental Physics

VOLUME 4

ATOMIC AND ELECTRON PHYSICS

PART B

FREE ATOMS

METHODS OF EXPERIMENTAL PHYSICS:

L. Marton, *Editor-in-Chief*

Claire Marton, *Assistant Editor*

Volume 4

Atomic and Electron Physics

PART B

Free Atoms

Edited by

VERNON W. HUGHES and HOWARD L. SCHULTZ

Physics Department
Yale University
New Haven, Connecticut

1967

ACADEMIC PRESS • New York and London

ACADEMIC PRESS INC.
111 Fifth Avenue, New York, New York 10003

United Kingdom Edition published by
ACADEMIC PRESS INC. (LONDON) LTD.
Berkeley Square House, London W.1

LIBRARY OF CONGRESS CATALOG CARD NUMBER: 67-23170

PRINTED IN THE UNITED STATES OF AMERICA

222958

CONTRIBUTORS TO VOLUME 4, PART B

Numbers in parentheses indicate the pages on which the authors' contributions begin.

G. E. BECKER, *Bell Telephone Laboratories, Incorporated, Murray Hill, New Jersey* (259)

HENRY M. CROSSWHITE, *Department of Physics, Johns Hopkins University, Baltimore, Maryland* (49)

CHARLES W. DRAKE, JR., *Department of Physics, Oregon State University, Corvallis, Oregon* (226)

K. G. KESSLER, *National Bureau of Standards, Washington, D. C.* (49)

R. M. MOBLEY, *Physics Department, Yale University, New Haven, Connecticut* (318)

H. E. RADFORD, *National Bureau of Standards, Washington, D. C.* (105)

DAVID T. WILKINSON, *Palmer Physical Laboratory, Princeton University, Princeton, New Jersey* (1)

KLAUS ZIOCK, *Department of Physics, University of Virginia, Charlottesville, Virginia* (214)

v

FOREWORD

After an interval, which somewhat exceeded our expectations, Volumes 4A and 4B are presented herewith to the scientific community. To a great extent the delay was due to the wealth of material; critical examination of the subject required repeated revision of the original schedule. In my foreword to Volume 2 of this treatise I mentioned the need to split the material into Volumes 4 and 7. I announced at that time that Professors Benjamin Bederson and Wade Fite have taken over the editorship of Volume 7 and we expected that this reorganization would be sufficient for a compact presentation of the single particle aspects of atomic and electron physics. We were too optimistic; the amount of material which had to be included in Volume 4 exceeded the bounds of a single volume and forced us into reorganizing it into the two halves presented here.

A consequence of this growth is that our "Methods of Experimental Physics" acquires more and more the character of an encyclopedia. While the organization and format differ from the conventional its contents comprise a reasonably complete presentation of the majority of the methods required by an experimental physicist. I say "the majority"; I am aware of certain methods not being presented adequately or at all, but it is our endeavor to fill these gaps, either in forthcoming volumes or in new editions of the existing ones.

I wish to thank Professors Vernon W. Hughes and Howard L. Schultz for their unflagging devotion and interest to the problem of producing such a book. They succeeded in gathering a remarkably good group of contributors; the results of their cooperation with the volume editors is offered here for the benevolent criticisms of the experimental physicists.

L. MARTON

April, 1967

PREFACE TO VOLUME 4

Volumes 4 and 7 of the "Methods of Experimental Physics" cover the field of atomic and electron physics. Volume 4 is restricted primarily to a treatment of the methods of experimental physics applicable to the study of individual particles as opposed to the study of the interaction of particles with one another. Due to the thoroughness and diligence of the authors of Volume 4, the amount of material exceeds a reasonable length for a single book, and therefore the volume appears in two parts as Volumes 4A and 4B. Volume 4A treats the topics of sources and detectors of particles. Volume 4B treats the methods for experimental studies of free electrons, positrons, atoms, and ions, organized according to the property under investigation, and also includes a chapter on basic techniques of ultra-high vacuum and gas purity.

These volumes are directed toward the research worker and graduate student in experimental atomic and electron physics. A major objective of the volumes has been to bring together a comprehensive treatment of all aspects of the subject of the methods of experimentation in atomic and electron physics. Leading experts contributing in their specialties to the volumes have made every effort to treat their topics with a high degree of completeness. Not only have they presented the most recent techniques but they have also given introductory background and theory useful to the student not intimately familiar with the subject. Usually, general methods, their advantages and limitations, are emphasized rather than detailed descriptions. Some parts of the volume treat highly specialized techniques not easily found in the literature.

Some overlap between Volume 4 and other volumes of this treatise, notably those dealing with Electronic Methods (Volume 2) and Nuclear Physics (Volume 5) exists. The amount of overlap present is unavoidable, even desirable, in the interest of completeness, and in a sense, it complements the presentations in other volumes. The overlap in nuclear physics technique is minimized as a result of the natural division on the basis of the energy of detected particles and radiations.

We wish to express deep appreciation to the contributors for their painstaking efforts and cooperation throughout this long venture, and to extend our thanks to the publisher, and especially to Dr. L. Marton, the Editor-in-Chief, for his constant help and encouragement.

VERNON W. HUGHES
HOWARD L. SCHULTZ

May, 1967

CONTENTS OF VOLUME 4, PART B

3. Properties of Free Electrons and Positrons

by DAVID T. WILKINSON

4. Properties of Atoms

5. Basic Techniques

CONTRIBUTORS TO VOLUME 4, PART A

I. AMES, *IBM Thomas J. Watson Research Center, Yorktown Heights, New York*

CARL E. ANDERSON, *General Electric Company, Space Science Laboratory, Philadelphia, Pennsylvania*

F. M. CHARBONNIER, *Field Emission Corporation, McMinnville, Oregon*

ROBERT L. CHRISTENSEN, *IBM Thomas J. Watson Research Center, Yorktown Heights, New York*

JAMES E. DRAPER, *Department of Physics, University of California, Davis, California*

W. P. DYKE, *Field Emission Corporation, McMinnville, Oregon*

H. A. FOWLER, *National Bureau of Standards, Washington, D. C.*

J. S. GREENBERG, *Physics Department, Yale University, New Haven, Connecticut*

G. A. HAAS, *Naval Research Laboratory, Washington, D. C.*

VERNON W. HUGHES, *Physics Department, Yale University, New Haven, Connecticut*

HIN LEW, *Division of Pure Physics, National Research Council of Canada, Ottawa, Canada*

EDGAR LIPWORTH, *Department of Physics, Brandeis University, Waltham, Connecticut*

L. MARTON, *National Bureau of Standards, Washington, D. C.*

FRANCIS M. J. PICHANICK, *Physics Department, Yale University, New Haven, Connecticut*

M. POSNER, *Physics Department, Yale University, New Haven, Connecticut*

W. RAITH, *Physics Department, Yale University, New Haven, Connecticut*

H. J. SHAW, *Microwave Laboratory, Stanford University, Stanford, California*

J. AROL SIMPSON, *National Bureau of Standards, Washington, D. C.*

L. W. SWANSON, *Field Emission Corporation, McMinnville, Oregon*

E. D. THERIOT, JR., *Physics Department, Yale University, New Haven, Connecticut*

N. REY WHETTEN, *General Electric Research and Development Center, Schenectady, New York*

CONTENTS OF VOLUME 4, PART A

Methods of
Experimental Physics

VOLUME 4

ATOMIC AND ELECTRON PHYSICS

PART B

FREE ATOMS

3. PROPERTIES OF FREE ELECTRONS AND POSITRONS*

3.1. Introduction and Summary

This chapter is concerned with our current empirical knowledge of the intrinsic properties of free electrons and positrons. The experiments upon which this knowledge is based are described and, when appropriate, discussed in some detail. Theory is mentioned only when the experimental result has some important bearing on the structure or justification of the theory. In keeping with the basic philosophy of this series, experiments of only historical importance are not discussed; however, an effort has been made to provide a route to these experiments through the references. Generally, the emphasis here is on the more modern experiments and techniques which give information about the properties of free electrons and positrons. A summary of the current state of affairs is given in Table I.

The word "free" is used here to mean "not bound into an atomic system." However, experiments on bound systems which advance our knowledge of the properties of the free particles are not excluded from this chapter. Some particle properties, such as the electron-proton charge difference, must necessarily be measured with bound systems but, generally, free particle experiments, when possible, are more precise. This is due mainly to the more complicated interactions of the bound particle which often make interpretation of the results, in terms of free particle properties, more difficult and more ambiguous.

The apparent overemphasis of experiments on the electron at the expense of the positron is unfortunate, but unavoidable. The fact is that, in comparison to the electron, the properties of the positron have not been precisely measured. There are probably two reasons for this lack of experimental work on the positron's properties; first, source and lifetime problems limit the scope of possible experiments, and second, theory strongly suggests the identity (except for charge) of electrons and positrons and a high precision experiment, as well as a certain amount of audacity, is required to challenge a well-founded theory. An effort has been made, usually at the end of each section, to examine what independent evidence there is concerning positron properties.

Finally, methods for measuring the states of free electrons are not

---

* Part 3 is by David T. Wilkinson.

discussed in this chapter. Readers are referred to Volume 5 of "Methods of Experimental Physics" for discussions of the measurement of momentum, energy, and polarization of electrons and positrons.

TABLE I.   Summary of the Experimental Values of the Properties of Electrons and Positrons as of January, 1966

Property	Value	References
Electron charge, e	$(4.802\ 98 \pm 0.000\ 20) \times 10^{-10}$ esu	[a]
Electron–proton charge difference	$<10^{-21}e$	[b]
Electron–positron charge difference	$<2 \times 10^{-15}e$	[c]
Electron mass, m	$(9.1091 \pm 0.0004) \times 10^{-28}$ gm	[a]
Electron–positron mass difference	$<3 \times 10^{-5}m$	[d]
Electron e/m	$(1.758\ 796 \pm 0.000\ 019) \times 10^{7}$ emu/gm	[a]
Electron magnetic moment	$\dfrac{\mu_e}{\mu_0} = 1 + \dfrac{\alpha}{2\pi} - (0.327 \pm 0.005)\dfrac{\alpha^2}{\pi^2}$	[e]
Positron magnetic moment	$\dfrac{\mu_{\text{pos}}}{\mu_0} = 1 + (1.0 \pm 0.1)\dfrac{\alpha}{2\pi}$	[f]
Electron electric dipole moment	$<2 \times 10^{-21}$ cm $\times e$	[g]
Positron electric dipole moment	$<8 \times 10^{-13}$ cm $\times e$	[h]

[a] "New Values for the Physical Constants," *Phys. Today* **17**, 48 (1964); E. R. Cohen, *in* "Methods of Experimental Physics" (I. Estermann, ed.), Vol. I, pp. 35–52. Academic Press, New York, 1959.

[b] J. G. King, *Phys. Rev. Letters* **5**, 562 (1960).

[c] Section 3.2.3.

[d] Section 3.3.2.

[e] D. T. Wilkinson and H. R. Crane, *Phys. Rev.* **130**, 852 (1963).

[f] Arthur Rich and H. R. Crane, *Bull. Am. Phys. Soc.* **11**, 121 (1965); *Phys. Rev. Letters* **17**, 271 (1966).

[g] P. G. H. Sandars and E. Lipworth, *Phys. Rev. Letters* **13**, 718 (1964).

[h] E. E. Salpeter, *Phys. Rev.* **112**, 1642 (1958); Section 3.6.4.

3.2. The Electron Charge, e

3.2.1. Summary of Experimental Methods

3.2.1.1.   Cloud and Drop Methods.

The first measurement of the electron charge, e, was reported by J. S. Townsend in 1897—the same year in which J. J. Thomson published his classic paper[1] on the nature of cathode rays. Townsend's experiment[2] consisted of measuring two quantities: (1) the total charge on a cloud of water vapor which had been formed by expanding an ionized gas and (2) the number of droplets in the cloud. The assumption was made that each droplet had condensed onto a single ion, so that the charge per ion was obtained by dividing the total charge by the number of droplets. Even though the "one ion per droplet" assumption could not be justified at the time, the fact remains that Townsend's value of e agrees with the modern value to within a factor of 2. Townsend's cloud method was modified and improved by Thomson[3] and Wilson.[4]

Wilson's modification was particularly important as it provided a steppingstone for later work. He added plates above and below the region occupied by the charged vapor cloud which enabled him to apply a vertical electric field to the vapor droplets. The rate of fall of the cloud was measured with and without the electric field and, assuming the validity of Stoke's law, the value of e could be computed from the force equation.

At this point (about 1906) R. A. Millikan became interested in the problem of a direct measurement of e. After experimenting unsuccessfully with the vapor cloud methods, Millikan devised his famous oil-drop experiment which is still, some 50 years later, the best method available for measuring e directly. The experiment is too well-known to be discussed here; details of the method and apparatus can be found in Millikan's papers[5] of 1913 and 1917. A short summary of the experiment is given by Klemperer.[6] Millikan's measurements were so scrupulous that later experimenters,[7-9] using modern detection techniques, have improved only slightly on the precision of the measurement.

3.2.1.2. F/N Method. Independent measurements of the Faraday constant, F, and Avogadro's number, N, can be used to give a value for e by simply taking the ratio of F to N. A better value is obtained if the

[1] J. J. Thomson, *Phil. Mag.* [5] **44**, 293 (1897).

[2] J. S. Townsend, *Proc. Cambridge Phil. Soc.* **9**, 244 (1897).

[3] J. J. Thomson, *Phil. Mag.* [5] **46**, 528 (1898); *ibid.* [6] **5**, 354 (1903).

[4] H. A. Wilson, *Phil. Mag.* [6] **5**, 429 (1903).

[5] R. A. Millikan, *Phys. Rev.* **26**, 198 (1908); *Phil. Mag.* [6] **19**, 209 (1910); *Phys. Rev.* **32**, 349 (1911); *Phil. Mag.* [6] **21**, 757 (1911); *Phys. Rev.* **2**, 109 (1913); *Phil. Mag.* [6] **34**, 1 (1917); "Electrons (+ and −), Protons, Photons, Neutrons, Mesotrons, and Cosmic Rays." Univ. of Chicago Press, Chicago, Illinois, 1947).

[6] O. Klemperer, "Electron Physics." Academic Press, New York, 1959.

[7] V.D. Hopper and T. H. Laby, *Proc. Roy. Soc.* **A178**, 243 (1941).

[8] E. Bäcklin and H. Flember, *Nature* **137**, 655 (1936).

[9] Y. Ishida, I. Fukushima, and T. Suetsugu, *Sci. Papers Inst. Phys. Chem. Research (Tokyo)* **32**, 57 (1937).

values of F and N are combined with the results of other experiments in an analysis which adjusts the values of several atomic constants to give the best consistency in the results of the several experiments. This "least-squares adjustment" is discussed in Volume 1 of this series by E. R. Cohen[10] and in a monograph by J. H. Sanders.[11] The values of e and the electron mass m which are given in Table I have been taken from the most recent adjustment[12] of this kind.

A painstaking measurement of the electrochemical equivalent of silver has recently been carried out at NBS.[13] (See Craig et al.[13] for a review of earlier work.) This measurement, when combined with measurements of the atomic weight of silver,[14] gives the value for the Faraday constant as $96{,}486.8 \pm 1.6$ coulombs/gram-equivalent-weight.

The most accurate method of measuring Avogadro's number consists of measuring the density, ρ, lattice spacing, d, and molecular weight, M, of a crystal whose structure is known. For a cubic crystal structure, Avogadro's number is simply $Mf/d^3\rho$, where f is the number of molecules per unit cell. However, a problem exists because d is measured by X-ray diffraction and is, therefore, determined in X units rather than in centimeters. The conversion factor, Λ, from X units to centimeters is only known to a few parts in 10^5 and this uncertainty ultimately limits the accuracy of measurements of N and, subsequently, the accuracy to which e can be found from the ratio F/N.

3.2.1.3. Shot Effect Method.   The shot effect was predicted theoretically by Schottky[15] even before instrumentation was available to observe it. By assuming only that electrons are emitted randomly and independently from a hot cathode, Schottky was able to show that the mean-square value of the fluctuations in the current of a temperature-limited diode should be

$$\overline{(\delta I)^2} = 2eI_0\,\Delta\nu, \tag{3.2.1}$$

where I_0 is the time-averaged diode current and $\Delta\nu$ is the bandwidth of the detection apparatus. Schottky went on to suggest that the electron charge could be determined from measurements of the other three quantities in his equation.

[10] E. R. Cohen, in "Methods of Experimental Physics" (I. Estermann, ed.), Vol. 1, pp. 35–52. Academic Press, New York, 1959.

[11] J. H. Sanders, "The Fundamental Atomic Constants." Oxford Univ. Press, London and New York, 1961.

[12] "New Values for the Physical Constants," Phys. Today 17, 48 (Feb. 1964).

[13] D. N. Craig, J. I. Hoffman, C. A. Law, and W. J. Hamer, J. Research Natl. Bur. Standards 64A, 381 (1960).

[14] W. R. Shields, D. N. Craig, and V. H. Dibeler, Proc. Intern. Conf. Nuclidic Masses, p. 519. Hamilton, Ontario, 1960.

[15] W. Schottky, Ann. Physik [4] 57, 541 (1918); ibid. 68, 157 (1922).

Early attempts[16,17] at this measurement were hampered by instrumental limitations and errors were, at best, a few per cent. Stigmark,[18] in a more recent measurement, was able to reduce the experimental error to 0.25 %, with most of this error due to instrumentation and calibration. It seems that a fundamental limitation on the accuracy of this experiment has not yet been reached, but roughly two orders of magnitude improvement is needed if the current uncertainty in e is to be reduced.

3.2.2. The Electron-Proton Charge Difference

The measurement of the electron charge in terms of absolute units is of great importance, but of more fundamental interest to physics, particularly elementary particle theory, is the question of whether or not the magnitude of the charge on different elementary particles is the

TABLE II.[a] Summary of Results of Electron-Proton Charge Difference Experiments

Method	Molecule	$\dfrac{\Delta Q(\text{molecule})}{e}$	$\dfrac{\delta q}{e} = \dfrac{\Delta Q(\text{molecule})}{(Z+N)\,e}$	References
Gas efflux	CO_2	$<2.2 \times 10^{-19}$	$<5 \times 10^{-21}$	b
	Ar	$(4 \pm 4) \times 10^{-20}$	$(1 \pm 1) \times 10^{-21}$	c
	N_2	$(6 \pm 6) \times 10^{-20}$	$(2 \pm 2) \times 10^{-21}$	c
	H_2	$(-2.5 \pm 1.5) \times 10^{-20}$	$(-1.3 \pm 0.8) \times 10^{-20}$	d
	He	$(4 \pm 2) \times 10^{-20}$	$(+1 \pm 0.5) \times 10^{-20}$	d
	$CHCl_3$	$<1.1 \times 10^{-16}$	$<9 \times 10^{-19}$	e
Molecular beam deflection	CsI	$<4 \times 10^{-13}$	$<1.5 \times 10^{-15}$	f
	CsF	$<2 \times 10^{-14}$	$<1.3 \times 10^{-16}$	g
	KF	$<1 \times 10^{-13}$	$<1.7 \times 10^{-15}$	g
	H_2	$<2 \times 10^{-15}$	$<1 \times 10^{-15}$	h
	D_2	$<2.8 \times 10^{-15}$	$<7 \times 10^{-16}$	h
	K	$(-3.8 \pm 11.8) \times 10^{-17}$	$(-1 \pm 3) \times 10^{-18}$	h
	Cs	$(1.3 \pm 5.6) \times 10^{-17}$	$(1 \pm 4) \times 10^{-19}$	h

[a] This table is mostly from reference h below.
[b] A. Piccard and E. Kessler, *Arch. sci. phys. et nat.* **7**, 340 (1925).
[c] A. M. Hillas and T. E. Cranshaw, *Nature* **184**, 892 (1959); *ibid.* **186**, 459 (1960).
[d] J. G. King, *Phys. Rev. Letters* **5**, 562 (1960).
[e] J. C. Zorn, *Bull. Am. Phys. Soc.* **9**, 45 (1964); private communication (1965).
[f] V. W. Hughes, *Phys. Rev.* **76**, 474 (1949); *ibid.* **105**, 170 (1957).
[g] J. C. Zorn, G. E. Chamberlain, and V. W. Hughes, *Bull. Am. Phys. Soc.* **5**, 36 (1960).
[h] J. C. Zorn, G. E. Chamberlain, and V. W. Hughes, *Phys. Rev.* **129**, 2566 (1963).

[16] C. A. Hartmann, *Ann. Physik* [4] **65**, 51 (1921).
[17] A. W. Hull and N. H. Williams, *Phys. Rev.* **25**, 147 (1925).
[18] L. Stigmark, *Arkiv Fysik* **5**, 399 (1952).

same. Very small upper limits have been placed on a possible electron-proton charge difference by experiments which fall into two categories: the gas efflux method and the molecular beam deflection method. A discussion of each method follows, and the results of experiments of this type are summarized in Table II.

3.2.2.1. Gas Efflux Method. The first experiment[19] designed specifically to test for an electron-proton charge difference was of the gas efflux type. A schematic drawing of a gas efflux apparatus is shown in Fig. 1.

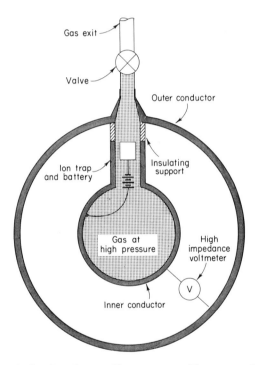

FIG. 1.   Schematic drawing of a gas efflux apparatus. Figure reproduced from Zorn.[20]

Initially the inner conductor is filled with gas under pressure and the potential difference between the inner and outer conductors is noted. The valve is then opened and gas leaves the inner conductor carrying with it an amount of charge

$$Q = n \times \Delta Q(\text{molecule}), \qquad (3.2.2)$$

[19] A. Piccard and E. Kessler, *Arch. sci. phys. et nat.* **7**, 340 (1925).

[20] J. C. Zorn, "Limit for the Electron-Proton Charge Difference from a Vapor Efflux Experiment." Univ. of Michigan (unpublished, 1964).

where n is the number of departed molecules and ΔQ(molecule) is the excess charge per molecule. The departure of change Q from the inner conductor results in a change of the voltmeter reading of $V = Q/C$, where C is the capacitance of the two-conductor system. (We assume here an ideal voltmeter with infinite impedance and zero input capacitance.) The molecular charge is then

$$\Delta Q\text{(molecule)} = \frac{C \cdot V}{n} , \tag{3.2.3}$$

and measurable values of $C \cdot V$ are typically $10^3 e$. Thus, it is apparent that the gas efflux method is capable of great precision because n is typically 10^{24} molecules and ΔQ(molecule) $\sim 10^{-21} e$.

Precautions must be taken to minimize charge leakage on the insulating supports and to avoid the exit of ions along with the "neutral" gas. The latter problem is solved by collecting ions on a negatively charged electrode in the throat of the inner conductor. Thus, ions and free electrons are swept out of the effluxing gas, but charged dust particles, because of their relatively large mass, can still escape from the system. Dust, then, must be scrupulously avoided in the filling gas and cleanliness of the inner vessel is essential.

Recent adaptations[21,22] of the gas efflux method were motivated, in part, by a suggestion[23] that an electron-proton charge difference might play an important role in cosmology. The work of King[22] is chosen for discussion here partly because he worked with hydrogen and helium gases for which the interpretation of ΔQ(molecule) in terms of an electron-proton charge difference is least ambiguous.

Cylindrical containers were used in King's experiment. The inner vessel (11.2 liters) was filled to a pressure of 18.6 kg/cm² with hydrogen or helium and then the gas was allowed to escape slowly; in the reported runs the efflux time was 140 seconds. An electrometer with a time constant of 60 seconds was used to monitor the potential difference between the two vessels as a function of time. The pressure inside the inner vessel was also recorded as a function of time in order to permit a calculation of the shape of the expected electrometer reading.

The results of King's experiment are reproduced in Fig. 2. Curves (b) and (c) show the electrometer reading averaged over twenty-one hydrogen runs and nineteen helium runs, respectively. It will be noted that the entire helium curve is negative [indicating ΔQ(helium) > 0],

[21] A. M. Hillas and T. E. Cranshaw, *Nature* **184**, 892 (1959); *ibid.* **186**, 459 (1960).

[22] J. G. King, *Phys. Rev. Letters* **5**, 562 (1960).

[23] R. A. Lyttleton and H. Bondi, *Proc. Roy. Soc.* **A252**, 313 (1959); F. Hoyle, *ibid.* **A257**, 431 (1960).

but that the hydrogen curve starts negative, then goes positive, with the net area under the curve being positive. The crosshatched region in Fig. 2 shows the area that would be expected under the electrometer curves if $\Delta Q(\text{molecule}) = 5 \times 10^{-20}e$ and $n = 5.4 \times 10^{24}$ molecules. By considering the area under the curves (b) and (c), King obtained the values of $\Delta Q(\text{molecule})$ listed in Table II.

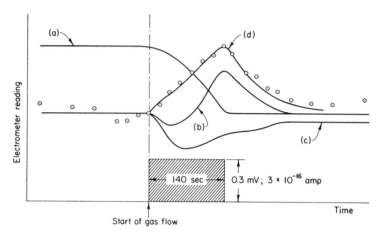

FIG. 2.   Results of King's experiment: (a) pressure in the inner vessel; (b) electrometer reading averaged over twenty-one hydrogen runs; (c) electrometer reading averaged over nineteen helium runs; (d) expected electrometer reading as computed from (a). Circles are obtained by subtracting curve (c) from curve (b). Figure reproduced from King.[22]

In interpreting the measured quantity, $\Delta Q(\text{molecule})$, in terms of an electron-proton charge difference, δq, the assumption is usually made that the neutron charge is equal to the electron-proton charge difference, so that

$$\delta q(\text{electron-proton}) = \frac{\Delta Q(\text{molecule})}{N + Z}, \qquad (3.2.4)$$

where $N + Z$ is the total number of neutrons and protons in the molecule. This view is rationalized by assuming that charge is conserved in β-decay and that the antineutrino is uncharged. Of course, the electron-proton charge difference obtained from the hydrogen measurement does not suffer from this ambiguity. The results of King can also be used to set an upper limit on the neutron charge. Taking the difference of results for hydrogen and helium causes the electron-proton charge difference to drop out and one is left with a result for the neutron:

$$\delta q(\text{neutron}) = (3 \pm 2) \times 10^{-20}e. \qquad (3.2.5)$$

Returning again to Fig. 2, we mention an interesting observation which King made concerning the shape of curves (b) and (c). Curve (a) of Fig. 2 shows the time dependence of the pressure in the inner vessel. From this curve, and the assumption that the effluxing gas is uniformly charged, he computed the expected shape of the electrometer reading, and this is shown as curve (d) in Fig. 2. King observed that if curve (c) is subtracted from curve (b), the difference (shown as circles in Fig. 2) is in good agreement with the shape of the expected curve (the height of curve (d) is adjustable). This interesting result could be explained if helium molecules were uncharged (perhaps the neutron and the hydrogen atom have equal charge of opposite sign) and hydrogen molecules carry a net charge of $(-7 \pm 2.5) \times 10^{-20}e$. Curve (c) is then interpreted as a spurious instrumental effect which is common to both helium and hydrogen runs. At this point a better understanding of the reasons for the shapes of curves (b) and (c) is needed, but this appears to be a difficult task as the effects are extremely small and possible causes are numerous.

Zorn[20,24] has recently modified the efflux method by using volatile liquids as the effluent material. Vacuum pumps are used to remove the vapor from the inner vessel at a controlled rate. The chief advantage of using a liquid, instead of high-pressure gas, is that for a given number of molecules, n, the inner container can be smaller, thus reducing the value of C in Eq. (3.2.3). The precision attained to date is not as good as that of the gas efflux method, but the limitations on precision are instrumental and are, therefore, subject to further improvement.

3.2.2.2. Molecular Beam Deflection Method. The beam deflection method was used by Hughes[25] and a group at Yale[26] to test a number of different molecules for a charge excess. These experiments have not attained the precision of the gas efflux experiments, but the beam deflection method gives a more direct test for the charge on molecules and the interpretation of a positive experimental result is more straightforward. A summary of the results of the molecular beam deflection experiments is given in the lower part of Table II.

A sketch of the molecular beam deflection method is shown in Fig. 3. The well-collimated beam is directed into a region of intense horizontal electric field; field strengths as high as 10^5 volts/cm are used. In the foreground of Fig. 3, but not shown, is a hot wire or a Pirani gauge detector which can be moved horizontally to scan the beam profile. By positioning the detector at points of maximum slope on one side of the

---

[24] J. C. Zorn, *Bull. Am. Phys. Soc.* **9**, 45 (1964); private communication (1965).

[25] V. W. Hughes, *Phys. Rev.* **76**, 474 (1949); *ibid.* **105**, 170 (1957).

[26] J. C. Zorn, G. E. Chamberlain, and V. W. Hughes, *Bull. Am. Phys. Soc.* **5**, 36 (1960).

undeflected beam profile, maximum sensitivity to horizontal deflection was obtained.

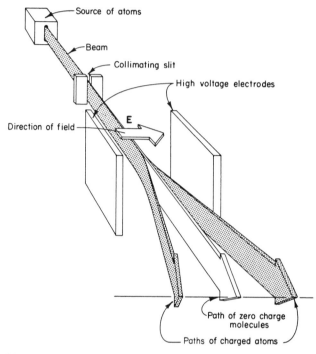

FIG. 3.   Sketch of molecular beam deflection method for measuring molecular charge excess. Figure reproduced from Zorn et al.[27]

Care must be taken to account for deflections of the beam due to induced electric moments which interact with electric field gradients at the ends of the deflecting plates. This was accomplished by using a subtraction technique[25] which makes use of the properties of electric forces under reversal of the direction of the electric field $\mathbf{E}$. The force on a molecule in an electric field is given by

$$\mathbf{F} = \Delta Q(\text{molecule})\mathbf{E} + \nabla(\mathbf{d} \cdot \mathbf{E}) + \cdots, \qquad (3.2.6)$$

where $\mathbf{d}$ is the induced electric dipole moment. Quadrupole and higher-order terms are shown by Zorn et al.[27] to be negligible in these experiments. In a simple experiment where $\mathbf{E}$ is simply turned on and off the second term in Eq. (3.2.6) can cause deflections which might be mistaken for an effect due to a finite $\Delta Q(\text{molecule})$. In order to avoid the effects of the $\mathbf{d}$ interaction the deflection caused by a *reversal* of $\mathbf{E}$

[27] J. C. Zorn, G. E. Chamberlain, and V. W. Hughes, *Phys. Rev.* **129**, 2566 (1963).

was measured. Since **d** reverses with **E**, the dipole force is in the same direction before and after reversal and any change in the beam position is due to the ΔQ(molecule) term.

The molecular beam deflection experiments have been used[27] to put an upper limit on the width of a possible distribution in the value of the elementary charge, e. If e were actually only a mean value about which the individual electron and proton charge were distributed, then each molecule in the beam would experience a different deflecting force, depending upon the exact values of the charges within that molecule. This would result in a broadening of the beam profile when the electric field is switched on. No such broadening was observed and an upper limit of 8 parts in 10^{15} was placed on the width of a possible distribution of e.

3.2.2.3. Suspended Sphere Method. In his work on measuring the electron charge, Millikan also made measurements of the proton charge[5] by observing the behavior of drops with a deficiency of electrons. He found that the electron-proton charges did not differ in magnitude by more than 1 part in 1500. Hughes[25] has reinterpreted Millikan's results by considering the effect of all proton-electron pairs in the drop and concludes that the electron-proton charge difference is less than $10^{-15}e$.

At least two attempts are currently being made to suspend solid spheres and observe deflections due to a small charge excess.[28,29] The method uses a magnetically suspended metal sphere which can be subjected to a strong horizontal electric field. Horizontal deflections, occurring when the field is switched on, are measured optically. The inherent precision of this method is very high. It is hoped that deflections due to changes in the sphere's charge of $\pm e$ will be observable and, since the number of atoms in a sphere is of order 10^{21}, the method is capable of detecting atomic charge excesses of $10^{-21}e$ or smaller. However, experimental difficulties are great due to the feebleness of the desired interaction and the many sources of competing effects.

3.2.3. The Electron-Positron Charge Difference

The author is not aware of any experiments which test directly for a difference in the magnitude of the charges on the electron and positron. However, an argument, making use of indirect evidence, can be made which places a small upper limit on this charge difference. A recent experiment[30] makes use of the Mössbauer effect to show that the upper limit on the charge of the 14.4-kev γ rays from Co^{57} is $10^{-15}e$. Let us assume that this limit also applies to the γ rays from electron-positron

[28] J. W. Trischka and T. I. Moran, *Bull. Am. Phys. Soc.* **5**, 298 (1960).

[29] E. Johnston and P. A. Franken, private communications (1964).

[30] L. Grodzins, D. Engelberg, and W. Bertozzi, *Bull. Am. Phys. Soc.* **6**, 63 (1961).

annihilation. In addition, we assume that charge is strictly conserved in the reaction $e^+ + e^- \rightarrow 2\gamma$ and obtain an upper limit on the electron-positron charge difference of $2 \times 10^{-15}e$.

3.3. The Electron Mass, m

3.3.1. Summary of Experimental Methods

3.3.1.1. Compton Scattering Method. Experiments which measure the electron mass, m, are not as direct as is Millikan's experiment for measuring e. However, several single experiments are done whose results can be interpreted in such a way as to give a value for m. One such experiment is to measure the change in wavelength that occurs in Compton scattering from free electrons. The wavelength change is given by

$$\Delta\lambda = \frac{h}{mc}(1 - \cos\theta),\tag{3.3.1}$$

for a photon scattered through angle θ. Precision measurements using this method could not improve the current value of m because Plank's constant, h, is not known with enough accuracy. However, a precision value for h/m would be most useful in the program used for adjusting the values of atomic constants.[10] The main difficulty in precision measurements of the Compton effect comes in trying to account for the binding energies of the scattering electrons.

3.3.1.2. Hydrogenlike Spectra Method. A measurement of the electron mass can be obtained by comparing the atomic spectra of H and He+. The energy terms for hydrogenlike atoms are arranged according to

$$E_n = \frac{R_\infty hcZ^2}{n^2\left(1 + \dfrac{m}{M}\right)},\tag{3.3.2}$$

where R_∞ is the Rydberg constant, n is the radial quantum number, and M is the nuclear mass. Thus, for He+ $(Z = 2)$ the level corresponding to $2n$ should coincide with the nth level of hydrogen except for a correction factor of approximately $m(M_H^{-1} - M_{He}^{-1})$ and m can be determined from the spectra because M_H and M_{He} are known from mass spectrometer experiments.

3.3.1.3. Annihilation Radiation Method. A third method for measuring the electron mass shows promise of attaining enough precision to give new information bearing on the value of m. A crystal spectrometer is used to measure the wavelength of the γ rays emitted when an electron and a positron undergo 2-photon annihilation.[31-33] Since annihilation occurs predominantly at low positron energies, the total γ ray energy is nearly equal to the sum of the rest masses of the electron and positron. Furthermore, momentum conservation requires that the γ ray energies are equal. If one accepts as a premise that the rest masses of electrons and positrons are equal, then the γ ray energy is just h/mc—the Compton wavelength. Accurate measurements of the annihilation radiation wavelength are, therefore, capable of giving values of h/m which could be used in the adjustment program[10] to improve the values of several atomic constants, including m.

However, there is a units calibration problem associated with precision measurements by this method. The crystal spectrometer is calibrated in terms of X units and so the conversion factor, Λ, from X units to centimeters must be used to reduce the measurements to cgs units. Unfortunately, Λ is only known to a few parts in 10^5, and so the accuracy with which h/m can be found by this method is limited. Even so, the annihilation wavelength method, in conjunction with improvements of the value of Λ, seems to hold the most promise for improving the accuracy with which m is known.

3.3.2. The Electron-Positron Mass Difference

The equivalence of the masses of the electron and positron is a cornerstone of current elementary particle theory. In fact, this equivalence is so fundamental that it is generally accepted and the empirical evidence in support of this basic assumption is not well known. Two experiments which give upper limits on the electron-positron mass difference are discussed below.

3.3.2.1. Upper Limit from Annihilation Radiation Wavelength. If one adopts the attitude that the electron-positron masses might be different, then the measurements of the wavelength of annihilation radiation take on a different significance than that described in Section 3.3.1.3. Here one assumes only that mass energy is conserved when an electron-positron pair annihilates at rest and derives, in a straightforward way, the following relationship:

$$\frac{\delta m}{m} = 2\frac{\lambda_A - \lambda_C}{\lambda_A}. \tag{3.3.3}$$

In this equation δm is the electron-positron mass difference, λ_A is the

[31] J. W. M. DuMond, *Phys. Rev.* **81**, 468 (1951).

[32] D. E. Muller, H. C. Hoyt, D. J. Klein, and J. W. M. DuMond, *Phys. Rev.* **88**, 775 (1952).

[33] J. W. Knowles, *Can. J. Phys.* **40**, 257 (1962).

measured wavelength of annihilation radiation, and $\lambda_C = h/mc$ is the Compton wavelength for electrons. The best value for λ_C is obtained from measurements of the fine structure constant, α, and the Rydberg constant, R_∞, via the relationship $\lambda_C = \alpha^2/2R_\infty$.

Early work[31] in measuring the wavelength of annihilation radiation indicated a discrepancy in the values of λ_A and λ_C and this was interpreted as evidence for a possible electron-positron mass difference. However, later, more precise, measurements of λ_A[32,33] have given values in agreement with the λ_C value to within experimental errors. The assigned experimental error in the most recent measurement of λ_A is about 30 parts in 10^6 and this gives an upper limit on δm of

$$\frac{\delta m}{m} < 30 \times 10^{-6}. \tag{3.3.4}$$

3.3.2.2. Mass Spectrometer Method. A second method for comparing the electron and positron masses uses a mass spectrometer, which actually compares m/e, not the masses directly. However, the argument in Section 3.2.3 places an upper limit on the difference in the magnitude of the charges of the electron and positron at $2 \times 10^{-15}e$, so that the experiment discussed below can be regarded as comparing the inertial masses of these particle. Since the mass spectrometer experiment is performed on electrons and positrons in their free state, the results can be interpreted more directly than are the results of the measurements on the wavelength of annihilation radiation. The precisions of the two methods are comparable. The remainder of this section is concerned with the mass spectrometer experiment of Page et al.[34]

The experimental method is based on the invariance of the Lorentz force

$$\mathbf{F} = e(\mathbf{E} + \mathbf{v} \times \mathbf{B}), \tag{3.3.5}$$

against reversal of the signs of e, $\mathbf{E}$, and $\mathbf{v}$. Thus, if the static fields $\mathbf{E}$ and $\mathbf{B}$ focus (in angle and energy) positrons from a source at point 1 onto a point 2, then the fields $-\mathbf{E}$ and $\mathbf{B}$ should focus electrons from a source at point 2 onto point 1. However, a difference in the values of m/e for the electron and positron would cause the two beams to achieve focus at different values of $\mathbf{E}$ or $\mathbf{B}$. In the experiment to be described here, $\mathbf{B}$ was held fixed throughout and values of $\mathbf{E}$ were measured at best focus of the two beams.

Figure 4 is a plan view of the double-focusing mass spectrometer used by Page et al.[34] A uniform magnetic field ($\sim$100 gauss) is applied to the region enclosed by the rectangle at the top; $\mathbf{B}$ is directed out of the page. Velocity selection is achieved by applying a (reversible) voltage V

[34] L. A. Page, P. Stehle, and S. B. Gunst, *Phys. Rev.* **89**, 1273 (1953).

to the plates C. The slits B and E are the foci of the spectrometer. A is a Na[22] line source of positrons which is also used as a collector for electrons. When positrons are being counted, the Geiger counter, GMC, is operative and aperture H is open. At J is a tungsten filament electron source whose potential, together with that of I, determines the electron beam energy. An aluminum foil at G is inserted during electron runs so that electrons are scattered into angles acceptable to the spectrometer. Electron source strength is monitored by the current collected at plate F.

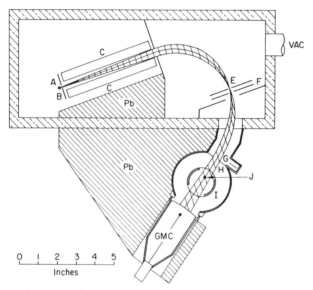

FIG. 4.   The electron-positron mass spectrometer of Page, Stehle, and Gunst. The plate (CC) spacing is exaggerated in order to show a positron beam traversing the apparatus. Figure reproduced from Page *et al.*[34]

Since the electron source did not have a broad energy spectrum, it was necessary to adjust the electron energy to the value acceptable to the spectrometer. To do this an alternating voltage was superimposed onto the dc accelerating potential. The collected electron signal then consisted of pulses (two per sweep cycle) which were equally spaced when the dc accelerating voltage was adjusted. Thus, the dc accelerating voltage was adjusted to minimize the component of the electron signal occurring at the sweep frequency and the component at the second harmonic of the sweep frequency was used to measure the electron beam strength.

The experimental results which were achieved by the mass spectrometer are indicated in Fig. 5. The tuning curves for electron and for positron beams are shown in Fig. 5(a). It is important to notice that the shapes of the tuning curves are the same. Also, since the sensitivity for detecting mass difference depends on how well the tuning curves can be located along the voltage axis, the fractional width of these curves is important.

In Fig. 5(b) the observed voltage, corresponding to the center of the tuning curve, is shown for alternate measurements on electron and positron beams. The secular drift is believed due to heating of the resistance divider used to monitor the voltage V. The drift rate was apparently constant so that straight-line interpolation between electron runs was justified. The results were examined for a systematic displacement of the positron results relative to the electron line; none was found.

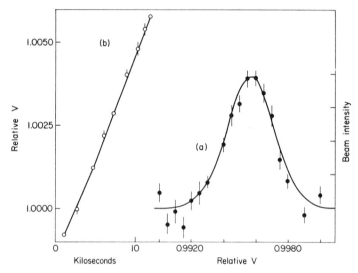

FIG. 5.   (a) Comparison of electron (solid curve) and positron (dots) tuning curves. (b) Voltage for optimum tuning for preliminary runs with electron (circles) and positron (dots) beams. Figure reproduced from Page et al.[34]

An electron-positron mass difference would affect the experimental results in the following way:

$$\frac{\delta m}{m} = \left[1 - \frac{v^2}{c^2}\right]^{-1} \frac{\delta V}{V}, \tag{3.3.6}$$

where v is determined by the velocity selector and δV is the difference between the values of V for optimum positron tuning and the extrapolated value of V for optimum electron tuning. The experimental results were that

$$\frac{\delta m}{m} = (26 \pm 71) \times 10^{-6}, \tag{3.3.7}$$

where the uncertainty is due mainly to counting statistics associated with the positron runs.

3.4. The Electron Charge to Mass Ratio, e/m

3.4.1. Classical Methods

Since the pioneering experiments of J. J. Thomson, which are generally hailed as the discovery of the electron, the experiments for measuring e/m for electrons have been varied and numerous. Many of the classical methods for measuring e/m were cleverly devised and the techniques used reflected much ingenuity on the part of the experimenters. However, the classical e/m experiments and methods are well known and are reviewed in many books,[6,35-37] and so they are not discussed here. Instead, we have chosen to describe two more modern experiments which can be used to obtain a value for e/m.

3.4.2. The Electron e/m from Two Precision Experiments

The current value of e/m (see Table I) is obtained from the adjustment program which combines the results of many modern experiments.[10] However, e/m can be obtained from the results of just two experiments with nearly the same accuracy as that reported by the adjustment program. Further improvement in the accuracy of these two measurements would make the value of e/m independent of the adjustment program.

The two quantities whose measurement gives e/m are the proton gyromagnetic ratio, γ_p, and the ratio of the Bohr magneton to the proton magnetic moment, μ_0/μ_p. Multiplication of these two quantities gives e/m for the electron.

3.4.2.1. The Proton Gyromagnetic Ratio, γ_p. The proton gyromagnetic ratio has been measured several times using, essentially, the same method, but quite different experimental techniques.[38-40] Briefly, the method is to measure the spin precession rate, ω_p, of protons in a magnetic field, B, which is calibrated in terms of absolute electrical units. Then,

$$\gamma_p = \frac{2\mu_p}{\hbar} = \frac{\omega_p}{B}. \tag{3.4.1}$$

[35] G. P. Harnwell and J. J. Livingood, "Experimental Atomic Physics," Chapter IV. McGraw-Hill, New York, 1933.

[36] J. B. Hoag and S. A. Korff, "Electron and Nuclear Physics," 3rd ed. Van Nostrand, Princeton, New Jersey, 1948.

[37] W. Gerlach, in "Handbuch der Physik" (H. Geiger, ed.), 2nd ed., Vol. 22, Part I, p. 1. Springer, Berlin, 1933.

[38] H. A. Thomas, R. L. Driscoll, and J. A. Hipple, *J. Research Natl. Bur. Standards* **44**, 569 (1960); *Phys. Rev.* **78**, 787 (1950).

[39] F. Kirchner and W. Wilhelmy, *Nuovo cimento* [10] **6**, Suppl. 1, 246 (1957); W. Wilhelmy, *Ann. Physik* [6] **19**, 329 (1957).

[40] R. L. Driscoll and P. L. Bender, *Phys. Rev. Letters* **1**, 413 (1958).

This important measurement, then, gives the relationship between the magnetic field, as defined in terms of the absolute ampere, and the proton resonance frequency, which is the quantity used in most laboratories to measure B.

The measurement of Driscoll and Bender[40] is the most recent and has the smallest quoted uncertainty. In this experiment, a sample of distilled water (2-cm-diameter sphere) was polarized in a 5-kg magnetic field and then shot, pneumatically, into the center of a precisely wound solenoid (100 cm long and 28 cm in diameter). The proton spins, which are initially oriented along the solenoid field, are reoriented to be perpendicular to the field by a 90° pulse at the resonant frequency (52.5 kc/sec). Subsequently, the polarization precesses in the solenoid field, and pickup coils, oriented normal to the solenoid axis, detect the resonance signal for about 3 seconds. In this way, ω_p is measured to about 1 part in 10^7. The magnetic field, B, is obtained from careful measurements of the solenoid geometry and current. Their result is $\gamma_p = (2.675\,13 \pm 0.000\,02) \times 10^4\,\text{sec}^{-1}\,\text{gauss}^{-1}$. The uncertainty stems mainly from the determination of the solenoid current in units of the absolute ampere.

3.4.2.2. μ_0/μ_p from Measurements of the Cyclotron Frequency of Low-Energy Electrons. The ratio of the Bohr magneton to the proton magnetic moment has been measured by several groups.[41-44] The method used in each of these experiments was to measure the angular rate of orbital motion, ω_c (the cyclotron rate), of low-energy electrons and the spin precession rate of protons, ω_p, in the same magnetic field. Then,

$$\frac{\omega_c}{\omega_p} \approx \frac{\mu_0}{\mu_p} = \frac{e}{mc\gamma_p}, \qquad (3.4.2)$$

where the first equality holds only to extent that ω_p can be corrected for diamagnetic effects in the proton sample and that a relativistic correction can be made to ω_c to account for the finite electron energies. Generally, these experiments are done with magnetic field strengths which give proton resonance at about 15 Mc/sec and electron cyclotron frequencies in the 10 Gc/sec range. Proton resonance is detected by conventional techniques and electron cyclotron resonance is detected by microwave absorption (except in Gardner and Purcell[41]) due to free electrons in a resonant cavity. The use of microwave absorption tech-

[41] J. H. Gardner and E. M. Purcell, *Phys. Rev.* **76**, 1262 (1949); J. H. Gardner, *ibid.* **83**, 996 (1951).

[42] S. Liebes and P. A. Franken, *Phys. Rev.* **116**, 633 (1959); *ibid.* **104**, 1197 (1956).

[43] W. A. Hardy and E. M. Purcell, *Bull. Am. Phys. Soc.* **4**, 37 (1959); private communications from W. A. Hardy (1965).

[44] J. H. Sanders, K. F. Tittel, and J. F. Ward, *Proc. Roy. Soc.* **A272**, 103 (1963).

niques for measuring free-electron cyclotron resonance is a useful technique and merits some discussion here.

In the experiment of Sanders, Tittle, and Ward[44] the electrons were produced by a hot tungsten filament at one end of a cylindrical cavity operating in the TE_{101} mode. The filament was screened by a grid to afford control of the electron density inside the cavity. This control is necessary because the electric fields due to space charge cause large shifts of the cyclotron resonance according to the formula

$$\frac{\Delta \omega_c}{\omega_c} = \frac{mc^2}{e} \frac{\langle E_r \rangle}{RB^2} ,$$ (3.4.3)

where $\langle E_r \rangle$ is the time-averaged radial electric field experienced by the orbiting electrons and R is the orbit radius. This difficulty was overcome by measuring the resonant frequency as a function of grid current and extrapolating the results to zero grid current (zero space charge).

Another problem with this method is the precise location of the region of the magnetic field where the absorption is taking place. It was expected that absorption would be due mainly to slow electrons near the grid and this was confirmed by a technique which is similar to one used earlier by Hardy and Purcell.[43] A small perturbing magnetic field is added to the main magnetic field in such a way that only in one plane are the perturbing field and the main field perpendicular. (A single small coil whose axis is perpendicular to the main field will do.) In this plane the magnitude of the total field is least altered by switching on the perturbing field. Therefore, by displacing the perturbing field along the direction of the main field, a position can be found where minimum shift of the resonant frequency is observed as the perturbing field is switched on and off. This determines the plane in which the absorption is taking place. The electron resonance apparatus could then be replaced by the proton resonance head such that the protons sampled the same portion of the magnetic field as had previously been occupied by the absorbing electron cloud.

The experiment of Liebes and Franken[42] for measuring μ_0/μ_p used several novel techniques. The cloud of free electrons was not produced by thermionic emission, but by photoelectric emission. A 5-mm ID Pyrex sphere was evacuated and coated inside with an invisible layer of potassium. Intense light beams, directed onto the bulb through an opening in one end of the microwave cavity, were used to cause photo-emission from the potassium layer. In this way, 10^4 to 10^5 free electrons with lifetimes of about 10^{-6} second could be obtained inside the bulb. The average electron energy was estimated to be 0.3 ev for illumination from an incandescent lamp and 1.5 ev when illuminated from a Hg lamp.

One curious feature of this technique was that maximum electron absorption occurred when only the top (or bottom) portions of the bulb were illuminated. The resonance absorption nearly disappeared when only the central region was illuminated. The experimenters were inclined to think that this was an effect of electrostatic trapping fields in the unlit portion of the bulb.

A drawing of the resonance head is shown in Fig. 6. The small spheres are the sample bulbs which are normally in the center of the cylindrical openings in the cavity block. The upper cavity is fitted with a sliding short for resonance tuning. The lower cavity contains an rf coil for the proton sample. The resonance head was mounted in such a way that rapid displacements could be made in order to place either the electron bulb or the proton bulb at a given point in the magnetic field. In this way, the resonant frequencies were obtained with the bulbs at the same location in the magnetic field.

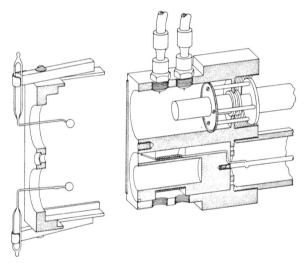

FIG. 6.   Cross section of the electron-proton resonance head used by Liebes and Franken. The sample holder is shown separated from the cavity block. The upper cavity is fitted for electron resonance and the lower cavity for proton resonance. Figure reproduced from Liebes and Franken.[42]

The shifts of electron cyclotron frequency due to electrostatic field gradients were carefully evaluated by Liebes and Franken. They showed that the orbital radius was small enough to assume that $\langle E_r \rangle$ in Eq. (3.4.3) is proportional to R. Thus, to a good approximation,

$$\frac{\Delta\omega_c}{\omega_c} = \frac{K}{B^2},$$
(3.4.4)

where K is independent of orbit radius and electron energy. So, in order to account for this shift, the frequency was measured over a range of magnetic field (750 to 1700 gauss) and plotted against B^{-2}. The data confirmed the relationship in Eq. (3.4.4); the results of a typical run are shown in Fig. 7. The left-hand intercept gives the unshifted value of ω_c/ω_p. Forty-two such runs were taken and analyzed to give the final result.

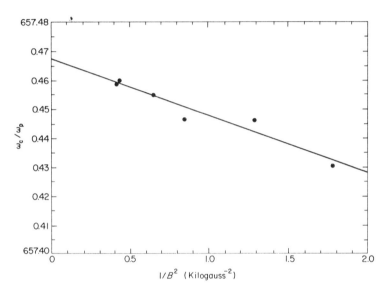

FIG. 7. A typical run from the experiment of Liebes and Franken. The linear dependence of ω_c/ω_p on B^{-2} is illustrated. The averages of forty-two runs, displayed in the same way, also showed good linearity. Figure reproduced from Liebes and Franken.[42]

After corrections for relativistic effects, and for field inhomogeneities due to magnetic contamination, the result is

$$\frac{\mu_0}{\mu_p(\text{spherical oil})} = 657.462 \pm 0.003, \tag{3.4.5}$$

where the uncertainty is due mainly to errors in the magnetic contamination corrections. The more recent result of Sanders, Tittle, and Ward is in excellent agreement with this value.

An unpublished experiment by Hardy and Purcell[43] has given a result for μ_0/μ_p which is not in agreement with that of Liebes and Franken. The electron cyclotron resonance was observed by using microwave absorption due to low-energy free electrons in a waveguide cavity.

Narrow slits in the cavity walls permitted electrons from a 1000°K filament to drift across the wide dimension of the cavity in the direction of the magnetic field. Electron resonance was observed with very low electron densities (a few electrons per cubic centimeter) so that space charge effects were negligible. However, systematic shifts due to static electric field gradients in the cavity were not directly evaluated; several indirect observations suggested that these were negligible. The main source of error in this work was due to the uncertainty associated with substituting a proton resonance probe into the magnetic field region where electron resonance had occurred. Rather large gradients in the magnetic field magnified this uncertainty. The final result* of this experiment is

$$\frac{\mu_0}{\mu_p(\text{spherical } H_2)} = 657.4676 \pm 0.0010. \tag{3.4.6}$$

After diamagnetic corrections have been made according to Liebes and Franken[42] and Hardy and Purcell[43] the result of Hardy and Purcell is

$$\frac{\mu_0}{\mu_p(\text{spherical oil})} = 657.4696 \pm 0.0010. \tag{3.4.7}$$

We are now in a position to obtain values for e/m from the results quoted above and compare them with the value of e/m in Table I which was obtained without recourse to the μ_0/μ_p experimental results. By first correcting the value of γ_p to apply to spherical oil samples and then multiplying, one gets

$$\frac{e}{m} = \frac{\mu_0}{\mu_p \gamma_p} = (1.758\ 790 \pm 0.000\ 015) \times 10^7 \text{ emu/gm}$$

(Liebes and Franken; Sanders, Tittle, and Ward),

$$= (1.758\ 811 \pm 0.000\ 013) \times 10^7 \text{ emu/gm}$$

(Hardy and Purcell), $\tag{3.4.8}$

where most of the uncertainty in these values comes from the experimental errors in γ_p. These results are in agreement with each other (due to the lower precision of γ_p) and in agreement with the value in Table I.

---

* Considerable confusion exists in the literature regarding the unpublished result of Hardy and Purcell. The author is indebted to W. A. Hardy for a direct communication of the results quoted here.

3.5. The Electron Magnetic Moment, μ_e

3.5.1. Introduction

Since Uhlenbeck and Goudsmit[45] first postulated the spinning electron with angular momentum $\hbar/2$ and magnetic moment $\mu_e = \mu_0 \equiv$ one Bohr magneton, the electron magnetic moment has played a leading role in the development of quantum theory. For instance, in his famous paper of 1927, Dirac[46] showed that an electron magnetic moment of μ_0 was a natural consequence of his relativistic wave equation. Twenty years later, Schwinger's[47] calculation of the radiative corrections to μ_e helped modern quantum electrodynamics to gain a foothold. Today, the agreement between the theoretical and experimental values of the electron magnetic moment provides one of the best checks on the theory of quantum electrodynamics.

Bohr was the first to point out that the uncertainty principle places certain limitations on experiments of the Stern–Gerlach type when applied to the measurement of the magnetic moment of electrons.[48] The uncertainty principle limits the accuracy of simultaneous measurements of the magnetic moment and the trajectory of a charged particle. For electrons, it happens that the splitting of the beams from a Stern–Gerlach magnet is smaller than the breadth of each beam and, therefore, statistical methods must be used in order to measure the magnetic moment. However, as we shall see, μ_e can be measured very accurately by experiments which do not provide detailed knowledge of the electron trajectory.

Interest in an accurate measurement of μ_e was kindled by Breit,[49] in 1947, when he suggested that the true value might be slightly larger than the Dirac value, μ_0. In this way, he explained the discrepancy between the theoretical and experimental values for the hyperfine splitting of hydrogen.[50] At the same time, quantum electrodynamics was developing from Bethe's[51] successful calculation of the Lamb shift[52] and, in 1948, Schwinger[47] used the new theory to show that radiative corrections give

$$\mu_e = \mu_0 \left(1 + \frac{\alpha}{2\pi}\right) = \mu_0(1.001\ 16), \tag{3.5.1}$$

[45] G. E. Uhlenbeck and S. Goudsmit, *Nature* **117**, 264 (1926).
[46] P. A. M. Dirac, *Proc. Roy. Soc.* **A117**, 610 (1927).
[47] J. Schwinger, *Phys. Rev.* **73**, 416 (1948); *ibid.* **76**, 790 (1949).
[48] N. F. Mott, *Proc. Roy. Soc.* **A124**, 425 (1929).
[49] G. Breit, *Phys. Rev.* **72**, 984 (1947).
[50] J. E. Nafe and E. B. Nelson, *Phys. Rev.* **73**, 718 (1947).
[51] H. A. Bethe, *Phys. Rev.* **72**, 339 (1947).
[52] W. E. Lamb, Jr. and R. C. Retherford, *Phys. Rev.* **72**, 241 (1947).

to first order in the fine structure constant, α. Experimentally, the first direct measurement of the radiative corrections to μ_e was made by Kusch and Foley.[53] Using atomic beam measurements of the Zeeman splitting in Ga, In, and Na they obtained

$$\mu_e = \mu_0(1.001\ 19 \pm 0.000\ 05). \tag{3.5.2}$$

Since these early discoveries most of the interest in the electron magnetic moment has centered around the higher-order predicitions of the theory. The calculation of the term of order α^2 has been carried out[54–56] and the current theoretical value for μ_e is

$$\mu_e = \mu_0 \left(1 + \frac{\alpha}{2\pi} - 0.328\ \frac{\alpha^2}{\pi^2}\right)$$
$$= \mu_0(1.001\ 159\ 615 \pm 0.000\ 000\ 005), \tag{3.5.3}$$

for $\alpha^{-1} = 137.0389 \pm 0.0006$. The Feynman diagrams for this calculation and their contributions to the observable radiative corrections to μ_e are shown in Fig. 8.

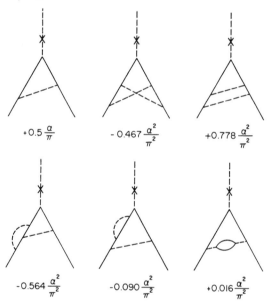

FIG. 8.   The radiative corrections to μ_e. Solid lines represent electrons, dashed lines represent photons, and x's indicate external fields.

[53] P. Kusch and H. M. Foley, *Phys. Rev.* **74**, 250 (1948).
[54] K. Karplus and N. M. Kroll, *Phys. Rev.* **77**, 536 (1950).
[55] C. M. Sommerfield, *Phys. Rev.* **107**, 328 (1957); *Ann. Physik* [6] **5**, 26 (1958).
[56] A. Peterman, *Helv. Phys. Acta* **30**, 407 (1957).

The experimental verification of this very accurate theoretical prediction has motivated a number of highly refined precision experiments, several of which will now be discussed.

3.5.2. Experiments on Bound Electrons

Experiments which measure μ_e fall into two classifications, those in which the electron is bound into an atomic system, and those in which the electron interacts only with macroscopic electromagnetic fields. In the latter case the electron is usually called "free." Although the first measurements[53] of the radiative corrections to μ_e were made on electrons which were bound into complicated atomic systems, the accuracy of such measurements is limited by uncertainties arising from the purity of the atomic state and from relativistic corrections. For this reason, hydrogen is used for precision measurements of the magnetic moment of bound electrons.

The most accurate determination of μ_e from bound electron experiments is obtained by combining the results of two separate measurements. One of the measured quantities is the ratio of the Bohr magneton to the proton magnetic moment, μ_0/μ_p; methods and experiments for measuring μ_0/μ_p are discussed in Section 3.4.2.2 in connection with the evaluation of e/m. The second quantity of interest here is μ_e/μ_p which has been measured with great precision by three groups.[57-59] In these experiments the frequency corresponding to a transition in the magnetic substates of the ground state of hydrogen and the frequency of proton magnetic resonance are measured in the same magnetic field. The ground state transition ordinarily used is $(1, 1) \leftrightarrow (0, 0)$ which in a strong magnetic field is the transition corresponding to flipping the electron spin. Atomic beam techniques[57] and microwave absorption techniques[58,59] have been employed in this measurement with the latter achieving the more precise results. Experiments of these types are discussed by H. E. Radford in Sections 4.1.2.6.1 and 4.1.2.6.2 of this volume.

The frequencies obtained in these experiments are used in the Breit–Rabi formula to give the ratio of the atomic g factor of the ground state of hydrogen to the g factor of the proton, g_j/g_p. By applying the accurately known relativistic correction, g_j is converted to g_e—the free-electron g factor. Thus, a value for μ_e/μ_p is obtained. The ground state of hydrogen has been shown[57] to be sufficiently pure that state

[57] S. H. Koenig, A. G. Prodell, and P. Kusch, *Phys. Rev.* **88**, 191 (1952).

[58] R. Beringer and M. A. Heald, *Phys. Rev.* **95**, 1474 (1954).

[59] E. Lambe, Ph.D. Thesis, Princeton University, 1959 (unpublished).

mixing effects on these measurements are negligible and nuclear effects have been ruled out with similar experiments on deuterium.[60] The results of experiments on μ_0/μ_p and μ_e/μ_p are summarized in Table III. The notation (oil) indicates that measurement is referred to a spherical proton resonance sample of mineral oil. The last entry in the table is the result of Lambe and Dicke, but corrected for diamagnetic effects. All of the error in this result is due to uncertainty in the correction factor. It is clear from the results in Table III that uncertainties in the measurement of μ_0/μ_p are now limiting the precision with which μ_e/μ_0 can be obtained from these experiments. Since the two latest results for μ_e/μ_p are in good agreement, we use the average of these in calculating μ_e/μ_0 below.

TABLE III.   Summary of Experimental Results for Bound Electron Measurements of μ_e/μ_0

Quantity	Result	Reference
μ_0/μ_p (oil)	657.475 ± 0.008	a
μ_0/μ_p (oil)	657.462 ± 0.003	b
μ_0/μ_p (oil)	657.469 6 ± 0.001 0	c
μ_0/μ_p (oil)	657.462 0 ± 0.002 4	d
μ_e/μ_p (oil)	658.228 8 ± 0.000 4	e
μ_e/μ_p (oil)	658.229 8 ± 0.000 3	f
μ_e/μ_p (H_2O)	658.227 59 ± 0.000 04	g
μ_e/μ_p (oil)	658.230 0 ± 0.000 3	h

[a] J. H. Gardner and E. M. Purcell, *Phys. Rev.* **76**, 1262 (1949); J. H. Gardner, *ibid.* **83**, 996 (1951).

[b] S. Liebes and P. A. Franken, *Phys. Rev.* **116**, 633 (1959); *ibid.* **104**, 1197 (1956).

[c] W. A. Hardy and E. M. Purcell, *Bull. Am. Phys. Soc.* **4**, 37 (1959); private communications from W. A. Hardy (1965).

[d] J. H. Sanders, K. F. Tittel, and J. F. Ward, *Proc. Roy. Soc.* **A272**, 103 (1963).

[e] S. H. Koenig, A. G. Prodell, and P. Kusch, *Phys. Rev.* **88**, 191 (1952).

[f] R. Beringer and M. A. Heald, *Phys. Rev.* **95**, 1474 (1954).

[g] E. Lambe, Ph.D. Thesis, Princeton University, 1959 (unpublished).

[h] E. Lambe and R. H. Dicke with diamagnetic corrections from Liebes and Franken[42] and Hardy and Purcell.[43]

The experimental results for μ_0/μ_p due to Liebes and Franken and due to Sanders, Tittle, and Ward are in good agreement. However, they disagree with the result of Hardy and Purcell [see footnote accompanying

[60] J. S. Geiger, V. W. Hughes, and H. E. Radford, *Phys. Rev.* **105**, 183 (1957).

Eq. (3.4.6)] which presumably supercedes the Gardner and Purcell result. We, therefore, calculate μ_e/μ_0 using both of these results:

$$\mu_e/\mu_0 = 1.001\ 168 \pm 0.000\ 005 \quad \text{(Liebes and Franken; Sanders,}$$
$$\text{Tittle, and Ward),}$$
$$= 1.001\ 156 \pm 0.000\ 002 \quad \text{(Hardy and Purcell).} \qquad (3.5.4)$$

3.5.3. Experiments on Free Electrons

3.5.3.1. Polarization Precession Methods. The first measurement of μ_e on free electrons was reported by Louisell, Pidd, and Crane in 1953.[61] The experiment was based upon the Mott double scattering theory[48] which predicts that electrons, when scattered through 90° of angle by a nuclear coulomb field, will emerge partially polarized along a direction perpendicular to the incident and scattered directions. A second 90° coulomb scattering results in an intensity asymmetry in the direction perpendicular to the plane determined by the momentum and the polarization of the beam at the second scatterer.

The method used to measure μ_e was to impose a uniform magnetic field, B, between the scattering foils and parallel to the electron trajectories (see Fig. 9). In this way, the direction of polarization was made to

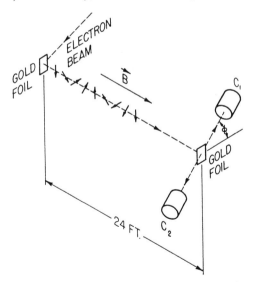

Fig. 9. Schematic diagram of the experiment which gave the first free-electron measurement of μ_e. The final polarization direction was determined by measuring ϕ for maximum intensity asymmetry in the counters.

[61] W. H. Louisell, R. W. Pidd, and H. R. Crane, *Phys. Rev.* **91**, 475 (1953); *ibid.* **94**, 7 (1954).

precess about the magnetic field direction with a circular frequency equal to $g(eB/2mc)$, where g is the free-electron g factor and $\mu_e = (g/2)\mu_0$. Therefore, measurements of B and of the precession rate constituted a measurement of μ_e/μ_0. The experimental parameters were such that the polarization rotated through about five revolutions between the scattering foils and, since the error in determining the final polarization angle was $\pm10°$, the accuracy was limited to $\pm0.5\,\%$. Therefore, the result of this experiment ($g = 2.00 \pm 0.01$) did not check the radiative corrections to μ_e, but did demonstrate the measurability, in principle, of the free-electron magnetic moment.

The experiment just described also provided a logical steppingstone to the ($g - 2$) experiment which is currently the most precise method for measuring the radiative corrections to μ_e/μ_0. A discussion of this experiment is postponed until Sections 3.5.4 and 3.5.5.

Farago[62] has proposed a method for comparing the orbital and the spin precession rates of electrons moving in a magnetic field. Polarized electrons, moving perpendicular to a uniform magnetic field, B, are obtained from a β-active source. A uniform weak electric field, E, is applied as shown in Fig. 10, so that the beam "walks" enough to miss

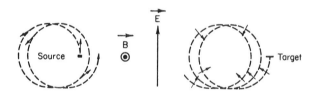

FIG. 10. Farago's method. The polarization directions, indicated by the arrows, correspond to settings of E and B which give about 250 orbital revolutions between the targets.

the back of the source on the first turn. The beam continues walking to the right for a distance almost equal to the orbital diameter. It then encounters a scattering foil, at which the final direction of polarization is determined from the intensity asymmetry in the direction perpendicular to the plane of the orbit. If the final polarization direction is measured as a function of the transit time between source and target, then a sine curve is obtained whose frequency is equal to the difference between the spin precession frequency and the orbital frequency of the circulating electrons. To the extent that $E/B \ll 1$, this difference frequency is proportional to $[\mu_e/\mu_0 - 1]$ (see Section 3.5.4). Thus,

[62] P. S. Farago, *Proc. Phys. Soc. (London)* **72**, 891 (1958); P. S. Farago, R. B. Gardiner, J. Muir, and A. G. A. Rae, *ibid.* **82**, 493 (1963).

Farago's method measures directly the radiative corrections to the free-electron magnetic moment. One particularly attractive feature of this method is that it is directly applicable to positrons.

3.5.3.2. Magnetic Resonance Methods. A resonance method which bears some resemblance to the method of Louisell et al. has been suggested by Tolhoek and DeGroot.[63] The electron polarization would be caused to precess in a magnetic field between two scattering foils, but, in addition, an rf magnetic field would be applied normal to the main field. With the radio-frequency tuned to the electron precession frequency, depolarization of the beam would be observed as a disappearance of the intensity asymmetry at the second scattering foil. Thus, one measures the free-electron precession frequency which, when combined with a measured value for the magnetic field, gives μ_e/μ_0.

Another class of experiments has been proposed,[64] but has not yet yielded results. In these experiments, very low-energy polarized electrons are trapped in a weak magnetic bottle and a radio-frequency field is applied. When either the orbital frequency or the magnetic precession frequency is applied, the electrons should gain energy and leave the trap to be detected. Thus, the circular frequencies of orbital motion, eB/mc, and spin precession, $(g_e/2)(eB/mc)$, are measured and g_e is obtained.

To date, only one resonance-type experiment has been successful in detecting the spin precession frequency of free electrons. The technique, developed by Demelt,[65] uses a transparent bulb containing sodium atoms in an argon buffer gas. The bulb is placed in a uniform magnetic field and the sodium atoms are polarized by illumination with circularly polarized resonance radiation (optical pumping). Free electrons are produced in the bulb by a periodic rf discharge which ionizes some of the argon. Through the mechanism of exchange collisions the free-electron cloud quickly assumes the polarization of the sodium atoms, and any effect which tends to depolarize the electrons also depolarizes the sodium. A change in the sodium polarization causes a change in the transmission of the resonance radiation which is detected by a photocell. Radio-frequency fields are applied to the bulb and a resonance is detected by the photocell output when the frequency corresponds to the free-electron spin precession frequency or to one of the Zeeman transition frequencies of the sodium ground state. In this way, the ratio of the free-electron g factor to the atomic g factor of the ground state of sodium has been measured to a few parts per million.[66] However, an accurate

[63] H. A. Tolhoek and S. R. DeGroot, *Physica* **17**, 17 (1951).

[64] F. Block, *Physica* **19**, 821 (1953).

[65] H. Demelt, *Phys. Rev.* **109**, 381 (1958).

[66] J. L. Hobart, Ph.D. Thesis, University of Michigan, 1962 (unpublished).

measurement of the sodium ground state g factor by an independent experiment is now needed in order to get g for free electrons by this method.

3.5.4. The Electron $(g - 2)$ Experiment—Method and Theory

3.5.4.1. The Ideal $(g - 2)$ Experiment. In 1953, Crane *et al.*[67] pointed out that, if polarized electrons were caused to move with their velocities perpendicular to a uniform magnetic field, then at a fixed azimuth on the cyclotron orbits one would observe the polarization precessing at a rate equal to the difference between the spin precession rate and orbital (cyclotron) rate. As we will now show, this difference precession rate, ω_D, is directly proportional to the "anomalous" part of the electron magnetic moment; i.e., it is proportional, not to μ_e, but to $[\mu_e/\mu_0 - 1]$, which we hereafter denote by a. This last quantity can also be written as $\frac{1}{2}(g - 2)$, where g is the free-electron g factor, and, hence, the conventional name "$(g - 2)$" for experiments of this type.

A simple calculation of ω_D can be made by considering a classical spinning electron with magnetic moment

$$\mu_e = \mu_0(1 + a),\tag{3.5.5}$$

which is moving perpendicular to a uniform magnetic field, B.

The orbital (cyclotron) rate is

$$\omega_c = \frac{eB}{\gamma mc},\tag{3.5.6}$$

where $\gamma = [1 - v^2/c^2]^{-1/2}$. The spin precession rate in the rest frame of the electron is

$$\omega_s' = \frac{2\mu_e}{\hbar} B' = \frac{eB'}{mc}(1 + a),\tag{3.5.7}$$

where $B' = \gamma B$ is the magnetic field in the rest frame. In transforming ω_s' into the laboratory frame we must take care to include the effects of Thomas precession which is well known for its role in atomic fine structure splitting. This effect of relativistic kinematics arises here because the circular electron orbits cause the rest frame to undergo accelerated motion.[68] As we shall see below, Thomas precession plays a

[67] H. R. Crane, R. W. Pidd, and W. H. Louisell, *Phys. Rev.* **91**, 475 (1953).

[68] L. H. Thomas, *Nature* **117**, 514 (1926); *Phil. Mag.* [7] **3**, 1 (1927). A lucid discussion of Thomas precession is given by J. Aharoni, "The Special Theory of Relativity," p. 48. Oxford Univ. Press (Clarendon), London and New York, 1959.

very important role in the $(g - 2)$ method. The Thomas precession rate for circular motion, of rate ω_c, can be written as

$$\omega_T = \omega_c(1 - \gamma). \tag{3.5.8}$$

The spin precession rate as seen from the laboratory is then

$$\omega_s = \frac{\omega_s{}'}{\gamma} + \omega_T, \tag{3.5.9}$$

where $(\gamma)^{-1}$ is the time dilatation factor. The four preceding equations can be combined to give the difference precession rate as

$$\omega_D \equiv \omega_s - \omega_c = a\,\frac{eB}{mc}. \tag{3.5.10}$$

Notice that ω_D is independent of the electron energy and is proportional to the anomalous part of the magnetic moment. A quantum mechanical calculation[69] of ω_D gives the same result as is given by this simple classical calculation.

From Eq. (3.5.10) we see that the difference frequency is zero for a Dirac electron $(\mu_e = \mu_0)$ circling in a magnetic field. That is, the laboratory spin precession rate just equals the cyclotron rate and the polarization direction maintains a constant orientation with respect to the radius vector from the center of the orbit. This equality of ω_c and ω_s is surprising in view of the fact that the spin precession is made up of two parts: a magnetic precession, $\omega_s{}'/\gamma$, and a purely kinematic precession, ω_T.

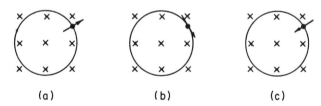

(a)   (b)   (c)

FIG. 11. Illustration of the ideal $(g - 2)$ experiment. The arrows indicate the polarization direction (a) initially, (b) after 250 orbital revolutions, and (c) after 500 orbital revolutions.

The idealized $(g - 2)$ experiment for real electrons $(a \approx 10^{-3})$ is illustrated in Fig. 11. Except at very relativistic energies, ω_s exceeds ω_c by about 0.1 % and, therefore, the difference precession rate is roughly 0.1 % of the cyclotron rate. Thus, about 1000 orbital revolutions are

[69] H. Mendlowitz and K. M. Case, *Phys. Rev.* **97**, 33 (1955); *ibid.* **100**, 1551 (1955).

required for a single revolution of the polarization direction as viewed from a fixed point on the orbit.

3.5.4.2. The Actual (g − 2) Experiment.   The actual (g − 2) experiment has been devised in such a way that the ideal conditions (electrons moving perpendicular to a uniform magnetic field) are satisfied as nearly as possible. Figure 12 is a sketch of the actual experiment.

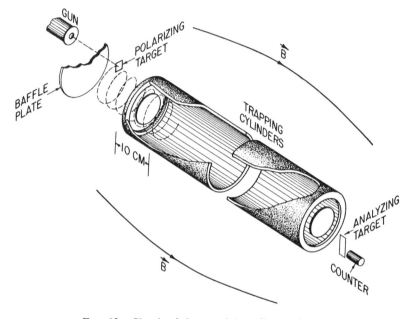

FIG. 12.   Sketch of the actual (g − 2) experiment.

A short pulse of electrons leaves the gun moving parallel to the magnetic field and is scattered from the polarizing target. Those electrons which are scattered to the right through an angle of about 89° are allowed to leave the vicinity of the target through a slit (not shown). This partially polarized beam starts traveling down the magnetic field in a helical path. If unperturbed, the beam will travel through the cylinders and strike the analyzing target. In order to keep the electrons in the magnetic field for a longer time and, hence, allow more cycles of the difference precession to take place, the electrons are trapped between the targets as follows.

As seen in Fig. 12, the magnetic field is slightly bottle-shaped; hence, the spiraling electrons are acted upon by the weak axial magnetic forces directed toward the median plane of the bottle. These forces are, of course, conservative and some perturbation of the orbits is needed in order to prevent the electrons from hitting one of the targets in a very short time. The perturbation is supplied by weak electric fields which are applied across the gap in the trapping cylinders shown in Fig. 12. At the time that the electron gun is pulsed, a negative potential is applied to the right-hand trapping cylinder; therefore, the electrons lose some axial energy when they cross the gap and are then turned around by magnetic forces before they reach the analyzing target. However, before they return to the gap, the potential is removed from the right-hand cylinder and the electrons do not regain the axial energy which they lost on their first crossing of the gap. Their axial energy is now insufficient to allow them to return to the polarizing target, and so they are trapped in the magnetic bottle and will continue to spiral from one end to the other with a beam lifetime determined by gas scattering. The process just described is called injection.

In order to eject electrons from the trap, so that their polarization can be analyzed, a negative potential is applied to the left-hand trapping cylinder in Fig. 12. The electrons which happen to be in this cylinder at the time of ejection are given sufficient axial energy, when they cross the gap, so that they reach the analyzing target at the right-hand end of the trap. The electron gun is then pulsed again and the cycle is repeated.

Since the bottle-shaped magnetic field acts like an energy well for the electrons, the trapping process may be illustrated as in Fig. 13. Sketch (a) shows the energy well with the electron gun turned on and both cylinders at ground potential and (b) shows the well with the right-hand

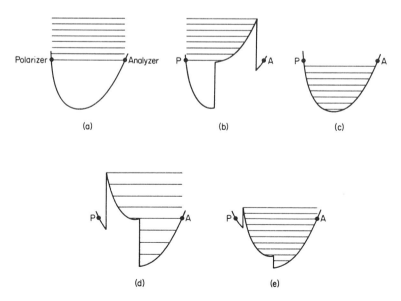

FIG. 13.   The trapping process from an energy-well point of view.

cylinder pulsed so as to inject electrons. In (c) the cylinder potential is back to zero and the electron gun is off; electrons are in the trap. Sketch (d) shows half of the electrons being ejected from the well; the electrons that are in the right-hand side, at the time that the left-hand cylinder is pulsed, remain in the trap. Sketch (e) shows the effect of using a low ejection voltage so that only electrons from the top of the well reach the analyzing target.

The counting rate of the Geiger counter in Fig. 12 depends upon the polarization direction of the electrons being scattered from the analyzing target. If this counting rate is measured as a function of trapping time (the time between cylinder pulses), then a cosine curve is obtained which alternates at a rate equal to the difference precession rate, ω_D. The measurement of ω_D and of the time-averaged magnetic field experienced by the trapped electrons constitutes a direct measurement of a through the use of Eq. (3.5.10).

For precision experiments of the type just described, Eq. (3.5.10) must be modified to conform with the nonideal conditions of the experiment. There are four important differences between the ideal and the actual $(g - 2)$ experiments. (1) As mentioned in the preceding paragraph, the nonuniformity of the magnetic field means that the time-averaged value of B over the electron orbits must be obtained. Another problem introduced by the bottle-shaped magnetic field is that of depolarization of the trapped beam. Mendlowitz and Case[69] investigated this problem and found that depolarization is small if

$$N < \frac{1}{5n\langle\theta^2\rangle_{\mathrm{av}}}, \qquad (3.5.11)$$

where N is the number of cyclotron revolutions, n is the falloff index of the magnetic field ($B \approx \mathrm{const}\ r^n$), and θ is the pitch angle of the trapped electrons. (2) The electron velocity is not perpendicular to the magnetic field; the effects of the finite pitch of the spiraling beam must be considered. (3) Stray electric fields cannot be avoided in the trapping region; therefore, Eq. (3.5.10) must be generalized to include the effects of possible electric fields. (4) Although theoretical considerations (see Section 3.6.1) make the existence of an electric dipole moment (EDM) for electrons very unlikely, this possibility should be considered here. The inherent precision of the $(g - 2)$ experiment makes it a good test for an electronic EDM.

Equation (3.5.10) will now be generalized to include the effects introduced by the actual experimental conditions. We first calculate the spin precession frequency for electrons moving with velocity **v** in magnetic and electric fields, $\mathbf{B}$ and $\mathbf{E}$. As viewed from the laboratory

$$\boldsymbol{\omega}_s = -\frac{e}{mc}\left[\frac{1}{1+\gamma}\frac{\mathbf{v}}{c}\times\mathbf{E}' + \frac{g_e}{2\gamma}\mathbf{B}' + \frac{\lambda}{\gamma}\mathbf{E}'\right], \qquad (3.5.12)$$

where the electron EDM $= \lambda(e\hbar/2mc)$ and the primes indicate fields in the electron's rest frame. The first term on the right is the Thomas precession, the second is the magnetic precession, and the third is the electric precession. Again, the γ^{-1} factors in the last two terms account for time dilatation. In terms of the laboratory fields $\mathbf{B}$ and $\mathbf{E}$

$$\boldsymbol{\omega}_s = -\frac{e}{mc}\left[\frac{\mathbf{B}}{\gamma} - \frac{1}{1+\gamma}\frac{\mathbf{v}}{c}\times\mathbf{E} + a\left(\mathbf{B} - \frac{\gamma}{1+\gamma}\mathbf{v}\cdot\mathbf{B}\frac{\mathbf{v}}{c^2} - \frac{\mathbf{v}}{c}\times\mathbf{E}\right)\right.$$

$$\left. + \lambda\left(\mathbf{E} - \frac{\gamma}{1+\gamma}\mathbf{v}\cdot\mathbf{E}\frac{\mathbf{v}}{c^2} + \frac{\mathbf{v}}{c}\times\mathbf{B}\right)\right]. \qquad (3.5.13)$$

Again, the magnetic moment anomaly, a, occurs naturally as a result of combining the Thomas precession and the magnetic precession terms.

Equation (3.5.13) is now written in cylindrical coordinates, r, θ, z, and all terms are time-averaged over the trapping time. Geometrical and kinematic arguments can then be used to simplify the right-hand side term by term. For example, the conditions of the experiment require that

$$\langle v_r\rangle_{\mathrm{av}} = 0 ; \qquad \langle v_z\rangle_{\mathrm{av}} \approx 0 ; \qquad \langle v_\theta\rangle_{\mathrm{av}} \approx v = \beta c ;$$

$$\langle B_r\rangle_{\mathrm{av}} \ll \langle B_z\rangle_{\mathrm{av}} ; \qquad \langle B_\theta\rangle_{\mathrm{av}} = 0 ; \qquad \langle E_i\rangle_{\mathrm{av}} \ll \langle B_z\rangle_{\mathrm{av}} .$$

In this way, one finds that to a good approximation

$$\langle\boldsymbol{\omega}_s\rangle_{\mathrm{av}} = -\frac{e}{mc}\left[\frac{\langle B_z\rangle_{\mathrm{av}}}{\gamma} + a\langle B_z\rangle_{\mathrm{av}} + \frac{\beta}{1+\gamma}\langle E_r\rangle_{\mathrm{av}}\right.$$

$$\left. - \frac{a\langle B_z\rangle_{\mathrm{av}}\gamma}{1+\gamma}\frac{\langle v_z^2\rangle_{\mathrm{av}}}{c^2}\right]\frac{\mathbf{z}}{z}$$

$$ - \frac{e}{mc}\left[\lambda\beta\langle B_z\rangle_{\mathrm{av}}\right]\frac{\mathbf{r}}{r}. \qquad (3.5.14)$$

The above approximations can also be applied to the orbital equation of motion to get the time-averaged cyclotron rate,

$$\langle\boldsymbol{\omega}_c\rangle_{\mathrm{av}} = -\frac{e}{mc}\left[\frac{\langle B_z\rangle_{\mathrm{av}}}{\gamma} + \frac{\langle E_r\rangle_{\mathrm{av}}}{\beta\gamma}\right]\frac{\mathbf{z}}{z}. \qquad (3.5.15)$$

The time-averaged difference precession $\langle\boldsymbol{\omega}_D\rangle_{\mathrm{av}}$ is found by subtracting Eq. (3.5.15) from Eq. (3.5.14). The quantity which is actually measured in the $(g-2)$ experiment is the magnitude of $\langle \omega_D \rangle_{av}$ which we will hereafter denote as ω_D. One finds that

$$\omega_D = \frac{e\langle B_z\rangle_{av}}{mc}\left[a - \frac{a\gamma}{1+\gamma}\frac{\langle v_z^2\rangle_{av}}{c^2} - \frac{\langle E_r\rangle_{av}}{\beta\gamma^2\langle B_z\rangle_{av}} + \frac{\lambda^2\beta^2}{2a}\right] \qquad (3.5.16)$$

to a sufficiently good approximation.

This result is similar to Eq. (3.5.10) except that B has been replaced by $\langle B_z\rangle_{av}$ and three correction terms have been added to the right-hand side. The first correction term arises from the nonzero pitch of the trapped electrons. The second accounts for possible radial electric fields in the trapping region; ω_D is relatively insensitive to the other two components of $\mathbf{E}$. Finally, the third correction term appears if the electron EDM is nonzero.

3.5.5. The Electron $(g-2)$ Experiments—Results

3.5.5.1. The First Experiment. The experiment described in the previous section was first carried out by Schupp, Pidd, and Crane[70] as a sequel to the Louisell, Pidd, and Crane[61] experiment. The goal, of course, was to measure $\langle B_z\rangle_{av}$ and ω_D as accurately as possible and then use Eq. (3.5.16) to obtain a. The measurement of these two quantities and the evaluation of the correction terms are discussed later in this section in connection with an improved version of the same experiment. Some experimental parameters are given in Table IV for both of these experiments.

TABLE IV.   Parameters of the $(g-2)$ Experiments

Parameter	Schupp, Pidd, Crane[70]	Wilkinson, Crane[71]
Solenoid dimension (cm)	600 × 30 diameter	240 × 60 diameter
Trap dimensions (cm)	78 × 18 diameter	61 × 15 diameter
Electron energy (kev)	50 to 100	45 to 114
Magnetic field (gauss)	82 to 117	94 to 153
Magnetic trap depth (gauss)	0.2 to 0.3	0.05 to 0.08
Energy well depth (ev)	150 to 210	27 to 65
Max. trap time (μsec)	300	1900

The final result of Schupp, Pidd, and Crane was

$$a = 0.001\ 160\ 9 \pm 0.000\ 002\ 4, \qquad (3.5.17)$$

[70] A. A. Schupp, R. W. Pidd, and H. R. Crane, *Phys. Rev.* **121**, 1 (1961).
[71] D. T. Wilkinson and H. R. Crane, *Phys. Rev.* **130**, 852 (1963).

where experimental error was mainly due to uncertainty in the values of the correction terms of Eq. (3.5.16) and partly due to experimental uncertainty in the value of $\langle B_z \rangle_{av}$. It should be noted that this experiment provided the first measurement of a for free electrons and, at the same time, obtained an accuracy as good as that of the best bound electron measurements. When written in the form of the theoretical power series for a the result in Eq. (3.5.17) becomes

$$ a = \frac{\alpha}{2\pi} - (0.1 \pm 0.4)\frac{\alpha^2}{\pi^2} . \qquad (3.5.18)$$

Therefore, the experimental coefficient of α^2/π^2 was in agreement with the theoretical value of 0.328, but fell just short of providing an experimental check on this value.

3.5.5.2. The Second Experiment. The success of the first $(g - 2)$ experiment provided the motivation for Wilkinson and Crane to undertake a second version of the experiment.[71] The goal of this new experiment was to improve the accuracy to a point where the theoretical coefficient of α^2/π^2 could be checked. Some of the improvements made are indicated in Table IV. Longer trapping times were obtained and the magnetic field gradient in the trap was reduced. These improvements allowed more accurate determination of ω_D and $\langle B_z \rangle_{av}$.

The magnetic field was controlled by a proton resonance regulator which used the frequency of a crystal-controlled oscillator as the reference. Another proton resonance head was used to map the magnetic field inside the magnetic bottle. Figure 14 is a graph of the azimuthally averaged magnetic field at the beam radius as a function of axial distance, z. It can be shown (see Wilkinson and Crane[71]) that the energy well has approximately the same shape as $B_z(z)$; therefore, an energy scale, corresponding to this setting of the magnetic field, is also given in Fig. 14.

The time-averaged magnetic field experienced by electrons trapped at a given energy level can be calculated from the magnetic field map. The results of such a calculation are shown in Fig. 14 for five different energy levels. Now, if we know the energy level from which electrons are ejected, the value of $\langle B_z \rangle_{av}$ can be found. Fortunately, there is an easy way to control the energy level from which electrons are ejected. By applying ejection voltages which are less than the depth of the energy well (measured in electron volts), only electrons from the higher levels are able to reach the analyzing target. Figure 13(e) illustrates the low-voltage ejection process. This trick was used in the second experiment to reduce the uncertainty in the value of $\langle B_z \rangle_{av}$.

The quantity $2\pi/\omega_D$ was measured by accurately locating in time two maxima of the asymmetry cosine curve and then dividing the time separating these maxima by the counted number of cycles between them. As in the previous experiment, ω_D and $\langle B_z \rangle_{av}$ were measured at

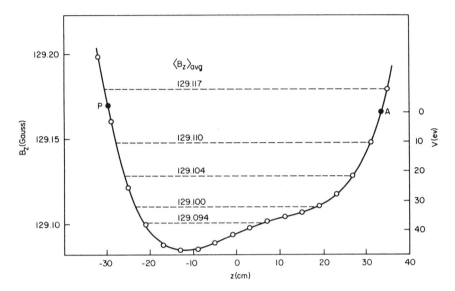

FIG. 14. The magnetic field in the trapping region after averaging over azimuth. This is one of four field settings used in obtaining the final data.

different electron energies and magnetic field settings. (The beam radius was kept constant.) In this way, the effects of radial electric fields and an electron EDM can be evaluated. Samples of the data used to determine ω_D are shown in Fig. 15.

The number of cycles, M, between two arbitrarily chosen maxima was determined as follows. Asymmetry data were taken around a trapping time halfway between the chosen maxima. If a maximum was found, then M was even; a minimum meant M was odd. Similar data at a trapping time one-third of the way between the maxima established whether $M - 1$, M, or $M + 1$ was divisable by 3. This procedure was repeated at shorter trapping times until a unique number for M was obtained.

It should be noted that a serious systematic error is avoided by determining ω_D between two *measured* maxima instead of between one measured maximum and the assumed maximum at zero trapping time. The absolute trapping time is difficult to determine with accuracy due to electronic delays and due to the finite time spread of the beam leaving the trap. However, changes in trapping time can be measured accurately because the spacing of the trapping pulses is determined by a crystal-controlled oscillator. The use of two measured maxima permits the measurement of ω_D by using only changes in trapping time; the absolute trapping time is not needed.

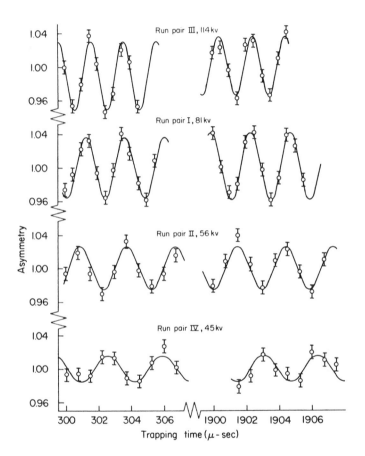

FIG. 15. Samples of the data used to determine ω_D.

The measurement of ω_D and $\langle B_z \rangle_{av}$ has now been described. Three other quantities in Eq. (3.5.16) can be determined directly from the data. The value of $\langle v_z^2 \rangle_{av}$ is related to the axial kinetic energy of the trapped electrons and the latter can be computed from the magnetic field map (see Wilkinson and Crane[71]). Also known in Eq. (3.5.16) are the values of β and γ from measurements of the total electron energy. We now solve Eq. (3.5.16) for a and arrange the terms so that all measured quantities appear on the right. Then

$$a - \frac{\langle E_r \rangle_{\text{av}}}{\beta \gamma^2 \langle B_z \rangle_{\text{av}}} + \frac{\lambda^2 \beta^2}{2a} = \frac{\omega_D}{\langle B_z \rangle_{\text{av}}} \frac{mc}{e} + \frac{a\gamma}{1+\gamma} \frac{\langle v_z^2 \rangle_{\text{av}}}{c^2}. \qquad (3.5.19)$$

The terms on the right-hand side were measured at four values of electron energy and the results are plotted in Fig. 16 against the coefficient of $\langle E_r \rangle_{\text{av}}$;

$$X = (\gamma^2 \beta \langle B_z \rangle_{\text{av}})^{-1}. \qquad (3.5.20)$$

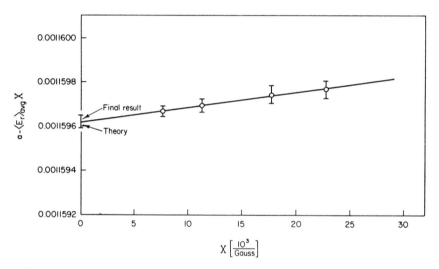

FIG. 16.   The measured values of the right-hand side of Eq. (3.5.19) plotted against the coefficient of $\langle E_r \rangle_{\text{av}}$.

The linearity of the points in Fig. 16 suggests that the energy shift observed in this experiment was indeed caused by a constant radial electric field. The slope of the results has the opposite sign from the slope that would be produced by an electronic EDM. Furthermore, this term would introduce some curvature into the results as plotted in Fig. 16. Therefore, when fitting the left-hand side of Eq. (3.5.19) to the measured results, it was assumed that the effect of the EDM term was negligible.

The least-squares fit of a straight line to the points in Fig. 16 gives the intercept at $X = 0$ as

$$a = 0.001\ 159\ 622 \pm 0.000\ 000\ 027. \qquad (3.5.21)$$

The experimental errors, shown by the error flags in Fig. 16, can be put into four categories. (1) About two-thirds of the experimental error results from uncertainty in the values of $\langle B_z \rangle_{av}$ and $\langle v_z{}^2 \rangle_{av}$ due to the uncertainty in the average level from which electrons are ejected. Fortunately, these two systematic errors tend to cancel in Eq. (3.5.19), for if the average energy level is chosen too high, then the value of $\langle B_z \rangle_{av}$ will be too large, but the calculated value of $\langle v_z{}^2 \rangle_{av}$ will also be too large. The remainder of the experimental error is made up of approximately equal contributions from (2) statistical errors in measuring ω_D, (3) possible undetectable drifting of the magnetic field, and (4) the present uncertainty in the value of $\gamma_p(m/e)$ (see Section 3.4.2.2) where γ_p is the proton gyromagnetic ratio.

3.5.5.3. Comments on the (g − 2) Experimental Results. The most interesting result of the experiment just described is the complete agreement between the experimental and theoretical values of a to order α^2/π^2. The agreement is best shown by writing the experimental result in Eq. (3.5.21) as

$$a = \frac{\alpha}{2\pi} - (0.327 \pm 0.005) \frac{\alpha^2}{\pi^2} \qquad (3.5.22)$$

and comparing the coefficient of α^2/π^2 to the theoretical value, 0.328. Referring to Fig. 8, we see that the contribution of each of the five α^2 Feynman diagrams is larger than the experimental error in Eq. (3.5.22). Therefore, the existence of each of these diagrams is necessary to the present agreement between theory and experiment. This agreement is one of the best justifications to date for the methods of modern quantum electrodynamics.

The value of the next term in the theoretical power series for a has recently been estimated to be $+ 0.15\alpha^3/\pi^3$.[72] However, this prediction cannot be checked by improved (g − 2) experiments until more accurate values of the constants α and $\gamma_p(m/e)$ are found from other experiments.

It was mentioned earlier that the (g − 2) experiment provides a sensitive test for the existence of an electric dipole moment for electrons. The experimental results have been analyzed to give an upper limit on the electron EDM and this work is described in Section 3.6.2.

One particularly appealing aspect of the free-electron (g − 2) experiments is the purity of the interaction being studied. To a high degree of precision only electron-photon interactions need to be considered; thus, nuclear size effects, possible strong interaction, etc., do not muddle the comparison of the experimental result to the theoretical prediction.

[72] S. D. Drell and H. R. Pagels, *Phys. Rev.* 140, B397 (1965).

3.5.6. The Positron Magnetic Moment, μ_{pos}

3.5.6.1. Experiments on Bound Positrons–Positronium. A value for μ_{pos} can be obtained by examing the results of precision experiments which determine the fine structure splitting of the ground state of positronium (see Section 4.1.2 of this volume). A large fraction of this splitting is due to the $\mu_e \cdot \mu_{pos}$ interaction, and so a comparison of theoretical and experimental values can be used to evaluate μ_{pos}. The current experimental results[73,74] are in good agreement with the theoretical[75] fine structure value and are also in good agreement with each other. An average of the three most precise experimental values gives

$$\nu_{\text{Exp}} = (2.0336 \pm 0.0004) \times 10^5 \, \text{mc/sec.} \qquad (3.5.23)$$

We now interpret this result in terms of a possible difference, $\delta\mu$, in the electron and positron magnetic moments. Since the magnetic interaction contributes $4/7$ of the total splitting[76] and the current experimental errors are ± 2 parts in 10^4, a limit of $3.5 \times 10^{-4}\mu_e$ can be placed on $\delta\mu$. With the electron magnetic moment precisely known, this result can be rewritten to give the positron magnetic moment as

$$\mu_{pos} = \mu_0 \left[1 + (1 \pm 0.3) \frac{\alpha}{2\pi} \right]. \qquad (3.5.24)$$

Thus, the first radiative correction to μ_{pos} is confirmed to $\pm 30\%$.

3.5.6.2. Experiments on Free Positrons. The method of Crane for measuring $(g - 2)$ for free electrons has now been applied to positrons.[77] The electron gun and polarizing target are replaced by a radioactive positron source (polarization $\approx v/c$). The post-trapping polarization direction is measured by causing the positrons to stop and form positronium in a strong magnetic field. The lifetime of positronium, thus formed, depends on the direction of the polarization of the incident positron, and so the time between the stopping of the positron (in plastic scintillator) and the appearance of annihilation radiation is a measure of this polarization (see Section 2.5.5.5 of Volume 5B of this series).

[73] M. Deutsch and S. C. Brown, *Phys. Rev.* **85**, 1047 (1952); R. Weinstein, M. Deutsch, and S. C. Brown, *ibid.* **94**, 758 (1954); *ibid.* **98**, 223 (1955).

[74] V. W. Hughes, S. Marder, and C. S. Wu, *Phys. Rev.* **106**, 934 (1957).

[75] R. Karplus and A. Klein, *Phys. Rev.* **87**, 848 (1952).

[76] H. A. Bethe and E. E. Salpeter, "Quantum Mechanics of One- and Two-Electron Atoms," p. 114. Academic Press, New York, 1957.

[77] Arthur Rich and H. R. Crane, *Bull. Am. Phys. Soc.* **11**, 121 (1965); *Phys. Rev. Letters* **17**, 271 (1966).

The first results of this experiment have given a value of

$$a_{\text{pos}} = (1.0 \pm 0.1)\,\frac{\alpha}{2\pi}, \qquad (3.5.25)$$

for the positron magnetic moment anomaly. Thus, the first radiative correction term is confirmed to $\pm\,10\%$ by these preliminary measurements. Further work is currently in progress.

3.6. The Electron Electric Dipole Moment, EDM

3.6.1. Introduction

The existence of an intrinsic electric dipole moment for an elementary particle would violate certain important symmetry principles. Landau[78] has argued that CP (charge conjugation $\times$ space inversion) is violated by a particle possessing an EDM and Lee and Yang[79] have shown that elementary particles must have zero EDM if either P or T (time reversal) is an invariant operation. Therefore, important symmetry principles are tested by precise experimental evidence on the possible existence of intrinsic electric dipole moments for elementary particles. A very precise experiment[80] has been performed on the neutron which places an upper limit of 3×10^{-20} cm $\times\ e$ on the magnitude of an EDM.

The first precise limit to be placed on the electron EDM was obtained from comparing the theoretical and experimental values of the Lamb shift. Calculation[81,82] of the perturbation of the Lamb shift due to an electron EDM showed that the agreement between experiment and theory (without EDM) would be destroyed if the electron EDM were larger than 4×10^{-14} cm $\times\ e$. Since then, several experimental tests of higher sensitivity have been reported.

3.6.2. Experiments on Free Electrons

3.6.2.1. Electron EDM from the $(g - 2)$ Experiment. The equations which were used to interpret the results of the electron $(g - 2)$ experiment (see Section 3.5.5) included a term to account for a possible electron EDM. However, in fitting Eq. (3.5.19) to the data (Fig. 16) the EDM term was dropped. If this term is retained and a three-parameter

[78] L. Landau, *Nuclear Phys.* 3, 127 (1957).
[79] T. D. Lee and C. N. Yang, *Brookhaven Natl. Lab.* No. 443(BNL) (T-91), 17 (1957).
[80] J. Smith, E. M. Purcell, and N. F. Ramsey, *Phys. Rev.* 108, 120 (1957).
[81] G. Feinberg, *Phys. Rev.* 112, 1637 (1958).
[82] E. E. Salpeter, *Phys. Rev.* 112, 1642 (1958).

$(a, \langle E_r \rangle_{av}, \lambda)$ least-squares fit is performed, then the values of a and $\langle E_r \rangle_{av}$ are nearly the same as before and a value of $\lambda = 2 \times 10^{-5}$ is obtained. Interpreting this result as an upper limit gives, for the free electron,

$$\text{EDM} < 4 \times 10^{-16} \text{ cm} \times e. \tag{3.6.1}$$

It has been suggested[83] that the effect of the electron EDM could be emphasized in the $(g - 2)$ experiment by applying a radial electric field in the trapping region (see Section 3.5.4). The magnitude of this field would be adjusted so as to cancel the magnetic precession of the electrons around the magnetic field direction and, thus, allow an EDM to cause precession around the radial direction. However, preliminary work on such an experiment indicated that depolarization of the trapped electrons, due to the radial gradient in the electric field, was stronger than had been expected, and the experiment was discontinued.

3.6.2.2. Electron EDM from High-Energy Scattering. Experiments[84,85] which measure the absolute differential cross sections for elastic scattering of high-energy electrons have been used to set an upper limit on the electron EDM. The precision of these experiments is, so far, about the same as that of the $(g - 2)$ experiment. The two experiments are complementary in that they test electrons at two widely different energies. The most recent result[85] from scattering experiments gives an upper limit on the EDM of 10^{-15} cm $\times e$ for 41.5 Mev electrons.

3.6.3. Experiments on Bound Electrons

3.6.3.1. Electron EDM from Atomic Beams. A method, bearing some resemblance to the one used for the neutron EDM experiment,[80] has been used to test for an intrinsic EDM in the Cs atom.[86] The result can then be interpreted to give an upper limit on the free-electron EDM. For this experiment an atomic beam apparatus of the separated-oscillating-field[87] type was equipped with parallel plates between the hairpins so that a strong transverse electric field could be applied to the magnetically precessing Cs atoms. Thus, any additional precession, caused by an induced electric moment or by an intrinsic EDM, would be detected as a shift in the resonant frequency when the electric field was turned on. The $(4, -3) \leftrightarrow (4, -4)$ Zeeman transition was used and

[83] D. F. Nelson, A. A. Schupp, R. W. Pidd, and H. R. Crane, *Phys. Rev. Letters* **2**, 492 (1959).

[84] G. R. Burleson and H. W. Kendall, *Nuclear Phys.* **19**, 68 (1960).

[85] J. Goldemberg and Y. Torizuka, *Phys. Rev.* **129**, 2580 (1963).

[86] P. G. H. Sandars and E. Lipworth, *Phys. Rev. Letters* **13**, 718 (1964).

[87] N. F. Ramsey, "Molecular Beams," p. 124. Oxford Univ. Press, London and New York, 1956.

the frequency and the magnetic field (a few gauss) were adjusted to give an operating point on the side of one of the narrow resonance peaks in the Ramsey pattern. This gives maximum sensitivity of the detected beam signal to shifts in the precession frequency and gives a beam signal which is proportional to small shifts in frequency.

The shift in precession frequency is expected to take the form

$$\delta\nu = K_1 E + K_2 E^2, \tag{3.6.2}$$

where the term quadratic in the electric field, E, comes from the Stark effect on the Zeeman levels and the term linear in E is due to an intrinsic EDM of the atom. The linear and quadratic effects were measured separately by applying an electric field of the form

$$E = E_{dc} + E_{ac} \sin \omega t. \tag{3.6.3}$$

One then finds that a time-dependent frequency shift should occur at a rate ω and with an amplitude of $(2K_2 E_{dc} + K_1)E_{ac}$. Since the detected beam signal is proportional to the frequency shift, the amplitude of the signal occuring at ω (25 cps) can be measured with $E_{dc} = 0$ to give K_1. As E_{dc} is changed, the amplitude of the ω component of the signal changes proportionally. The value of K_2 is obtained from the slope of a plot of signal (25 cps) vs E_{dc}.

Early results of this experiment are shown in Fig. 17. The slope of the results indicates that there is indeed a small Stark shift in the Zeeman levels being studied; however, of interest here is the nonzero value of $\delta\nu$ at $E_{dc} = 0$. The value of the intercept corresponds to an EDM for Cs of 2×10^{-19} cm $\times e$. This is interpreted by the experimenters as an upper limit because of the possible existence of a systematic effect which would cause the results in Fig. 17 to be displaced vertically. The effect is due to motional magnetic fields ($\mathbf{v} \times \mathbf{E}$) which give rise to a spurious signal at rate ω if $\mathbf{E}$ and $\mathbf{B}$ are not exactly parallel in the precession region. Attempts are being made to evaluate this possible systematic effect.

The interpretation of the Cs atom EDM in terms of an EDM for the free electron must be done carefully. It has been observed[82,88,89] that a neutral aggregate of nonrelativistic charged particles does not exhibit an EDM even though the charged particles themselves have nonzero EDM's. This is simply because the aggregate must polarize in order to prevent acceleration of the charged particles and the local electric field at the particles adjusts to zero. However, if the charged particles are

[88] R. L. Garwin and L. M. Lederman, *Nuovo cimento* [10] 11, 776 (1959).
[89] L. I. Schiff, *Phys. Rev.* 132, 2194 (1963).

moving with relativistic velocities within the aggregate, then the electric field in the particle's rest frame can be nonzero, even though the time-averaged laboratory electric field is zero, and effects of the charged particle's EDM can be observed.

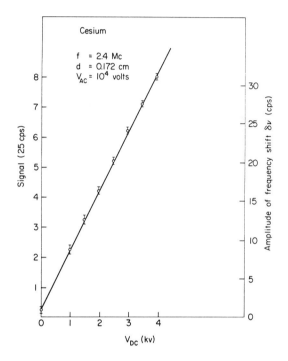

FIG. 17. Early results of the Cs atom EDM experiment. Figure reproduced from Sandars and Lipworth.[86]

The effect of a free-electron EDM on the Cs atom EDM has been calculated[90] with the surprising result that the atomic EDM is some 100 times larger than that of the free electron. Therefore, the upper limit which this experiment can place upon the free-electron EDM is 100 times smaller than the limit actually measured for the Cs atom. The upper limit obtained in this way is

$$\text{EDM} < 2 \times 10^{-21} \, \text{cm} \times e, \tag{3.6.4}$$

which is an improvement of five orders of magnitude over earlier experimental limits.

[90] P. G. H. Sandars, *Phys. Letters* **14**, 194 (1965).

3.6.4. The Positron Electric Dipole Moment

One expects from the symmetry principles that the upper limits for an electron EDM might also apply to positrons. However, these same symmetry principles are open to question if an EDM is found. It is important, therefore, to ask whether any experimental upper limit on the positron EDM exists, even though the limit is not as small as that for the electron.

There seems to be only one current experimental result which yields an upper limit on the positron EDM. Salpeter[82] has computed the effect of a possible electron-positron EDM on the fine structure separation of the ground state of positronium. Then, by using 1 part in 4000 as an upper limit on the possible discrepancy between theory (without EDM) and experiment, he obtained

$$\text{EDM} < 8 \times 10^{-13} \, \text{cm} \times e. \tag{3.6.5}$$

With the electron EDM now known to be very much smaller, this can be roughly interpreted as an experimental upper limit on the positron EDM. Further reductions in this upper limit can be expected to come from improved positronium fine structure measurements, from high-energy positron scattering cross sections, and from experiments, now in progress, to measure $(g - 2)$ for the positron.

4. PROPERTIES OF ATOMS

4.1. Energy Levels

4.1.1. Optical Spectroscopy*

4.1.1.1. Introduction. Experimental spectroscopy encompasses the methods of observing the flux density or intensity of radiation as a function of wavelength, time, and state of polarization. The most frequently investigated relationship is that of intensity as a function of wavelength, known as the spectrum. This article will deal with the methods of obtaining, observing, detecting, and analyzing the spectra of atoms in the optical region. The best presently developed means of measuring wavelength in this region are much more accurate than those of measuring intensity, and it is with the former that we shall mainly be concerned. The question of intensity will, of course, be of importance to us in discussing the relative advantages of sources, spectrometers, and detectors. We shall not, however, treat in detail the methods of making the best intensity measurements and determining transition probabilities as these subjects are covered elsewhere in this volume (see Chapter 4.2). Polarization will be considered here mainly in connection with methods of observing and analyzing the transverse Zeeman effect (Section 4.1.1.2.5); where we deal with two orthogonal plane polarizations. Finally, only a brief mention will be given of the techniques for studying light sources which vary in brightness with time, that is, of time-resolved spectroscopy.

A further limitation of this article is that it will be confined to the experimental methods of optical atomic spectroscopy. We shall assume that the reader is familiar with the elementary principles of atomic structure and with the spectroscopic notations used to describe that part of this structure which results from the interactions of the outer electrons with each other, with the electronic core, and with the nucleus. This information may be found at varying depths of treatment in a number of easily available sources,[1-5] and its omission here

---

[1] M. Born and E. Wolf, "Principles of Optics." Pergamon Press, Oxford, 1957.

[2] B. Edlén, in "Handbuch der Physik—Encyclopedia of Physics (S. Flügge, ed.), Vol. 27, p. 80. Springer, Berlin, 1963.

[3] H. E. White, "Introduction to Atomic Spectra." McGraw-Hill, New York, 1934.

[4] H. G. Kuhn, "Atomic Spectra." Academic Press, New York, 1962.

[5] G. Herzberg, "Atomic Spectra and Atomic Structure." Dover, New York, 1944.

---

* Section 4.1.1 is by K. G. Kessler and H. M. Crosswhite.

will allow a more thorough discussion of experimental spectroscopy.

In a brief review of a field such as this, the discussion will of necessity be somewhat superficial. We hope, however, to give an outline of the problem and, with appropriate references, guide the reader toward the solution of his particular problem.

It will be helpful to the reader if he notices at the beginning that the next three sections of this article follow in division of material the choices one must make when confronted with a problem open to investigation by spectroscopic means: the *source* of the appropriate line or spectrum, the dispersive arrangement or *spectrometer*, and the *detector*. The choices made will depend on, among other things, the wavelength range of the spectrum and the desired accuracy. This matching of instrumentation to problems in physics is discussed in Section 4.1.1.5, with particular emphasis on the methods of analysis and the effect of the experimental limitations on our knowledge of the positions and other properties of the electronic energy levels in atoms. Before beginning our discussion of the above components we will define some units, terms, and concepts necessary for an understanding of the following sections.

4.1.1.1.1. UNITS. The traditional and fundamental unit of wavelength in optical spectroscopy is the angstrom, symbol Å, now defined as exactly 10^{-10} meter. By adoption of a resolution, the 11th General Conference of Weights and Measures (October, 1960) has defined the meter as equal to 1650763.73 wavelengths in vacuum of the orange line of krypton-86 arising from the transition $5p[\frac{1}{2}]_1 - 6d[\frac{1}{2}]_1^0$ (pair-coupling notation). The wavelength in vacuum of this krypton line, the primary standard, is thus 6057.80210(5) Å.

The reciprocal centimeter, cm^{-1}, is the most generally useful unit when we are considering electronic energy levels in atoms. The energy difference, E, between two levels may be expressed in cm^{-1}, since $E = hc\sigma$, where as usual h is Planck's constant, c is the velocity of light, and σ is the wave number difference between the levels, expressed in cm^{-1} in the cgs system. Since wave number differences are determined with accuracies considerably higher than that to which hc is known, it is usual in spectroscopy to use the cm^{-1} as the unit of energy. If two levels are separated by a wave number difference σ, a transition between the levels will have the vacuum wavelength λ_{vac} (Å) $= 10^8/\sigma$ (cm^{-1}). Thus when observations are made in vacuum, measurements of wavelength and wave number are entirely equivalent.

The cm^{-1} is now frequently called the kayser, symbol K. In high-resolution spectroscopy the milliangstrom (1 mÅ $= 10^{-3}$ Å) and the millikayser (1 mK $= 10^{-3}$ K) are frequently used units. Those who usually work with frequency units will note that 1 cm^{-1} corresponds to approximately 30,000 Mc and 1 mK to approximately 30,000 kc. The gross features of atomic structure are conveniently presented in units of the kilokayser (1 kK = 10^3 K). Wavelengths longer than 10,000 Å are often given in microns (μ), (1 μ = 10^4 Å = 10^{-3} mm). Some workers express optical wavelengths in millimicrons or nanometers (1 mμ = 1 nm = 10 Å), a unit which will not be used here.

4.1.1.1.2. GENERAL REFERENCES. The subject of optics is covered in a variety of texts, including the classics by Wood[6] and Drude[7] and the more recent books by Jenkins and White,[8] Sommerfeld,[9] Strong,[10] and Ditchburn.[11] Books on the theory of atomic spectra include Born and Wolf,[1] Condon and Shortley,[12] White,[3] Edlén,[2] Kuhn,[4] and Herzberg.[5] Experimental applications are discussed by Sawyer[13] and Harrison et al.,[14] and spectrochemical analysis by Brode,[15] Ahrens,[16] Nachtrieb,[17] and Twyman.[18] The theory of hyperfine structure and isotope shift are covered by Kopfermann[19] and the instrumentation for these studies by Tolansky[20,21] and Candler.[22]

In the line of tables of atomic wavelengths, the most complete is that compiled and listed by wavelength by Harrison and assistants at MIT.[23] Less extensive, since they cover only the principal multiplets,

[6] R. W. Wood, "Physical Optics." Macmillan, New York, 1934.

[7] P. Drude, "Lehrbuch der Optik." Hirzel, Leipzig, 1912.

[8] F. A. Jenkins and H. E. White, "Fundamentals of Optics." McGraw-Hill, New York, 1957.

[9] A. Sommerfeld, "Optics" (translated by O. Laporte and P. A. Moldauer), Vol. 4. Academic Press, New York, 1954.

[10] J. Strong, "Concepts of Classical Optics." Freeman, San Francisco, California, 1958.

[11] R. W. Ditchburn, "Light." Blackie, Glasgow and London, 1954.

[12] E. U. Condon and G. H. Shortley, "Theory of Atomic Spectra." Cambridge Univ. Press, London and New York, 1963.

[13] R. A. Sawyer, "Experimental Spectroscopy." Prentice-Hall, Englewood Cliffs, New Jersey, 1951.

[14] G. R. Harrison, R. C. Lord, and J. R. Loofbourow, "Practical Spectroscopy." Prentice-Hall, Englewood Cliffs, New Jersey, 1948.

[15] W. R. Brode, "Chemical Spectroscopy." Wiley, New York, 1943.

[16] L. H. Ahrens "Spectrochemical Analysis." Addison-Wesley, Reading, Massachusetts, 1950.

[17] N. H. Nachtrieb, "Principles and Practice of Spectrochemical Analysis." McGraw-Hill, New York, 1950.

[18] F. Twyman, "The Spectrochemical Analysis of Metals Alloys." Chem. Publ. Co., New York, 1941.

[19] H. Kopfermann, "Nuclear Moments" (translated by E. E. Schneider). Academic Press, New York, 1958.

[20] S. Tolansky, "An Introduction to Interferometry." Longmans, Green, New York, 1955.

[21] S. Tolansky, "High-Resolution Spectroscopy." Pitman, New York, 1947.

[22] C. Candler, "Modern Interferometry." Hilger & Watts, London, 1951.

[23] "M.I.T. Wavelength Tables." Wiley, New York, 1939.

but more carefully evaluated are those by Moore,[24] which are listed both by element and by wavelength in a finding list. A fairly complete listing of principal lines of the elements can be found in the American Institute of Physics Handbook[25,25a] and in the Handbook of Chemistry and Physics.[26]

The preceding tables, although generally reliable for wavelength precision and identification, contain, at best, only rough estimates of intensity. References to more precise intensities can be found in a bibliography by Glennon and Wiese.[27] An extensive list of spectral intensities has been published by Meggers *et al.*[28] and some of these entries have been reduced to approximate oscillator strengths by Corliss and Bozman.[29]

Tables of atomic energy levels have been assembled by Moore.[30] Energy level diagrams of some atoms are published in the classical book by Grotrian[31] and more recently by Merrill.[32]

A comprehensive treatment of resonance problems, line widths, lifetimes, etc., is given by Mitchell and Zemansky.[33] Birnbaum[34] has written a comprehensive summary of the laser field.

4.1.1.1.3. OPTICAL WAVELENGTH RANGE. The range of wavelengths to be dealt with in this article extends from a few hundred angstroms in the vacuum ultraviolet to about 13000 Å in the near infrared. This range is characterized by the decreasing reflectivity of coatings at the short-wavelength end and by the decrease in sensitivity of photographic detectors at the long-wavelength end. Hence our restriction as to the meaning of "optical range" is made to some extent on the basis of instrumentation. However, it may also be noted that this range is

---

[24] C. E. Moore, *Natl. Bur. Standards (U.S.) Tech. Note* **36** (1959); *Natl. Bur. Standards (U.S.), Circ.* **488**, Sect. 1, H to V (1950); Sect. 2., Cr to Nb (1952); Sect. 3, Mo to La and Hf to Ac (1958).

[25] "American Institute of Physics Handbook," Section 7. McGraw-Hill, New York, 1963.

[26] "Handbook of Chemistry and Physics." Chem. Rubber Publ. Co., Cleveland, Ohio, 1964.

[27] B. M. Glennon and W. L. Wiese, *Natl. Bur. Standards (U.S.), Monograph* **50** (1962).

[28] W. F. Meggers, B. F. Scribner, and C. H. Corliss, *Natl. Bur. Standards (U.S.), Monograph* **32**, Part I arranged by Elements; Part 2 arranged by Wavelength (1961).

[29] C. H. Corliss and W. R. Bozman, *Natl. Bur. Standards (U.S.), Monograph* **53** (1962).

[30] C. E. Moore, *Natl. Bur. Standards (U.S.), Circ.* **467**, Sect. 1, H to V (1949); Sect. 2, Cr to Nb (1952); Sect. 3, Mo to La and Hf to Ac (1958).

[31] W. Grotrian, "Graphische Darstellung der Spektren von Atomen und Ionen mit ein, zwei und drei Valenzelektronen." Springer, Berlin, 1928.

[32] P. W. Merrill, *Carnegie Inst. Wash. Publ.* **610**, 103–167 (1956).

[33] A. C. G. Mitchell and M. W. Zemansky, "Resonance Radiation and Excited Atoms." Cambridge Univ. Press, London and New York, 1934.

[34] G. Birnbaum, "Optical Masers," Academic Press, New York, 1964.

essentially determined by the values of the atomic constants and the purposes of optical atomic spectroscopy. For these purposes we need to analyze those atomic radiations which arise from transitions between electronic energy levels corresponding to states differing only in the outer electrons. The greatest part of the total oscillator strength associated with such transitions in any neutral atom or ion of moderate ionization is accounted for by lines lying in the above region. Thus the observation and analysis of a well-developed spectrum throughout this region enables one to obtain the positions and other properties of the basic electronic energy levels for the atom being studied.

4.1.1.1.3.1. *"Visible" and Near Infrared.* This region is bounded on the short-wavelength side by the transmission limit of glass at about 3500 Å and on the long-wavelength side by the decreasing sensitivity of detectors. Sensitized photographic emulsions can be used to about 13,000 Å, and photocells can be used to about 12,000 Å. Both have a rapidly decreasing sensitivity beyond 8000 Å. It is a region in which nearly all instruments have a high efficiency. Most common optical materials are highly transparent, metallic reflectivities are high, and very high-efficiency multilayer dielectric films are available. This region shades, on the long-wave side, into the region of infrared techniques, where sulfide cells, bolometers, and thermocouples are used as detectors.

The visible–near IR region also corresponds to that over which the level of blackbody radiation is high for readily attainable temperatures. Tungsten lamps are excellent sources of continuum. The techniques of absorption spectroscopy are therefore easily applied. The availability of efficient blackbodies also makes absolute flux density measurements possible.

4.1.1.1.3.2. *Near Ultraviolet.* This region is an extension of the previous one, the principal difference being that most glasses are opaque, thereby eliminating glass prisms, lenses, and windows. From 3500 Å, this region extends downward to about 1900 Å. This lower limit is determined by the transmission limits of both quartz and air. It is a region characterized by highly efficient detectors and high resolving power instruments. Above 2300 Å, photographic materials and photoelectric cells attain their maximum efficiency. Below 2300 Å, gelatin becomes opaque, and either fluorescent coated plates or Schumann plates must be used. The opacity of glasses leads to some limitations in the availability of lenses. For most purposes, simple quartz lenses are suitable, and excellent quartz–calcium fluorite achromatic lenses are available. Since suitable high-index dielectric layers are difficult to obtain for this region, interferometry is limited largely to the use of metallic films. The reflectivity of pure aluminum is quite good and is generally used in this region.

Blackbody radiation for easily attained temperatures falls off very rapidly toward the UV; thus absolute calibrations of radiant flux become increasingly difficult and less precise toward the shorter wavelength portion of the spectrum. Other sources of continuum, such as the hydrogen continuum, are however available for absorption studies.

4.1.1.1.3.3. *Near Vacuum Ultraviolet.* Below about 1900 Å, air becomes opaque, thus necessitating a drastic change in instrumentation. Source, spectrograph, and detector must be either in a vacuum or in a transparent gas such as helium. Only a limited number of materials such as the fluorites are transparent; hence gratings are almost universally used as the dispersing element. Windows are, however, available down to about 1100 Å, the transmission limit for lithium fluorite. It is the short-wave transmission limit of available transparent materials that sets the lower bound of this region.

The necessity of maintaining a good vacuum (generally below 10^{-5} mm Hg) or an atmosphere of clean, transparent gas adds considerably to the experimental problems. Good, high-reflectivity materials are still available for gratings, but virtually no interferometry has been done. Most light sources can still be used in modified form, and both Schumann and coated photographic plates are quite satisfactory. Phototubes may be windowless or have fluorite windows, or they may be coated with a material such as sodium salicylate which fluoresces strongly.

4.1.1.1.3.4. *Middle Vacuum Ultraviolet.* This region differs from the previous only in that no suitable materials transparent in this region are known. All work must therefore be done in vacuum and without the use of windows. This greatly limits the number of available light sources, which must operate either in vacuum or in an atmosphere of inert gas in a windowless chamber. Sources of structureless continuum radiation are not readily available. Phototubes must be either windowless or coated with a fluorescent material. The lower limit of this region is near 500 Å, where metallic reflectivities become very low, and helium becomes opaque.

4.1.1.1.3.5. *Far Vacuum Ultraviolet.* Below 500 Å, the reflectivities of all known materials decrease drastically. Gratings operated near normal incidence therefore become extremely inefficient. Near grazing incidence, however, it is possible to obtain reasonably high reflectivities, and virtually all instuments in this region utilize gratings at grazing incidence. Since all reflections are prohibitively inefficient, concave grating spectrographs, which use only a single reflection, are universally used. Otherwise, the problems here are the same as in the previous region. The lower limit of this region runs into the soft X-ray region, somewhere near 10 Å.

4.1.1.2. Spectroscopic Light Sources. Any source of radiation in the "optical" regions can be considered a potential source for spectroscopic studies. The variety of these sources is so great that even an adequate system of classification becomes difficult. We shall attempt in this discussion to consider only a few examples of sources that either are illustrative of a general type or have a wide applicability in themselves.

The light sources studied may be considered in two classes:

(1) Applications in which spectroscopy is used as a diagnostic tool on existing sources of light. This would include such sources as the sun, the airglow, the plasma pinch, or a rocket flame. In these experiments, the source configuration and conditions either are beyond the control of the experimenter or are determined by other factors pertaining to the experiment. Here the task of spectroscopy is to measure one or more parameters as a diagnostic aid in evaluating a more complex situation. This class of sources is probably the most frequently encountered and in many instances the most interesting. The tremendous variety of these sources and the fact that their design evolves from the conditions imposed by other considerations preclude any useful discussion of such sources in this section.

(2) Sources designed to study specific atomic or molecular properties. The design of the source and its operating parameters are at the disposal of the spectroscopist. Included are all of the classical sources of spectroscopy: those used in the analysis and classification of spectra, in the determination of transition probabilities, and in spectrochemical analysis. A few examples are discussed below. The classification selected is not intended to be logically complete and the examples chosen are presented as a group covering a range of different problems that are frequently encountered.

4.1.1.2.1. CONTINUOUS EMISSION SOURCES. Sources of continuous (rather than discrete) radiation find their principal application as sources of background against which discrete or sometimes continuous absorptions can be measured. The ideal source for this application would have constant intensity structureless spectral distribution over the region of the spectrum under study, and zero intensity elsewhere.

In the near ultraviolet, visible, and near infrared, an excellent continuum can be obtained from incandescent solids, such as tungsten strip lamps, at moderate temperatures. If the incandescent material is "black" over the region covered, the spectral distribution will follow Planck's law.[35] A tungsten lamp at a temperature of 2900°C is quite useful over the visible portion of the spectra and up to several microns into the infrared. The Planck curves fall off relatively slowly in the

[35] F. K. Richtmyer and E. H. Kennard, "Introduction to Modern Physics." McGraw-Hill, New York, 1942.

infrared but most of the radiation remains in the region below a few microns. The problem at longer wavelengths therefore concerns not only the reduced absolute intensity in this region but also the interference by the scattered light from the large fraction of the energy at shorter wavelengths. A considerable gain in signal-to-noise can be achieved by the use of materials such as "globars" which have a low emissivity in the visible and near infrared and a high emissivity at longer wavelengths.

In the visible and near infrared such sources are extensively used for the study of molecular absorption bands in solids, liquids, and gases. Application to industrial control problems is commonplace and a variety of excellent spectrometers, usually containing an appropriate source, is available commercially.

Toward the ultraviolet the Planck curve falls off very rapidly at temperatures attainable in incandescent solids. The fraction of the radiation below 3000 Å becomes extremely small, and no truly satisfactory source exists for shorter wavelengths.

Continua other than the incandescent continuum are available in selected regions. These, however, are usually very limited in extent and frequently suffer from a superposition of a discrete line spectrum. It must also be remembered that at thermal equilibrium the intensity of radiation at any wavelength cannot exceed the radiation predicted by the Planck law at the temperature of the radiator. These continua generally involve electronic transitions in atoms or molecules, from a continuum to a bound state.

A common and commercially available source for the region from 3500 to approximately 1700 Å is the hydrogen continuum source. The radiation comes largely from the Balmer continuum and is quite free of discrete lines within this range.

A number of other rare gas continua have been described.[36-38] The approximate wavelength ranges over which these are effective are

Element	Wavelength range (Å)
Hydrogen	3500–1700
Xenon	2200–1470
Krypton	1850–1250
Argon	1650–1070
Neon	1000– 750
Helium	1000– 600

[36] W. C. Price, *Advan. Spectroscopy* **1**, 56 (1959).
[37] P. G. Wilkinson and Y. L. Tanaka, *J. Opt. Soc. Am.* **45**, 344 (1955).
[38] R. E. Huffman, Y. L. Tanaka, and J. C. Larrabee, *Appl. Optics* **2**, 617 (1963).

These rare gas continua are unfortunately overlaid with numerous emission lines.

Some success has been achieved by using vacuum spark discharges through a capillary to produce continua below the limit of helium near 500 Å. This radiation which is emitted by the material eroded from the quartz or ceramic walls of the capillary was first produced by Lyman and hence is called the Lyman continuum. Improved versions of this tube have been described by Garton.[39,40] The continuum, though quite strong, is heavily overlaid with emission lines, and extends to approximately 350 Å. Another modification of the vacuum spark source has been developed by Vodar and associates [41,42] who report continua, again with emission lines, as far as 80 Å.

A continuum completely devoid of line structure and one whose energy spectrum can be calculated is produced by the radially accelerated electrons in such high-energy machines as electron synchrotrons.[43] The intensity and spectral range covered depend upon the energy and radius of curvature of the electron beam. For a 180-MeV synchrotron with a 1.5-meter radius of curvature the intensity per angstrom reaches a maximum at about 400 Å and falls off rapidly below about 100 Å. Higher-energy machines yield spectra well into the X-ray region.

An interesting characteristic of the synchrotron radiation is its high degree of polarization[44] which should be of considerable interest for studying optical properties of materials in the vacuum ultraviolet. To date, this source has been used to study interesting structure and the absorption spectra of rare gases.[45]

4.1.1.2.2. DISCRETE EMISSION SOURCES. Most sources for the excitation of atomic or molecular line spectra,[46] whether they be flames or high-voltage sparks, are essentially thermal in nature, and a reasonable approximation to thermodynamic equilibrium may be assumed. If the emitting plasma is at an electron temperature, T, then the population of any state, i, is proportional to $g_i \exp(-E_i/kT)$ where E_i and g_i are the energy and statistical weights of the state i.

The lowest excitation temperatures are produced by furnaces or chemical flames. Such sources excite only the lowest-lying levels and are quite useful for the production of molecular vibration-rotation

[39] W. R. S. Garton, *J. Sci. Instr.* **30**, 119 (1953).
[40] W. R. S. Garton, *J. Sci. Instr.* **36**, 11 (1959).
[41] J. Romand and B. Vodar, *Spectrochim. Acta* **8**, 229 (1956).
[42] G. Balloffet, J. Romand, and J. Kieffer, *Spectrochim. Acta* **18**, 791 (1962).
[43] P. L. Hartman and D. H. Tomboulian, *Phys. Rev.* **91**, 1577 (1953).
[44] R. P. Madden and K. Codling, *J. Opt. Soc. Am.* (in press).
[45] R. P. Madden and K. Codling, *Phys. Rev. Letters* **10**, 516 (1963).
[46] W. Lochte-Holtgreven, *Repts. Progr. in Phys.* **21**, 312 (1958).

spectra, but have rather limited applicability in the excitation of atomic spectra.

The low-voltage Pfund-type arc is quite simple to construct and operate and has had wide application in the excitation of neutral atomic spectra. A very simple and satisfactory arc can be constructed by connecting two electrodes to a 220-volt dc line in series with a ballast resistance of between 20 and 200 ohms. Electron temperatures up to 6000°K can easily be achieved in such arcs in the body of the plasma and somewhat higher temperatures are observed near the cathode.

An extremely stable form of the dc arc has been developed by Lochte-Holtgreven and his associates at Kiel.[47,48] The plasma in these arcs is constrained by cooled walls to a narrow channel. Currents of up to 75 amp are passed through channels 2 to 4 mm in diameter and produce very stable plasmas with temperatures up to 12,000°K.

Higher excitation temperatures can be achieved with a high-voltage condensed spark.[49] Many forms of such sparks have been described, but they all consist essentially of a condenser, within the wide range of a few tenths to a few thousands of a microfarad, charged to a potential of somewhere between 10 and 50 thousand volts. The condenser is discharged through a series inductance-resistance circuit containing a spark gap (or gaps). Electron temperatures up to about 50,000°K can be achieved. Like the dc arc, this source can be used to observe the spectra of nearly all materials by using that material either as electrodes or as the gas in the space between electrodes. The spark in its usual form excites primarily the second (singly ionized) spectrum with some first and some third spectra.

The excitation temperature of a spark depends most critically upon the peak current during discharge. To achieve the highest temperatures, it is necessary to delay the spark breakdown until the condenser is charged to a high potential, and then to minimize the inductive and resistant elements in the discharge circuit.

Since the breakdown voltage at greatly reduced pressures is much higher than that at atmospheric pressures, high temperatures and high excitations can be achieved with a low-pressure or vacuum spark[50,51] or with high-temperature pinched plasmas.

For intermediate degrees of ionization, the ring discharge[52] is useful,

[47] H. Maecker, Z. Naturforsch. 11a, 457 (1956).
[48] W. Lochte-Holtgreven, Repts. Progr. in Phys. 21, 312 (1958).
[49] H. Kaiser and A. Wallraff, Ann. Physik [5] 34, 297 (1939).
[50] B. Edlén, Z. Physik 100, 621 (1936).
[51] A. G. Shenstone, Repts. Progr. in Phys. 5, 210 (1939).
[52] L. Minnhagen, B. Petersson, and L. Stigmark, Arkiv Fysik 16, 541 (1960).

especially where material must be conserved or contained. High-power pulsed electrodeless discharges have also been used.

A form of the condensed spark known as a "gliding spark"[53-55] has recently been introduced. The spark between electrodes is contained in a small cavity, a few millimeters on a side, in an insulating material such as lavite. The potentials used are quite low (about 1000 volts) but the capacitance is higher (a few microfarads) than that used in high-voltage sparks. If the inductive and capacitive elements in the discharge circuit are variable over wide ranges, a large variety of excitation temperatures can be achieved. It is, therefore, possible to excite preferentially spectra of different ionizations (up to about the third ionization). This permits the identification of lines from the various degrees of ionization, a separation which is essential before any analysis of the spectra can be carried out. By proper selection of conditions, self-reversal of many of the spectral lines can also be observed.[56] This self-reversal is extremely useful in identifying transitions involving either the ground state or metastable states.

The spectra of gases traditionally have been excited in Geissler tubes. These low-pressure lamps are readily excited with high-voltage luminous sign transformers. More recently, it has also been found convenient to excite gases by coupling a tube containing the gas at a few millimeters pressure to a microwave field.[57] Commercial diathermy units operating at 2450 Mc and rated at 100 watts input are generally used as the power supply. The coupling to the lamp may be achieved either with a directional reflector or with a cavity surrounding the lamp.

The pressure of gas within the electrodeless tubes is generally between 1 and 10 mm Hg. The application of electrodeless lamp excitation to more refractory elements has been achieved in recent years by filling the quartz tube with a compound of the element under study, usually a halide that has a vapor pressure exceeding a few microns at temperatures below a few hundred degrees.[58]

Quartz tubes containing either the halide alone or the halide plus a few millimeters of a rare gas emit, when raised to an appropriate temperature and excited by a microwave field, reasonably pure atomic spectra of a neutral atom. If the vapor pressure of the halide is sufficiently high, as is the case for thorium iodide, no carrier gas is needed. It is

[53] B. Vodar and N. Astoin, *Nature* **166**, 1029 (1950).
[54] K. Bockasten, *Arkiv Fysik* **9**, 457 (1955).
[55] J. Sugar, *J. Opt. Soc. Am.* **53**, 831 (1963).
[56] J. Sugar, *J. Research NBS* **66a**, 321 (1962).
[57] W. F. Meggers and F. O. Westfall, *J. Research NBS* **44**, 447 (1950).
[58] E. F. Worden, R. G. Gutmacher, and J. G. Conway, *Appl. Optics* **2**, 707 (1963).

frequently necessary to regulate the temperatures of the lamps, and hence the halide vapor pressure.

The excitation of the halide vapor produces, in addition to the spectrum of the element under study, the spectra of the halide molecule, the halogen atom, and, where used, the rare gas atom. Possible interference between lines in these spectra can be ascertained by taking successive observations with different halides and carrier gases. Those lines common to the several spectra can then be identified with the element studied.

The electrodeless lamp generally produces only the spectrum of the neutral atom, with a weak admixture of the spectrum of the singly ionized atom. A somewhat higher excitation temperature can be achieved by using a ring discharge.[52]

4.1.1.2.3. NARROW LINE SOURCES. Spectroscopic light sources that produce very sharp emission (or sometimes absorption) lines are needed: (1) for wavelength standards where the sharpness of the line is an aid to precise definition of its wavelength and (2) for the study of hyperfine structure and isotope shift where closely grouped lines must be separated.

The principal sources of line broadening[4,13,21,33] are as follows:

(1) Zeeman and Stark broadening, caused by the interaction of magnetic and electric fields, respectively, with the radiating or absorbing atom. The effects can be made quite negligible by avoiding strong external fields and keeping the charge density low in the emitting plasma.

(2) Pressure and resonance broadening, caused by collisional effects between atoms. This can be made negligible by operating at reduced pressures.

(3) Hyperfine structure and isotope shifts, which if unresolved, produce broadened lines. In the selection of lines for wavelength calibration, it is therefore best to choose those emitted by single even-even isotopes, thus eliminating both isotope shifts and hyperfine structure.

(4) The natural line width which is that width attributable to the lifetime of spontaneous photon emission in the atom:

$$\Delta \nu = \frac{1}{2\pi\tau} \qquad (4.1.1.1)$$

where $\Delta \nu$ is the width of the line in frequency units and τ is the lifetime of the upper level in the transition which produced the line. The limitation imposed by the natural line width can be circumvented only through the process of stimulated emission, as in a laser.[34] The lifetimes of most atomic transitions are in the range of 10^{-7} to 10^{-8} seconds. Thus the natural line widths will be 10^{-3} to 10^{-4} cm^{-1} or 1.6 to 16 Mc.

(5) Doppler broadening which sets the limit in most sources. It is produced by the thermal motion of the emitting atoms and its width at half-maximum is:

$$\Delta\nu = \frac{2\nu}{c}\sqrt{\frac{2RT\ln 2}{M}} = 7.16 \times 10^{-7}\nu\sqrt{\frac{T}{M}} \qquad (4.1.1.2)$$

where ν is the wave number of the lines, T is the absolute temperature, M is the molecular weight, R is the gas constant, and c is the velocity of light. The Doppler width of a spectrum line at 5000 Å from an atom of mass 100 at room temperature is 0.025 cm^{-1} or 0.006 Å.

Gaseous discharge tubes of either the Geissler or electrodeless forms can be operated at fairly low pressure and at low currents. The chief contributing factor to line width is therefore the Doppler effect. A narrow width can be achieved by operating the discharge tube at a low temperature and by using an emitting atom of large mass.

The very narrow width, 0.011 cm^{-1}, of the present international standard of length and of wavelength, the 6056 Å line of krypton-86, is achieved by operating a discharge tube containing a moderately heavy single isotope at 63°K. Another widely used length standard, the mercury-198 lamp, achieves its narrow line, 0.018 cm^{-1}, by operating with much heavier atoms at a somewhat higher temperature. No very significant improvement in the line width of the discharge tube over that obtained by these sources is possible, since heavier elements tend to have lower vapor pressures and cannot therefore be operated at low temperatures.

Since both krypton and mercury have relatively simple spectra, neither is a very suitable source of calibration wavelengths for high-dispersion spectrographs. For this purpose, arcs, hollow cathodes, and electrodeless discharge tubes containing the elements iron[59] or thorium[60] have come into wide use. Iron has the advantage of a somewhat simpler spectrum with easily recognized patterns of lines.[61] Used either in the hollow cathode or in an electrodeless discharge lamp, it yields a spectrum rich enough and sharp enough for all but the highest resolving power instruments. Thorium, being somewhat heavier and a single isotope, yields slightly sharper lines, and the large number of lines in its very complex spectrum makes it a very suitable calibration source for high-dispersion instruments.[62] Considerable work has been done on both these calibration sources.

[59] R. W. Stanley and W. F. Meggers, *J. Research NBS* **58**, 41 (1957).
[60] R. W. Stanley and W. F. Meggers, *J. Research NBS* **61**, 95 (1958).
[61] H. M. Crosswhite, Johns Hopkins Spectroscopic Report No. 13 (1958).
[62] R. Zalubas, *Natl. Bur. Standards (U.S.) Monograph* **17** (1960).

The cool hollow cathode tube produces sharp spectrum lines by operating at the temperature of liquid nitrogen.[21] At this temperature, discharge tubes are nearly useless, since all but a few materials have negligible vapor pressures. In the hollow cathode tube, the principal conducting material is a rare gas. Helium, neon, or argon is generally used. The material to be studied is imbedded in the walls of the cathode and the atoms of that material are ejected into the plasma columns by ionic bombardment of the cathode wall by gaseous atoms. Once in the plasma, they are excited by collisions of the second kind with excited gas atoms, and subsequently radiate very sharp spectrum lines. Hollow cathode tubes operated in this way have attained Doppler line widths very closely approximating the predicted line widths at liquid nitrogen temperatures. Since these tubes can be used with virtually any element, they have been extremely useful in the study of hyperfine structure and isotope shifts.

Atomic beam sources[21] reduce and nearly eliminate Doppler broadening by observing, in a beam, only those atoms whose thermal velocity is oriented in a particular direction. By observing this beam, normal to the direction of motion, extremely sharp lines can be produced. In an atomic beam of isotopic mercury, lines 0.0015 cm^{-1} wide have been produced at 2537 Å.[63]

4.1.1.2.4. LASER SOURCES. The recent development of laser light sources [34,64] has given the spectroscopists several classes of sources whose application to interesting problems in physics has only just begun. We will consider two general classes of these devices: (1) solid-state pulsed lasers capable of very intense radiation, and (2) continuous wave gas lasers capable of producing extremely monochromatic radiation.

The extremely high electromagnetic field generated by the solid-state lasers has been utilized in the study of nonlinear phenomena[65] and for vaporizing refractory materials for spectrochemical analysis.[66] These lasers are, however, difficult to excite in single-mode operation, and frequency of the light emitted is not very stable.

The gas laser, though generally it has far less power can be operated continuously with a highly monochromatic output whose line width may be only a few cycles out of 10^{14} cps. This output can also have a long-term stability of better than one part in 10^9.[67]

The application to metrological problems is an obvious consequence of the monochromaticity and stability, and a new superior wavelength

[63] R. L. Barger and K. G. Kessler, *J. Opt. Soc. Am.* **51**, 827 (1961).

[64] *J. Appl. Optics*, Suppl. 1, (1962).

[65] P. A. Franken and J. F. Ward, *Revs. Modern Phys.* **35**, 23 (1963).

[66] R. W. Terhune, *Solid State Design* **4**, 38 (1963).

[67] T. S. Jaseja, A. Javan, and C. H. Townes, *Phys. Rev. Letters.* **10**, 165 (1963).

standard of lengths is certainly forthcoming. The problem to be overcome is the design of a sensor and servo that will adjust the cavity resonance frequency to some feature of a spectrum line that is itself nearly independent of pressure shifts and other perturbations.

The wavelength of the emitted laser lines can be shifted somewhat by tuning the resonant cavity, thus permitting absorption studies at fantastically high resolving power. Unfortunately, the maximum amplitude of this shift is somewhat less than the Doppler width of the stimulated atoms, that is, of the order of 0.01 Å.

The solid-state laser has also been applied to the study of the Raman effect.[66,67a,b,c] Many more applications are under study and will be reported in the near future.

4.1.1.2.5. ZEEMAN SOURCES. For the analysis of atomic spectra (Section 4.1.1.5.1) Zeeman spectra constitute a valuable source of information since the observed patterns lead to the assignment of J quantum numbers and Lande g values for the observed transitions.[3] Observations can be made either on the light emitted in the direction of the magnetic field (circular polarization) or on that emitted normal to the direction of the field (linear polarization). The latter is used almost exclusively since it is easier to produce and analyze and contains more information.

Since the light sources used are generally quite small, the magnetic field need be constant (within a few per cent) over only about 1 cm³. It should, however, be as strong as possible. With iron core magnets 35,000 to 40,000 oersteds can be attained, and large air core solenoids such as the Bitter magnet at MIT can produce fields in the range of 100,000 to 250,000 oersteds. The development of superconducting magnets holds promise of future improvement in the ease with which such large fields can be produced.

The most convenient technique for producing Zeeman spectra in emission is with an electrodeless tube (Section 4.1.1.2.2) between the poles of the magnet. Small dc arcs can also be used, but these are rather difficult to maintain since the magnetic force on the charged particles tends to extinguish the arc when the arc is perpendicular to the magnetic field. One technique for surmounting this problem is to attach a vibrator to open and close the arc gap at a rapid rate.

To obtain the maximum information from the spectrum, it is necessary to observe separately the two polarizations. This is most easily accomplished by a Wollaston prism[8] in conjunction with a nearly stigmatic spectrograph. The magnitude of the magnetic field is readily obtained

[67a] S. P. S. Porto and D. L. Wood, *J. Opt. Soc. Am.* **52**, 251 (1962).

[67b] B. P. Stoicheff, *Phys. Letters* **7**, 186 (1963).

[67c] N. Bloembergen, "Non-linear Optics." Benjamin, New York, 1965.

if Lande g values are known for some of the lines observed in the spectrum. Impurity lines are frequently useful for this purpose.

Discussions of the Zeeman effect can be found in White[3] and in an article by Meggers.[68] Line components which result from transitions in which the change in the magnetic quantum number ΔM is ± 1 will be polarized normal to the magnetic field. The magnitude of the level splitting in a field of H gauss is:

$$\Delta \nu = \frac{eHg}{4\pi mc} M , \qquad (4.1.1.3)$$

or, if $\Delta\sigma$ is in cm^{-1} and H in gauss, $\Delta\sigma = 4.67 \times 10^{-5}\, gHM$.

4.1.1.3. Dispersive Instruments.* The fundamental and defining function of spectroscopy is the study of the radiation emitted, by such sources as are described in the previous section, as a function of wavelength. The required dispersion can be accomplished by utilizing either dispersion in a transparent medium, such as a prism, or the wavelength dependence of interference effects, as in a grating or interferometer.

A spectrograph is an instrument which displays, generally for photographic recording, a broad portion of the spectrum. The dispersive element may be a prism or a grating (including echelles). The range of wavelength displayed may be changed, but it is not designed primarily for continuous scanning.

A monochromator differs from a spectrograph in having an exit slit through which a very small portion of the dispersed spectrum passes. The spectrum is scanned past this exit slit and behind it is located a detector such as a photoelectric cell. Instruments have been designed to combine the features of both spectrograph and monochromator. The spectroscope, an instrument designed for visual observations, will not be discussed.

Interferometers, like gratings, utilize interference effects to achieve dispersion. Gratings obtain their resolving power by combining a very large number ($\sim 10^{-5}$) of beams at a few (most frequently three or less) orders of interference. The interferometer resolving power is obtained by combining a few (< 100) beams at high (10^4–10^6) orders of interference. Since the spectral range between orders of an interferometer is very small, it is almost invariably necessary to use interferometers in conjunction with a second- and lower-order dispersive instrument such as a spectrograph.

A few hybrids such as the echelle (Section 4.1.1.3.1.5) and the

---

[68] "Zeeman Effect," Encyclopedia Britannica. Some editions contain an error in that the appearance diagrams for the type 3 and type 6 in Table II are interchanged. The type 3 should have an even number of components, the type 6 an odd number.

* See also Vol. 1, Chapter 7.3, and Vol. 3, Chapter 2.4.

SISAM (Section 4.1.1.3.2.1) are also discussed briefly below, as is the technique of Fourier transform spectroscopy.

4.1.1.3.1. SPECTROGRAPHS. Although Rowland's development of a precision ruling engine and his invention of the concave grating mounting made posible grating spectrographs which could exceed the largest prism instruments in resolving power, it was many years before the early disadvantages of limited availability, low efficiency, and high ghost intensity could be overcome. In the past 20 or 30 years these have been largely eliminated, so that in most modern high-performance instruments gratings have superseded prisms. We will therefore treat prism instruments only briefly, paying more attention to recent trends in grating designs. For greater detail see Harrison[69] and others.[70,71]

4.1.1.3.1.1. *Prisms.* A typical mounting for prism spectrographs is shown in Fig. 1. The principal components are an adjustable slit S,

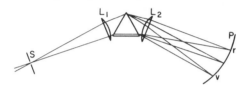

FIG. 1. Prism spectrograph.

collimating lens L_1, the prism, camera lens L_2, and the photographic plate P. In spectrographs which use uncorrected lenses the plate is inclined at rather high angles to the refracted rays because the focal length for the violet end of the spectrum (v) is less than for the red (r). Larger prism spectrographs often are of the Littrow design (Fig. 2)

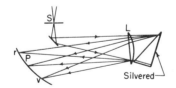

FIG. 2. Littrow prism spectrograph.

in order to get double benefit from the prism material. A serious objection to this arrangement is the large amount of light scattered from the lens L to the plate P.

4.1.1.3.1.2. *Concave Diffraction Grating Spectrographs.* Early diffraction

[69] G. R. Harrison, R. C. Lord, and J. R. Loofbourow, "Practical Spectroscopy." Prentice-Hall, Englewood Cliffs, New Jersey, 1948.
[70] R. A. Sawyer, "Experimental Spectroscopy." Dover, New York, 1963.
[71] W. R. Brode, "Chemical Spectroscopy." Wiley, New York, 1943.

gratings were ruled on optically flat glass or metal surfaces. Speculum metal (an alloy of copper and zinc) was commonly used. These were mounted in a Littrow arrangement similar to that of Fig. 2, with the grating substituted for the prism.

In 1882 Rowland announced his theory of the concave grating and tested it by making observations on the solar spectrum of higher precision than any previously reported. The basic analysis of the optical properties of the Rowland circle mountings was given by Rowland himself, although much more systematic treatments have since been given (Beutler in particular).[72,73]

The optical principles are indicated schematically in Fig. 3. Let a circle be drawn tangent to the grating at its center with a diameter D equal to the radius of curvature D of the grating. Then light entering a slit S placed on this circle will be diffracted in such a way that the resulting spectrum will be brought to a focus on this same circle.

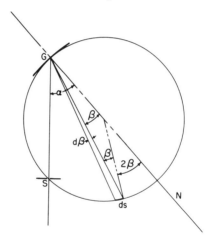

FIG. 3.   Rowland circle.

If the central ray of the incident beam makes an angle d with the grating normal, the diffraction angle will be β for a wavelength λ given by the grating equation

$$n\lambda = a(\sin \alpha + \sin \beta), \qquad (4.1.1.4)$$

where n is the order number and a is the grating spacing. For a fixed d the angular dispersion will be given by

$$\frac{d\lambda}{d\beta} = \frac{a}{n} \cos \beta \qquad (4.1.1.5)$$

[72] H. G. Beutler, *J. Opt. Soc. Am.* **35**, 311 (1945).
[73] T. Namioka, *J. Opt. Soc. Am.* **49**, 446 (1959).

and the linear dispersion by

$$\frac{d\lambda}{ds} = \frac{d\lambda}{d\beta}\frac{d\beta}{ds} = \frac{a\cos\beta}{Dn}, \qquad (4.1.1.6)$$

where D is the diameter of the Rowland circle and s is the position of a spectrum line as measured along the circumference of the Rowland circle. (The decreasing focal length $D\cos\beta$ is compensated by the fact that the focal curve is inclined at an angle β.) The dispersion will be nonlinear except very near the grating normal. As Rowland himself was interested in making precision wavelength measurements and as he had few calibration standards, it was important that he confine himself to the region of normal dispersion. The Rowland mounting for the concave grating was designed for this purpose. The grating and plate holder were connected by a rigid bar, the ends of which could move along two mutually perpendicular rails, the slit being placed at the intersection of these rails. At the center of the plate, β was always zero. Different spectral regions were obtained by varying the angle of the incident light. The light source itself was not moved, as the optic axis remains fixed. The dispersion is thus the same for all spectral regions photographed. This mounting is seldom used now.

Other versions soon appeared, notably the Paschen–Runge mounting,[74] in which the slit, grating, and focal plane remain fixed. The layout is thus similar to that of Fig. 3. The advantage of this system is that the whole spectrum may be photographed simultaneously.

A much more compact version than either of these was described in detail by Eagle,[75] but was in fact used earlier by Lyman[76] in his work in the vacuum ultraviolet (Fig. 4). The slit S and optic axis are fixed, but

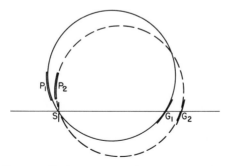

FIG. 4.   Eagle mounting of a concave grating.

[74] C. R. Runge and F. Paschen, *Abhandl. K. Akad. Wiss. Berlin* **1** (1902).

[75] A. Eagle, *Astrophys. J.* **31**, 120 (1910); *Proc. Phys. Soc. (London)* **23**, 233 (1911).

[76] T. Lyman, *Astrophys. J.* **23**, 181 (1906); "The Spectroscopy of the Extreme Ultraviolet," 2nd ed. Longmans, Green, New York, 1928.

for different spectral regions the grating is rotated and simultaneously moved from position G_1 to G_2. It is also necessary to move the plate holder from P_1 to P_2 by rotation about an axis that runs through the slit position.

The Rowland circle concave grating approximation is appropriate only if the grating size is kept within certain limits. For a 15.2-cm (6-in.) grating the corresponding radius of curvature is about 6.4 meters (21 feet). This is also about the size needed to make the diffraction width of the spectrum line commensurate with the grain size of sensitive photographic emulsions. With this restriction, all aberrations except astigmatism are within the diffraction width. If the light source does not fill an appreciable part of the length of the slit, loss of light intensity can be a problem, as the astigmatism can be severe. It is minimized with the Eagle mounting, at a sacrifice of the spectral coverage of the Paschen mounting.

A concave grating mounting which does not use the Rowland circle was suggested by Wadsworth[77] and improved by Meggers[78] by the substitution of a concave mirror for the collimating lens (see Fig. 5).

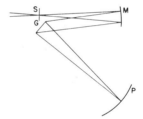

FIG. 5.   Wadsworth mounting of a concave grating.

The mirror M renders the light falling on the grating parallel. The diffracted light focused near the normal of the grating will form images free of astigmatism. The image will in general be brighter than in Rowland circle mountings, but at a cost of increased coma and spherical aberrations.

The largest gratings ruled by Rowland were 10 cm (4 in.) long and 6 in. wide but subsequently Michelson[79] at the University of Chicago, Babcock at Mt. Wilson, Wood and Strong at Johns Hopkins, and Harrison at MIT have made larger ones, the latter being as much as 10 in. wide with resolving powers of about 1,000,000. Randall at the

[77] F. L. O. Wadsworth, *Astrophys. J.* 1, 232 (1895); 3, 54 (1896).

[78] W. F. Meggers, *Natl. Bur. Standards (U.S.), Sci. Papers* 14, 371 (1918); W. F. Meggers and K. Burns, *ibid.* 18, 185 (1922).

[79] A. A. Michelson, *Nature* 88, 362 (1912).

University of Michigan has made even larger ones for use in the infrared, where the optical and mechanical tolerances are correspondingly less severe.[80] Other major advances were the development by Anderson and Babcock,[81] and by Wood,[82] of shaping the grooves to concentrate the light at high angles of diffraction, Strong's demonstration of the techniques for aluminizing glass blanks,[83] and Harrison's development of interferometric control of the ruling engines.[84] However, available ruling engines could not keep up with a growing interest in spectroscopic research, and it was not until the replication processes were developed enough that the quality of the replicas was equal to that of the original that the supply could be considered adequate.[85,86] For greater historical detail a number of recent papers are available.[80,86−89]

4.1.1.3.1.3. *Plane Grating Monochromators.* Before World War II the photographic plate was the principal detector used, but when the high-gain photomultiplier tube was introduced a number of suggestions for applications to spectroscopy were made.[90−94] Dieke showed that a resolution could be obtained equivalent to that from photographic plates. The first photoelectric instruments were merely modifications of photographic instruments, which was not in fact the optimum design. The development of the photomultiplier (and subsequently the PbS infrared detector) and increasing availability of large well-blazed plane gratings has led to the reconsideration of monochromator designs, and this in turn has inspired further development of plane grating photographic instruments.

A large concave grating cannot be made which has a uniform blaze over its entire surface, because of the varying angle that the diamond makes with the grating surface. Furthermore, the size of the grating is limited by the spherical approximation. An early photoelectric instrument

[80] H. M. Randall, *Rev. Sci. Instr.* 3, 396 (1932); *J. Opt. Soc. Am.* 44, 97 (1954).

[81] H. D. Babcock, *J. Opt. Soc. Am.* 34, 1 (1944).

[82] R. W. Wood, *Phil. Mag* [6] 20, 770 (1910); *J. Opt. Soc. Am.* 37, 733 (1947).

[83] J. Strong, *Phys. Rev.* 43, 498 (1933); 49, 295 (1936); *Astrophys. J.* 83, 401 (1956).

[84] G. R. Harrison, N. Sturgis, S. P. Davis, and Y. Yamada, *J. Opt. Soc. Am.* 49, 205 (1959).

[85] J. U. White and W. A. Fraser, U. S. Patent 2,464,738 (1947).

[86] R. F. Jarrell and G. W. Stroke, *Appl. Optics* 3, 1251 (1964).

[87] G. R. Harrison, *J. Opt. Soc. Am.* 39, 413 (1949).

[88] J. Strong, *J. Opt. Soc. Am.* 41, 3 (1951); 50, 1148 (1960).

[89] H. W. Babcock, *Appl. Optics* 1, 415 (1962).

[90] D. H. Rank, R. J. Pfister, and P. D. Coleman, *J. Opt. Soc. Am.* 32, 390 (1942).

[91] E. A. Boettner and G. P. Brewington, *J. Opt. Soc. Am.* 34, 6 (1944).

[92] M. F. Hasler and H. W. Dietert, *J. Opt. Soc. Am.* 34, 751 (1944).

[93] G. H. Dieke and H. M. Crosswhite, *J. Opt. Soc. Am.* 35, 471 (1945).

[94] J. L. Saunderson, V. J. Caldecourt, and E. W. Peterson, *J. Opt. Soc. Am.* 35, 681 (1945).

at Johns Hopkins University was a converted photographic Wadsworth, but this was soon abandoned in favor of a Czerny–Turner monochromator[95] with a 125 cm × 175 cm plane grating and 1- and 2-meter off-axis parabolas. The success of this instrument led Fastie[96] at Leeds and Northrup to investigate the properties of a type originally proposed by Ebert[97] (Fig. 6). Fastie's original motivation was mechanical stability

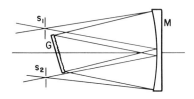

FIG. 6.   Ebert–Fastie monochromator.

but he was able to show that the optical symmetry could be put to good use.[96] The off-axis parabola system operates perfectly only at one point. However, if the numerical aperture of an off-axis sphere is kept greater than ten the only aberration of consequence is astigmatism. If circular slits are used the astigmatism will always be parallel to the exit slit and relatively long slits may be used with no loss of resolution.[98]

Design of spectroscopic instruments generally implies some compromise among speed, resolving power, and spectral range. In the following we will assume that near-theoretical resolution is desired. The primary consideration will then be the requirements needed to keep the optical aberrations within the diffraction limits of the spectrum line.

Design considerations are different for monochromatic and photographic instruments, and it is in general poor policy to attempt to modify a photographic spectrograph for use as a monochromator. For the moment we will assume that we are not limited by the light source and that the full length of the entrance slit is illuminated.

Consider a monochromatic source S (see Fig. 7) of brightness B (in ergs per cm²-sec-steradian). The area of the image on the entrance slit to the spectrograph will be magnified by a factor D_1^2/D_0^2; however, the solid angle ω_1 is smaller than ω_0 by the same factor, so that the image brightness in directions within the cone ω_1 is also B, neglecting losses

[95] M. Czerny and A. F. Turner, *Z. Physik* **61**, 792 (1930).

[96] W. G. Fastie, *J. Opt. Soc. Am.* **42**, 641 and 647 (1952); **43**, 1174 (1953).

[97] H. Ebert, *Wied. Ann.* **38**, 489 (1889).

[98] W. G. Fastie, H. M. Crosswhite, and P. Gloersen, *J. Opt. Soc. Am.* **48**, 106 (1958).

of the lens L_0. The angle ω_1 will generally be more than sufficient to fill the grating; the useful aperture will be

$$\omega_1' = \frac{HW \cos \alpha}{F_1^2} \tag{4.1.1.7}$$

where H and W are the dimensions of the grating (approximately the square of the numerical aperture $f_1 = W \cos \alpha / F_1$). The three internal optical elements are not necessarily distinct; in fact in the Rowland circle mountings all three are physically the same.

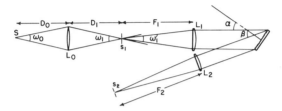

FIG. 7.   Schematic spectrograph and illuminating optics.

The useful radiative power entering the entrance slit of dimensions s_1, l_1 will be $B s_1 l_1 HW \cos \alpha / F_1^2$ ergs per sec. If the grating has an efficiency T for the particular wavelength (and order) diffracted in the direction of the detector, the total power contained in the cone ω_1 will be

$$P = TB s_1 l_1 HW \cos \alpha / F_1^2 \text{ ergs per sec.} \tag{4.1.1.8}$$

In order that this entire signal fall on the detector, the exit slit width must be sufficiently large; optimum results are obtained if both are put equal to the diffraction width for the wavelength of interest. However, this width is not necessarily the same for both slits, as the grating will appear foreshortened differently for the two angles α and β. We will have

$$s_1 = f_1 \lambda = F_1 \lambda / W \cos \alpha, \tag{4.1.1.9}$$

$$s_2 = f_2 \lambda = F_2 \lambda / W \cos \beta, \tag{4.1.1.10}$$

and

$$s_1/s_2 = F_1 \cos \beta / F_2 \cos \alpha. \tag{4.1.1.11}$$

This may be seen directly from the grating equation $n\lambda = a(\sin \alpha + \sin \beta)$. For a fixed wavelength, $\cos \alpha \, d\alpha + \cos \beta \, d\beta = 0$, where $d\alpha = s_1/F_1$ and $d\beta = s_2/F_2$. This apparent magnification of the entrance slit is of some importance in applications of both spectrometers and spectrographs when high angles of diffraction are used. It is however accompanied by a proportionate dispersion, so that the resolving power is not affected.

If the optimum slit values given by Eq. (4.1.1.9) and (4.1.1.10) are used, Eq. (4.1.1.8) may also be written

$$P = TB \frac{s_2 \cos \beta}{F_2} \frac{l_2}{F_2} HW \qquad (4.1.1.12)$$

where we have also chosen the exit slit length l_2 to be just equal to the magnified image of the entrance slit. If however the slit widths are in a different ratio than that given by (4.1.1.11), Eq. (4.1.1.8) or (4.1.1.12) will be correct depending on whether $s_1 \cos d/F_1$ is smaller or larger than $s_2 \cos \beta/F_2$.

Let us assume that (4.1.1.8) is valid. For a given grating, the signal available does not depend in an essential way on the choice of focal length. If F_1 were doubled one could by choosing a different external lens double the magnified image and hence double l_1. Since the dispersion is now double, the slit width s_1 may also be doubled for the same resolution. Hence the signal P in (4.1.1.8) will be unchanged.

If a continuous light source is used, the brightness B in Eq. (4.1.1.8) must be replaced by the expression $B(\lambda)d\lambda$, so that the signal power will be given by

$$P = TB(\lambda) \frac{a}{n} \frac{s_1 \cos \alpha}{F_1} \frac{s_2 \cos \beta}{F_2} \frac{l_1}{F_1} HW \qquad (4.1.1.13)$$

where we have taken the wavelength increment as $\Delta\lambda = as_2 \cos \beta/nF_2$. For a continuous source, the signal power is thus proportional to the product of the two slit widths.

4.1.1.3.1.4. *Plane Grating Spectrographs.* The availability of large plane gratings has also inspired development of plane grating spectrographs. In this case it is necessary to sacrifice some of the symmetry of the Ebert monochromator in order to obtain spectral range. In this case it is therefore necessary to restrict the numerical aperture to values greater than $f/40$ rather than $f/10$ as for the monochromator. If the entrance slit is placed below the grating the spectrum will appear above, but still dispersed laterally. However, the astigmatism is parallel to the spectrum line only at the central position, so that in order to minimize this the grating must have very short rulings and the slit and plate holder placed off-axis as little as possible.

A better arrangement seems to be the side-by-side one, and in this case it is also better to use the more general Czerny–Turner two-mirror system rather than the Ebert. In general, because of the large off-axis angles needed to provide for sufficient spectral coverage, the higher-order spherical aberrations, particularly coma, become very large. However, Fastie has shown[99] that, by choosing the positions of the

---

[99] W. G. Fastie, U.S. Patent 3,011,391 (1963).

mirrors properly with relation to the grating, the coma distortions can be made to cancel at the center of the plate and, if the numerical aperture is kept sufficiently large, can also be made negligibly small at the ends. Several mathematical studies of these systems have been recently made.[100–103]

4.1.1.3.1.5. Cross Dispersion Instruments. A 5-meter vacuum spectrograph of this type has recently been installed at Johns Hopkins, with a replica of a 25-cm interferometrically ruled Harrison grating. However, as the spacing is only 300 grooves per mm and as the blaze angle is approximately 60°, relatively high orders of interference are used. As the spectrograph is intended for use in the vacuum UV to about 1100 Å, this comes to over 50 orders. This is reminiscent of Wood's echelette gratings.[82] In the visible and near infrared, overlapping orders can be avoided by the use of narrow-band interference filters, but for higher orders an additional dispersing element operating at right angles (crossed dispersion) is required. For the Johns Hopkins instrument Fastie has designed a LiF_2-coated concave mirror and plane grating system similar in layout to the plane grating spectrograph described first by Monk.[101,104,105]

In 1898 Michelson[106] proposed a method of obtaining high resolving power by constructing a very coarse grating (echelon) from a number of glass plates, made as nearly identical as possible, thus working in very high orders of interference rather than with a large number of rulings. It was not until 1926, however, that a successful construction was reported by Williams.[107] The resulting spectra in some ways resembled that from interferometers. Because the free spectral range was so low, interpretation of the spectra was difficult.

Harrison has proposed a compromise between the echelon and Wood's echelette which he calls an echelle, having of the order of ten grooves per mm and produced by a milling and grinding process,[108] and has recommended a mounting in which the echelle is internally mounted in the collimated beam of a prism spectrograph. An echelle spectrograph constructed at Johns Hopkins uses instead a 6.4-meter (21-foot) Wadsworth spectrograph mounted on its side, with the Wadsworth

[100] G. R. Rosendahl, *J. Opt. Soc. Am.* **51**, 1 (1961); **52**, 408 and 412 (1962).

[101] M. V. R. K. Mutry, *J. Opt. Soc. Am.* **52**, 768 (1962).

[102] A. B. Shafer, L. R. Megill, and L. Droppleman, *J. Opt. Soc. Am.* **54**, 879 (1964).

[103] K. Kudo, *Sci. of Light (Tokyo)* **9**, 1 (1960); *J. Opt. Soc. Am.* **55**, 150 (1965).

[104] G. S. Monk, *J. Opt. Soc. Am.* **17**, 358 (1928).

[105] A. H. C. P. Gillieson, *J. Sci. Instr. and Phys. in Ind.* **26**, 335 (1949).

[106] A. A. Michelson, *Astrophys. J.* **8**, 37 (1898).

[107] W. E. Williams, British Patent 312,534 (1926); *Proc. Opt. Conv.* **2**, 982 (1926); *Proc. Phys. Soc. (London)* **45**, 699 (1933).

[108] G. R. Harrison, *J. Opt. Soc. Am.* **39**, 522 (1949).

grating dispersion in a vertical direction, the echelle being horizontal. The echelle is a Bausch and Lomb replica of a 7.85 grooves/mm (200 groove/in.) Harrison original, with about 900 rulings, blazed at approximately 60°. Two 40-cm plates record the first-order Wadsworth spectra between 4000 and 8000 Å, the corresponding echelle orders being of the order of 500. The resulting spectra are very compact, consisting of many short strips, each about 4 cm^{-1} in extent. Tousey's group at the Naval Research Laboratory has used a 73 groove/mm echelle rocket spectrograph to obtain high-resolution solar spectra.[109]

4.1.1.3.1.6. *Vacuum Ultraviolet Instruments.* Below 2000 Å, molecular oxygen becomes opaque, and it is necessary to work with an evacuated spectrograph, as Schumann[110] first showed in 1893. It was also necessary for him to prepare photographic plates with a bare minimum of gelatin, as this also absorbs light below about 2300 Å. He used a lithium fluoride prism spectrograph and recorded spectra down to 1200 Å, without however being able to make wavelength measurements. Lyman[76] designed a concave grating spectrograph similar to what is now called an Eagle, and measured spectra of various gases and metals down to 500 Å. Below this point the reflectivity of all known grating materials is so low at angles of incidence near the normal that the grating efficiency becomes very low. However, at high angles of incidence the reflectivity is high, as Hoag demonstrated in 1927,[111] and grazing incidence spectrographs are able to reach wavelengths which merge into the X-ray region.

These early grating spectrographs were all Rowland circle types.[112] Harrison[113] however constructed an off-plane (slit located outside the plane of dispersion) Eagle which is considerably more compact than the conventional version, an important consideration in vacuum spectrograph design. If the off-plane rays are less than a degree, no serious distortion results.[114,115]

Rowland circle mountings are not easy to adapt to use as monochromators because of the need for making several adjustments simultaneously. Seya[116] and Namioka[117] have found conditions under which fairly large deviations from the Rowland circle can be tolerated, with however rather severe limitations on the numerical aperture. This

[109] J. D. Purcell, D. L. Garrett, and R. Tousey, *Proc. 3rd Intern. Space Sci. Symp., Washington, D.C., 1962* p. 781 (1963); R. Tousey, *Space Sci. Rev.* 2, 3 (1963).
[110] V. Schumann, *Akad. Wiss. Wien* 102, 2A, 625 (1893).
[111] J. B. Hoag, *Astrophys. J.* 66, 225 (1927).
[112] H. A. Rowland, *Phil. Mag.* [5] 15, 469 (1882); 16, 192 (1883); *Nature* 26, 211 (1882).
[113] G. R. Harrison, *Rev. Sci. Instr.* 2, 600 (1931); 4, 651 (1933).
[114] P. G. Wilkinson, *J. Mol. Spectroscopy* 1, 288 (1957).
[115] T. Namioka, *J. Opt. Soc. Am.* 49, 460 (1959).
[116] M. Seya, *Sci. of Light (Tokyo)* 2, 8 (1952).
[117] T. Namioka, *Sci. of Light (Tokyo)* 3, 15 (1954); *J. Opt. Soc. Am.* 49, 951 (1959).

allows the spectrum to be scanned with only the grating angle being changed. See also the discussion by Greiner and Schäffer.[118]

The generally low reflectivity of materials in this region has made the concave grating mounting particularly desirable because of the single reflecting surface, but Hass[119] has shown that if rapidly deposited aluminum is immediately overlaid with a protective coating of magnesium fluoride a high reflectivity down to 1100 Å can be obtained. This makes plane grating monochromators and spectrographs also feasible down to this limit.

4.1.1.3.2. INTERFEROMETERS. Of all dispersive instruments, the most compact, versatile, and elegant is the interferometer. To adequately discuss its many variations and applications would be (and has been[22,120,121]) the subject of complete volumes. We will limit our discussion here to the more common forms and applications.

Only the Michelson and Fabry–Perot interferometers will be treated in this section. A large variety of interferometers, principally those using Fizeau fringes, are extremely useful in the evaluation of surfaces, metrology, and similar problems,[20,120] but find only negligible application to studies of atomic properties. Lummer–Gehrcke plates and echelons[21,22,121] have been almost completely superseded by the Fabry–Perot interferometer. The latter is far more versatile and convenient to construct and use. Only the reflection echelon merits serious consideration, as a potential device for high-resolution interferometry in the wavelength regions below 1100 Å, where no transparent materials are available.

Two excellent review articles on the subject are available,[122,123] and the reader is referred to these for a more detailed exposition of the subject. Progress since 1960 has been confined largely to improved technology inspired chiefly by the requirements of the laser. Given the incentive of a large demand backed by adequate compensation, commercial suppliers of interferometer flats and multilayer dielectric coatings are now able to supply interferometer plates flat to within 0.005 fringes or better, and with reflectivities above 99 % over most of the near ultraviolet, visible, and infrared.

A review of recent laser developments[34] is certainly not within the scope of this section. We must, however, recognize the influence of this

[118] H. Greiner and E. Schäffer, Optik 14, 263 (1957); 15, 51 (1958).

[119] G. Hass and R. Tousey, J. Opt. Soc. Am. 49, 593 (1959).

[120] S. Tolansky, "Multiple Beam Interferometry." Oxford Univ. Press (Clarendon), London and New York, 1948.

[121] E. Gehrcke, "Die Anwendung der Interferenzen." Vieweg, Braunschweig, 1906.

[122] P. Jacquinot, Repts. Progr. in Phys. 23, 267 (1960).

[123] H. G. Kuhn, Repts. Progr. in Phys. 14, 64 (1951).

new field of "active" interferometer cavities on the classic or "passive" field of interferometry. The entrance into the field of the electrical engineer has not only introduced a new jargon, but, by viewing the interferometer as an electromagnetic cavity resonator, he has added to our basic understanding of the instrument. Connes[124] deviated from the plane interferometer and introduced the confocal Fabry–Perot, and subsequent investigators have generalized this innovation to a variety of combinations of sphericities.[125]

4.1.1.3.2.1. *Michelson Interferometer.* The simplest and most versatile interferometer is the Michelson.[20,22,126] It has found wide applications in such fields as metrology and high-resolution spectroscopy, and its variants have been used to measure index of refraction and the progress of a shock wave. The basic principle in each of its modifications includes, first, the splitting of the amplitude of a wave front by means of a partially transmitting and partially reflecting surface into two beams. These beams then traverse different paths and are recombined at a semitransparent surface. In the Michelson, the two semitransparent surfaces to which each of the beams is returned are the same element. In the Mach–Zender interferometer these two surfaces are distinct.

If the two optical paths are very nearly equal, and if there is a small angle between the combining wave fronts, then Fizeau fringes (fringes of equal thickness) are formed. This type of interferometer is widely used in metrology, particularly with white light fringes.[22] Its application to spectroscopy and the study of atomic properties is very limited.

If, on the other hand, the emergent wave fronts are strictly parallel, then Haidinger fringes (fringes of equal inclination) are formed. Since the image of these fringes is at infinity, a real image of the fringe pattern will be formed in the focal plane of the camera lens. Normally, the interferometer is operated in parallel light from the source, which is then brought to the focus in this same focal plane. The fringes will therefore be superimposed on the image of the source, and if the source is a point source then its image will also be a point source whose intensity will be determined by its location relative to the image of the fringe system.

If the source is an extended source, then the extended image of that source will, for a balanced beam splitter, be modulated by the super-imposed fringe system:

$$I = I_0 \cos^2 \left(\pi \frac{2d}{\lambda} \cos \theta \right) \qquad (4.1.1.14)$$

[124] P. Connes, *J. phys., radium* **19**, 262 (1958).
[125] G. D. Boyd and H. Kogelnick, *Bell System Tech. J.* **41**, 1347 (1962).
[126] A. A. Michelson, *Phil. Mag.* [5] **24**, 463 (1887); **31**, 338 (1890); **34**, 280 (1892).

where I_0 is the intensity that would be present in the absence of inter-ference, $2d$ is the difference between the two optical paths, λ is the wavelength of the radiation, and θ is the angle between the direction of propagation through the interferometer and the normal to the mirrors. Maxima of this fringe system occur at angles θ satisfying the equation:

$$n\lambda = 2d \cos \theta \qquad (4.1.1.15)$$

where n is an integer and denotes the order of interference. The order of interference at the center of the fringe pattern ($\theta = 0$) is $n_0 = 2d/\lambda$, and

$$n = n_0 \cos \theta. \qquad (4.1.1.16)$$

In practice, θ is nearly always very small, and $\cos \theta$ can be expanded as $1 + \theta^2/2$; thus

$$n = n_0(1 + \theta^2/2). \qquad (4.1.1.17)$$

The nth and $(n - 1)$th rings are separated by a difference in their angles squared that is a constant:

$$\theta_{n-1}^2 - \theta_n^{\ 2} = 2/n_0 = \lambda/d. \qquad (4.1.1.18)$$

If the fringe pattern is brought to a focus on a screen by a lens of focal length F, then the difference in radii squared for two successive rings will be

$$\Delta(R^2) = \lambda F^2/d. \qquad (4.1.1.19)$$

If the fringe pattern is plotted as a function of the radius squared, the rings will be equidistant, and their intensity distribution will be that of a cosine function, plus a constant background, for monochromatic radiation.

If the radiation observed contains more than one component of fre-quency, each will produce such a cosine distribution, and the resultant will be the sum of their various contributions. If these frequencies are close together, the shape of the curves will remain very nearly that of the cosine distribution, but the amount of continuum background will change as a function of the phase relationship of the individual compo-nents. It is therefore not possible, as in the case of the Fabry–Perot interferometer, to resolve closely spaced spectrum lines.

The intensity observed at the center of the fringe pattern ($\theta = 0$) is given by $I = I_0 \cos^2(2\pi d/\lambda) = I_0[1 + \cos 4\pi(d/\lambda)]$. For a complex spectrum containing more than one line, the intensity at any plate separation, d, will be determined by the superposition of the various components:

$$I = \sum_i I_i \cos^2(2\pi d/\lambda_i). \tag{4.1.1.20}$$

The intensity, I, can be obtained as a function of the path difference, d, by observing the output of a Michelson interferometer as the position of one of the plates is varied. The Fourier transform of this function will give the intensity as a function of λ, or the spectrum of the source. This technique in its simplest form was used by Michelson to infer the existence of closely spaced doublets.[127]

Michelson defined a quantity which he called the visibility:

$$V = \frac{I_{\max} - I_{\min}}{I_{\max} + I_{\min}}. \tag{4.1.1.21}$$

For a single completely monochromatic line the visibility will always be one. For a pair of such lines, λ_1 and λ_2, of equal intensity, the visibility at $d = 0$ will be unity, and will vary in a sinusoidal manner as a function of d, being equal to 0 for values of d for which N is equal to an odd integer and equal to 1 for values of d for which N is an even integer in the relation

$$d = \frac{N}{4} \frac{\lambda_1 \lambda_2}{|\lambda_1 - \lambda_2|}. \tag{4.1.1.22}$$

If the two spectral lines have a finite width of $\Delta\nu$ wave numbers, the visibility curve will again vary as a sinusoid of decreasing amplitude approaching 0 with increasing d. This limit will be effectively reached when $d = 1/2\Delta\nu$. In the more general case, the visibility curve is the Fourier transform of the spectrum.

The development of large digital computers and more versatile analog computers has permitted the application of Fourier transform spectroscopy to more complex spectra.[128,129] The technique can yield a very high resolving power, but its application is extremely time consuming in all but the simplest spectra. It has, however, found successful application to the far infrared regions where conventional spectrometers are seriously energy-limited.

The basic principle of the Michelson interferometer can be applied to a variety of problems. In its various applications, it can be used to compare the index of refraction along one path with that along a second

[127] A. A. Michelson, "Light Waves and their Uses." Univ. of Chicago Press, Chicago, Illinois, 1902.

[128] J. D. Strong and G. Vanasse, *J. phys., radium* **19**, 192 (1958).

[129] J. Connes, *J. phys., radium* **19**, 197 (1958).

path, as in the Jamin interferometer, or to measure the linear translation of one mirror relative to the other, in terms of the wavelength of a monochromatic light source as a unit of length, for the precise measurement of distance.

An interesting variation of the Michelson interferometer is one used by Connes.[130] He called his instrument the "Spectrometre Interferentiel à Sélection par l'Amplitude de Modulation," or "SISAM" for short. In this instrument a pair of matched gratings is substituted for the mirror reflectors in the Michelson interferometer. Only radiation of that wavelength, λ, which obeys the grating equation, $n\lambda = 2d \sin i$, will be refracted back on itself. If the gratings are identical and are turned to the same angle, i then the instrument will act as a Michelson interferometer for that particular wavelength.

If the path difference in this interferometer is now varied, that radiation and only that radiation at the wavelength satisfying the above equation will be modulated. A spectrum can be observed by recording the modulation intensity as the two gratings are turned slowly in unison.

The advantage of this system is that it yields a resolving power equivalent to that of the grating alone, together with the larger light gathering power of the interferometer of the same resolution. It is therefore particularly suited to infrared studies where severe energy limitations are normally encountered. Its principal disadvantage is the great precision with which the two gratings must be rotated in synchronism.

4.1.1.3.2.2. *Fabry–Perot Interferometer*. The most widely used interferometer for high-resolution spectroscopy and for precise wavelength determinations is the Fabry–Perot interferometer. This instrument, long the tool of spectroscopists seeking the utmost in either resolving power or wavelength measurement precision, has more recently taken an active role as a resonant source in its laser applications.

The instrument in its plane version is conceptually, at least, the simplest of instruments. It consists merely of a pair of very flat partially transparent reflectors that are maintained completely parallel to each other. The frustrations encountered in application result from the difficulty of obtaining reflectors flat to $\pm 5 \times 10^{-6}$ mm or better with reflection coefficients in excess of 90 % without a prohibitive absorption loss, and of maintaining these plates parallel to $\pm 10^{-7}$ radians. Nevertheless, Fabry–Perot interferometry is still the easiest and most effective way of obtaining high resolution.

As in the case of the Michelson interferometer in which the emergent wave fronts are parallel, the interference fringe pattern in the Fabry–

---

[130] P. Connes, *J. phys., radium* 19, 215 (1958).

Perot is to be seen at infinity. The intensity of the Fabry–Perot fringes at an angle θ to the plate normal and for an optical separation of the plates of d is

$$I = \frac{T^2}{(1-R)^2} \cdot \frac{1}{1 + \dfrac{4R}{(1-R)^2} \sin^2 \left(\dfrac{2\pi d}{\lambda} \cos \theta\right)} \cdot \qquad (4.1.1.23)$$

The transmission, reflection, and absorption coefficients of the partially reflecting layers on the two interferometer plates are $T, R,$ and A $(T + R + A = 1)$.

The factor

$$\frac{1}{1 + \dfrac{4R}{(1-R)^2} \sin^2 \left(\dfrac{2\pi d}{\lambda} \cos \theta\right)}$$

gives the fringe distribution for ideal plates, for which $A = 0$. The argument $2\pi d/\lambda \cos \theta$ is the same as that in the case of the Michelson interferometer, and, as in that case, it leads to a set of circular fringes whose spacing is uniform on a scale of radii squared. The shape of this curve depends only upon the value of the reflectivity R. The reciprocal of the width at half maxima of the fringes in units of one free spectral range is known as the finesse, $F = \pi \sqrt{R}/(1 - R)$, of the interferometer, and is a measure of its resolving power.

The factor

$$\frac{T^2}{(1-R)^2} = \left(1 - \frac{A}{1-R}\right)^2 \qquad (4.1.1.24)$$

determines the intensity of the fringes. The efficiency of the instrument (intensity at the peak of the fringes) is given by this factor.

The ratio of minimum to maximum intensity in the fringe pattern is given by

$$\frac{I_{\min}}{I_{\max}} = \frac{(1-R)^2}{(1+R)^2} \cdot \qquad (4.1.1.25)$$

As in the case of the Michelson interferometer, fringe maxima occur for values of $d, \lambda,$ and θ satisfying the equation

$$n\lambda = 2d \cos \theta , \qquad (4.1.1.26)$$

where n is an integer.

The fringe pattern can be observed photographically by using an extended source and photographing the fringes with a camera focused at infinity. If a wide range of spectrum is to be studied, the camera lens should be an achromat over the wavelength region. A fringe pattern will appear for each component of a spectrum line present in the radiation.

If the spectrum is at all complex, it is customary to add a secondary source of dispersion. This can be accomplished by placing a spectrograph slit in the focal plane of the fringes. The circular fringe patterns for each wavelength component will be brought to a focus on the slit. The portion of the pattern that passes through the slit will be again brought to a focus in the focal plane of the spectrograph, dispersed along the focal plane. A wide slit is customarily used, and the resultant photograph has the appearance of a conventional spectrogram with wide slits, where upon each slit image is superimposed the interference pattern for that particular line (Fig. 8).

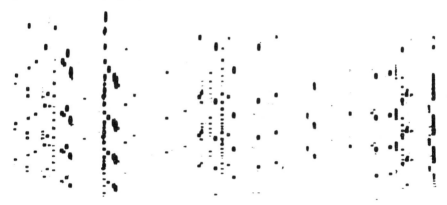

FIG. 8. Interferogram obtained by crossing a Fabry-Perot interferometer with a prism spectrograph. Note the large number of components (up to ten) visible in some of the lines in this spectrum showing the hyperfine structure of technetium.

The Fabry–Perot interferometer has an extremely high resolving power, limited only by the reflectivities attainable, the uniformity of the plates, and the maximum value of d for which one still obtains stability of the instrument. In the visible portion of the spectrum, excellent reflectivities can be obtained with multilayer dielectric coatings,[122] and reflectivities higher than 99 % can be achieved. In the ultraviolet, however, good dielectric layers are not available, and one is usually constrained to use aluminum, with a reflection coefficient in the neighborhood of 85 %.

Since it is possible to obtain both the greatest finesse and highest efficiency with dielectric multilayer coatings at wavelengths above 3500 Å, such coatings are generally preferred where the highest resolving power is needed over a limited spectral range. Since these plates are, however, dependent for their reflectivity upon the interference phenomena between alternate layers of low- and high-index materials, each one-quarter wavelength thick, these films are effective over only a relatively narrow band of wavelengths. Even within their range of high reflectivity, the phase change on reflection varies rapidly as a function of wavelength. These films are, therefore, of very limited use in studying a broad spectral region of more than about 3000 Å (although this can be broadened somewhat by varying the thickness of the successive layers). The rapid variation of phase change on reflection also introduces rather large corrections when precise intercomparison is attempted between monochromatic lines that are separated by more than a few angstroms.

Above 4000 Å, semitransparent layers of silver also have very high reflectivity, in excess of 90 % when fresh, but they also tarnish very readily.

Since there are no very satisfactory materials having high indices of refraction below 3500 Å that are both transparent and stable, most interferometry for the ultraviolet is carried out with plates coated with pure aluminum. Fresh layers of aluminum, if properly prepared, yield high values of reflectivity well into the ultraviolet.[131]

In actual practice, the resolving power of the interferometer is limited not only by the reflectivity of its plates, but also by their flatness. The flatness limit in practice is, for exceptional plates, about 1/200 fringe, or 15 Å. There is, therefore, nothing to be gained even for the best plates by using reflectivities in excess of 98 % unless, as in the case of a laser, only a very small, and hence very flat, area of the plate is to be used.

Good interferometer plates are normally made of a good grade of optical quality quartz. The nonreflecting surfaces of these plates are normally set at an angle of about 10' of arc to the reflective surface so that interference patterns formed by reflection at these surfaces will be thrown to one side. In the configuration utilizing the auxiliary dispersion of a spectrograph, if the width of the source image is comparable to the width of the slit, then it is a simple matter to place the wedge angle of the plates in such a manner that the extraneous interference patterns will not pass through the slit.

Since the resolving power of the interferometer depends critically on the parallelisms of the plates, it is important that these be carefully adjusted and that they maintain a constant and uniform spacing. In the better instruments, the plates are kept a fixed distance apart by Invar or quartz spacers.

The optical path between the plates is, of course, a function of the index of refraction of the space between the plates. If the instrument is operated in air, great care must be taken to avoid air currents and changes in the pressure and temperature of the air in the interferometer. Since the index is, to first order, a function only of the density, considerable

[131] R. P. Madden, in "Physics of Thin Films" (G. Hass, ed.), Vol. 1, p. 123. Academic Press, New York, 1963.

stability can be achieved by sealing the interferometer in a fixed volume of air. The effect of the index can of course be entirely eliminated by enclosing the interferometer in a vacuum chamber. For most work, a forepump vacuum is entirely adequate.

The adjustment for parallelism of interferometers can be accomplished quite readily for interferometers having plate separations up to about 20 cm. This adjustment can be accomplished by removing the camera lens and looking toward an extended source, whose image will be seen at infinity, and on it will be superimposed a series of ring patterns. If a mercury lamp is used, the pattern will be simple enough for critical adjustments. If the eye is now moved about, the fringe pattern will appear to move across the surface of the plates. The ring at the center will appear to expand if the portion of the interferometer through which it is viewed has a thicker spacing, and will appear to contract if the spacing is too small. The plates can be adjusted to be parallel to within 1/100 fringe or better with this test which is most critical if the length of the interferometer is so adjusted that a fringe is just beginning to appear at the center of the pattern. Very slight changes in plate separation will then cause very marked changes in the intensity at the center.

An excellent and convenient line to use in adjusting interferometers is the green line (5460 Å) of mercury-198 from a cooled electrodeless lamp. This source may be used for interferometers up to about 18 cm in length. By warming up such a lamp somewhat above room temperature, a narrow self-reversal can be formed in the green line. This self-reversed line can be used to extend the range of interferometer adjustment to about 24 cm.

For longer interferometers, a technique devised by Meissner[132] using images of very fine quartz fibers is very useful. In this technique, the images of the fibers produced by multiple reflections are superimposed by tilting the interferometer plates. Observation of these images is through a microscope of several hundredfold magnification. When optimum alignment is achieved a bright spot will appear at the intersection of the fibers.

Gas lasers will, of course, produce radiation sufficiently monochromatic for the adjustment of very long interferometers. They are, however, potentially very harmful to the eye if viewed directly, and should be used, if at all, only when observed reflected by a nonspecular diffuse reflector.

A number of excellent comprehensive articles and books on the application of the Fabry–Perot interferometer are available.[20–22,122,133]

Photoelectric observations with the Fabry–Perot interferometer can

[132] K. W. Meissner and V. Kaufman, *J. Opt. Soc. Am.* **49**, 434 (1959).
[133] K. W. Meissner, *J. Opt. Soc. Am.* **31**, 405 (1941); **32**, 185 (1942).

be accomplished by observing a slit image which is scanned through the fringe pattern by slowly tilting the entire interferometer with reference to the optic axis.[134] It is, however, more convenient to observe the center of the fringe pattern, that is, to view with the photocell only those rays which leave the interferometer within a small angle of the normal to the plates. For optimum resolution this angle should be small compared to the angular half-widths of the fringes. Scanning is, in this case, accomplished by slowly varying the optical path between the interferometer plates. This can be accomplished by physically moving the plates apart. Magnetostrictive or piezoelectric spacers have both been used successfully to accomplish this. The former has the advantage of a larger range of motion, the latter the advantage of low power dissipation and better high-frequency response. Both can be used in a servo loop. A convenient and frequently satisfactory method of scanning is to place the interferometer in a vacuum-tight housing and slowly leak in a gas. This changes the index of refraction and hence the optical path.

The Fabry–Perot interferometer is usually used in conjunction with a medium to large prism spectrograph. A nearly stigmatic instrument is essential since the dispersion of the interferometer is normal to that of the spectrograph. Most grating instruments are not sufficiently stigmatic, and even with prism instruments it is usually necessary to alter the focal curve to more nearly correspond to the stigmatic focus in the direction of the Fabry–Perot dispersion.

4.1.1.4. Detectors. A wide variety of radiation detectors has found application in spectroscopy. The type of detector to be used in a particular application is dictated first by the spectral regions studied and second by the nature of the information sought, as will be discussed below. Since many of the detectors to be discussed are proprietary products whose characteristics are constantly being improved and whose variety is ever increasing, the investigator entering the field is advised not only to seek latest information from the leading manufacturers, but also to inquire into the products of the smaller less well-known fabricators.

The oldest detector, the human eye, is still extremely useful in checking the alignment of instruments, and occasionally for survey applications. Although its sensitivity with a threshold of approximately ten quanta is comparable with that of the better detectors, it has been almost completely replaced in most serious research work and will not be discussed here.

4.1.1.4.1. THE PHOTOGRAPHIC PLATE.* The most widely used and the most versatile detector is the photographic plate. In its simplest

[134] C. J. Humphreys and E. Paul, Jr., *J. phys. radium* **19**, 424 (1958).

* See, for some aspects of the characteristics of the photographic emulsion, Vol. 5A, Chapter 1.7.

form, it consists of a thin emulsion of silver halide in gelatin supported on a glass plate or film backing. The sensitivity range of such plates extends from approximately 2200 Å in the ultraviolet to 5000 Å in the visible.

The upper limit of the range is set by the quantum threshold for the photochemical reaction that sensitizes the individual silver halide grains. This threshold can be substantially lowered by the addition of certain sensitizing dyes, and sensitized emulsions containing various dye combinations are commercially available. These emulsions are designated by upper-case alphabetical suffixes in the Kodak emulsion designations (such as the F in 103 aF). A wide variety of such emulsions have been devised for special requirements.[134a,b] For broad general coverage, however, the following series will be found quite adequate: O sensitization up to 5000 Å, F up to 6800 Å, N up to 8700 Å, M up to 10,000 Å, and Z from 10,000 to 12,000 Å.

The sensitivity of all these emulsions decreases rapidly with increasing wavelengths and the Z emulsion over its range is more than two orders of magnitude slower than the unsensitized plate at 4000 Å. Very strong spectrum lines have been photographed slightly beyond 13,000 Å with excessively long exposures.

In order to obtain the optimum sensitivity for M and Z plates, it is necessary to sensitize the emulsion with ammonia before use. The plate should be bathed for 3 min in a chilled (approximately 5°C) solution of 1 % ammonium hydroxide and should then be rinsed in a bath of absolute alcohol and dried as rapidly as possible in a stream of room-temperature air. Unless refrigerated, these plates will fog in a few hours. They should, in any case, be exposed and processed as soon as possible after sensitization.

At shorter wavelengths, the ordinary photographic range is limited by the absorption characteristics of gelatin, which rapidly becomes opaque below 2300 Å. Two types of plates are available for extending this range to shorter wavelength.

The "UV sensitized" plates are produced by coating the surface of a gelatin emulsion with a material that will fluoresce when exposed to shorter-wavelength photons. The secondary photons given off by the fluorescent material have a sufficiently long wavelength to penetrate the gelatin and to form a latent image. Such plates can be prepared by coating an ordinary plate with mineral oil or with a commercially available compound. These coatings must be thoroughly removed by washing the plate in ethylene chloride or cyclohexane after exposure and before

[134a] J. W. Mitchell, *Repts. Progr. Phys.* **20**, 433 (1957).

[134b] Kodak Plates and Films for Science and Industry, Eastman Kodak Co., Rochester, New York.

development (concentrations of ethylene chloride fumes can be toxic and this chemical should be used only in a well-ventilated dark room).

Another approach to this spectral region is that taken by the Schumann and SWR types of plate. These circumvent the problem of absorption in the gelatin by greatly reducing the gelatin concentrations near the surface of the emulsion. The developable silver halide lies in a very thin but dense layer on the surface. Such plates are more sensitive than the coated plates, but have a very high contrast and, since the silver halide grains are exposed, these plates are very susceptible to abrasion and pressure damage. The sensitivity of such plates extends on into the X-ray region.

The sole U.S. supplier, the Eastman Kodak Co., offers both plates and films in a variety of emulsions to which various dyes have been added. For most spectroscopy work in the laboratory the 103 and 103a types are used. The latter is especially formulated for weak exposures where the exposure time is in excess of 5 min. These emulsions are very fast and have a moderately low granularity. A slight increase in speed can be obtained with type I with somewhat greater granularity. Emulsions having greater resolving power at a considerable sacrifice in speed are also available.

The photographic plate's principal advantage over other detectors is that it can simultaneously record information at high resolution over a broad spectral range. Since it integrates energy for long periods of time, it is extremely useful on weak sources and yields for such sources a high signal-to-noise ratio. The photographic plate is also excellent for precise wavelength measurements. With suitable comparators, the positions of sharp lines in a typical spectrum can be measured reproducibly to better than a micron.

As used in a rotating drum spectrograph,* the photographic film is capable of presenting time-resolved information over an extended spectral range. In general, however, time-resolved information is most easily obtained with photoelectric detectors which yield such information continuously and without the annoyance and delays of the development process.

The principal disadvantages of the photographic plate are its low quantum efficiency and the nonlinearity of its response. At the lower end of its sensitivity range it has a threshold of energy below which plate darkening does not occur, and at the upper end of its range it has a saturation level. Between these limits the response curve is far from linear and its slope depends upon a variety of factors such as the condi-

* A rotating drum spectrograph is one in which the photographic film is moved rapidly in the focal plane in a direction normal to the dispersion. With such spectrographs, time resolution in the microsecond range can be achieved.

tions of manufacture, the age of the emulsion, the temperature and humidity at time of exposure, and the temperature, chemical composition, and duration of the development process. In spite of these factors, fairly precise (approximately 1 %) intensity ratio measurements over narrow spectral ranges can still be accomplished by carefully calibrating the plate and by meticulous attention to such factors as uniform development and careful microphotometry. Such techniques were highly developed by spectrochemists before the advent of commercial photoelectric instruments.

4.1.1.4.2. PHOTOELECTRIC DETECTORS.* Of all the various photoelectric detectors developed since the barrier layer cell, the only type widely applicable to spectroscopic techniques is the electron multiplier phototube. A full discussion of multiplier phototubes is certainly not in order here and an enumeration of available tubes would be out of date in a very short time. A few general comments are, however, in order.

At the time of this writing, no completely satisfactory standards and conventions for the specifications of sensitivity and signal-to-noise ratio were in effect. Since individual tubes of a particular type vary by as much as an order of magnitude in their characteristics, such specifications are useful only if limits are indicated. If the requirements of the particular experiment are such as to demand the utmost of the tube characteristics and if the research budget allows, it is advisable to obtain a number of samples of each tube type and to select those that best match the requirements of the experiment at hand.

Apparent phototube noise can also be generated by leakage currents in the phototube base or in its sockets. Since potentials of 1000 volts and up are generally used, it is essential that all insulators separating the leads be kept absolutely clean and dry. A defective socket or sloppy soldering can easily ruin an otherwise good experiment. The leakage problem becomes particularly troublesome in those experiments in which the phototube is cooled in order to reduce the dark current.

Phototubes are quite comparable to the photographic emulsion in spectral range but have a higher quantum efficiency. The long-wavelength limit of the phototube sensitivity is determined by the work function of the photosensitive cathode. As in the case of the photographic plates, the sensitivity decreases rapidly in the infrared. The long-wavelength limit of the infrared-sensitive S1 photocathode is about 12,000 Å. This tube has a maximum quantum efficiency of 0.4 % at 8000 Å and 0.1 % at 10,000 Å. The photocathode used most commonly in the visible and near ultraviolet is the S4 which has a maximum photoefficiency of 10 % near 5000 Å, falling off rapidly above 6000 Å.

* See also Vol. 2, Chapter 11.1.

The short-wave limit of the phototube is determined by the transmission characteristics of its window. Tubes designed primarily for the visible cutoff at about 3000 Å. Ultraviolet transmitting glass envelopes as used in the 1P28 can extend this limit to about 2200 Å. Further extension to about 1850 Å can be achieved with quartz windows. The present limit of window materials is represented by lithium fluoride which transmits in thin layers down to about 1050 Å. Below this limit one must operate either with windowless[135,136] tubes or with tubes coated with a fluorescent material.[137]

Although the overall photon efficiency of the coated tube is smaller by approximately a factor of three or four than the windowless tubes in the far ultraviolet, the fluorescent-coated tube is much more convenient to use and there is evidence that its response is nearly linear over wide spectral ranges. The fluorescence from sodium salicylate peaks in the 4000 to 5000 Å region, matching the sensitivity curve of the S4 photosurface in conjunction with which it is usually used. In order to increase the capture efficiency of the secondary photons it is, of course, advisable to use a photocell whose cathode is on the inner surface of its window.

Windowless photomultipliers can, of course, work efficiently only in a good vacuum, usually 10^{-6} mm or better. In addition, since such tubes will be occasionally exposed to air, the photosurface must be able to tolerate such poisoning. In the vacuum ultraviolet, the photon energies are sufficiently high to overcome the work functions of most metals. This feature permits the construction of photomultipliers for the detection of ultraviolet photons that are completely insensitive to photons in the visible region.

It is possible to use almost any photomultiplier geometry in a windowless phototube provided that appropriate materials are used for the cathodes and dynodes. Beryllium copper is a frequently used material since its sensitivity is not affected by exposure to air.

A recently developed and novel electron multiplier[138] has been widely used windowless applications. In place of the usual dynodes at successively higher potentials, this tube utilizes a continuous potential drop across a high-resistance surface. The electron multiplication takes place on a slab of insulating material coated with a conductive layer and placed in a magnetic field which is parallel to the surface and normal to the gradient of the electric field applied to the conductive layer. Electrons striking the layer at its negative end initiate electron

[135] S. E. Williams, *J. Quant. Spectroscopy & Radiative Transfer* **2**, 621 (1962).
[136] L. Dunkelman, *J. Quant. Spectroscopy & Radiative Transfer* **2**, 533 (1962).
[137] F. S. Johnson, K. Watanabe, and R. Tousey, *J. Opt. Soc. Am.* **41**, 702 (1951).
[138] G. W. Goodrich and W. C. Wiley, *Rev. Sci. Instr.* **32**, 846 (1961).

avalanches that proceed toward the positive electrode in small cycloids, gaining energy in each cycloid and thereby causing electron multiplication each time that the electron packet strikes the surface. Such multipliers can also be used without a magnetic field in a parallel plate configuration or in a cylindrical configuration.

Multiplier phototubes are available in a variety of configurations. In selecting a tube for a particular application, it is, of course, necessary to choose one whose spectral response covers the desired range. It is also advisable to choose one with at least nine stages of amplification.

In spectroscopic applications, the phototube is generally placed a short distance behind the exit slit of a monochromator or spectrograph. The useful area of the cathode is therefore rather small—a fraction of a millimeter by perhaps a centimeter. The remainder of the cathode yields no signal but does, by thermionic emission, contribute to the dark current. Since this dark current determines the sensitivity limit of the phototube, it is advisable to use as small a photocathode as possible.

In a good, selected nine-stage multiplier phototube with an amplification factor of 10^6, the dark current at the anode will be about 10^{-9} amp per cm^2 of the photosurface. This implies an electron emission current from the photocathode of about 10^4 electrons per second. If the cathode has a 10 % photon efficiency, this means that the dark current is equivalent to a signal flux of 10^5 photons per second. It is, of course, the statistical fluctuations in this dark current that are troublesome in most experiments. The root-mean-square fluctuation in the dark current, $\overline{\Delta I}$ over frequency range Δf, for a phototube whose amplification factor is N and whose dc dark current is I_0 is:

$$\overline{\Delta I} = \sqrt{2e}\, N I_0 \cdot \Delta f$$

where e is the electron charge.

For the detection of weak signals it is, of course, necessary to increase the signal-to-noise ratio by using a narrow bandwidth, Δf, if the signal has a characteristic frequency, f, or a long-time constant if the observations are on a dc phenomenon. The latter is equivalent to a narrow-band response at $f = 0$.

The dark current, since it is generated by thermionic emission, can be reduced by cooling the photosurface to dry ice or liquid nitrogen temperatures. Cooling techniques are, however, at best somewhat messy since the low temperatures involved necessitate elaborate precautions to prevent water condensation and temperature effects in the instrument. Cooling techniques are generally profitable only in experiments involving either photon counting or very long integration times on very weak signals. Furthermore, the charge mobility in many photosurfaces is so drastically reduced at these lower temperatures that, unless the photo-surface has an added conductive layer, the sensitivity will be greatly reduced at lower temperatures.

Photon counting techniques can be useful at very low signal levels, especially if the signal has a short duty cycle, since, by accepting counts only at specified times, the signal-to-noise ratio can be greatly increased. It should be noted, however, that pulse-height discrimination techniques which are so useful in scintillation detectors in the X-ray and gamma ray regions are not applicable in the optical region. Each primary photon ejects but one electron from the cathode and the pulse that it produces at the anode is indistinguishable from that produced by thermionic electrons emitted by the cathode.

In the infrared beyond 1.2 μ, both photographic plates and photo-electric detectors become insensitive. Although atomic spectra extend well into this range, the infrared has, by tradition and practice, been primarily the province of the molecular spectroscopist who has developed a complete technology covering this field.* The problems have been more generally related to chemistry and the chemical industries rather than to physics and the results have been the commercial development of a complete line of very high quality and sophisticated instruments.

These instruments can be applied to problems in atomic spectroscopy with an unfortunate but presently unavoidable decrease in sensitivity by several orders of magnitude below that in the visible region.

4.1.1.5. Spectroscopy Applied to Problems in Physics. Spectroscopy, as considered here, is a technique and a powerful probe which can be used to acquire information about a wide variety of phenomena. A complete dissertation on the range of applications, even in the field of physics, is well beyond the limitations of this volume and its authors. Instead, a few representative and illustrative examples will be considered.

4.1.1.5.1. ANALYSIS OF SPECTRA. The classic and, until recently, the most widespread application of spectroscopy was to the analysis of atomic spectra. The problem here, simply stated, is to deduce and describe the energy levels of an atom or ion from observations on its spectrum. Nearly all that we know of the electronic structure of atoms has been derived by these techniques.

The analysis of a spectrum involves an interesting inductive experience: given a series of spectrum lines, to construct the array of atomic energy levels, transitions between which produce the observed spectrum. For one- and two-electron spectra, this analysis is quite simple. The number of possible electron configurations is limited, the coupling scheme is well-known, and the number of lines in the spectrum is

_____
* See Vol. 3, Chapter 2.2.

relatively small. Most of these spectra were analyzed in the thirties and the principal remaining problem has been to observe the intersystem transitions between singlet and triplet and between doublet and quartet systems in the lighter elements which exhibit nearly pure L-S couplings, and where, therefore, such transitions are quite strongly forbidden.

The complexity of atomic spectra increases rapidly with the introduction of d electrons in the transition elements. The simple L-S coupling scheme which adequately describes the simpler spectra begins to lose its validity. As configurations multiply and overlap, mixing of terms becomes so great that the significance of the L-S notation becomes misleading. A particular level may be 60 % ^3F and 30 % ^1F and the remaining 10 % may be an admixture from a variety of other levels. For obvious reasons of typography and ease of identity, such a level is frequently labeled simply as ^3F. Once this has been done, it is all too easy to take the notation literally, and to forget its true complexity.

The ultimate in complexity is reached with the addition of f electrons in the rare earth elements. Here, in general, neither L-S nor j-j notation have any validity and the proliferation of energy levels leads to extremely complex spectra. Since these spectra illustrate the extreme example of a problem in analysis, we shall deal with it in some greater detail.

The first task leading to the analysis of the spectrum is, of course, production of the proper spectrum (see Section 4.1.1.2.2). Chemically pure samples of nearly all of the elements are now available, so that the contamination of the spectrum with impurity lines presents a negligible problem to modern spectroscopists. Generally, only the strongest lines of a few contaminates will appear. In the case of sources, such as electrodeless lamps or hollow cathode tubes where a carrier gas is used, lines introduced by the carrier gas can readily be eliminated by observing the same spectra with several different gases, and selecting only those lines in common between the spectra from the several sources.

A more severe problem is the separation of the spectra due to different degrees of ionization. A relatively cool source such as a dc arc or an electrodeless discharge will excite mainly transitions in the neutral atom. Lines in the spectrum of the singly ionized atoms will be present, but weak. The problem is to distinguish these from weak lines in the spectrum of the neutral atom. In the case of the dc arc, the intensity of the second spectrum lines is greatly enhanced near the electrode, and this sometimes yields sufficient information for proper identification.

In general, however, it is necessary to compare two different sources. Historically this was done with the dc arc and the condensed spark, hence the nomenclature: arc for the neutral, spark for the ionized spectra. In a typical case, lines strong in the arc but weak in the spark were identified with transitions in the neutral atom. Lines strong in the spark and weak in the arc were identified with the singly ionized atom and lines strong in the spark and missing in the arc were attributed to higher ionizations.

The separation of first and second spectra is especially difficult in the case of the lanthanides and actinides. The low ionization potential and the high and nearly uniform density of states in these atoms and ions leads to far more subtle changes in the intensities of transitions as a function of plasma temperature.

Since the principle involved in the separation is simply that a hotter plasma will have a greater concentration of higher ionization species, such a separation can be achieved with a variety of sources (Section 4.1.1.2.2).

Complex spectra and particularly those of the rare earth elements display an extremely high density of lines. In the spectrum of neutral thorium, for instance, some 25,000 lines have been observed between 2000 and 10,000 Å. In order to properly resolve these lines, and also, as will be shown later, to aid the analysis, it is necessary to observe such spectra with the highest available resolution and dispersion (see Section 4.1.1.3.1). Nearly all such work has been done in the past with 7-meter (21-foot) radius gratings ruled 600 to 1200 lines per mm. More recently, a few larger instruments utilizing 10-meter gratings have been used and a limited application has been made of plane gratings in either Ebert–Fastie or Czerny–Turner mountings. Echelle instruments yield a somewhat improved resolving power, but absolute wavelength measurements are more difficult and less reliable.

Since a successful analysis depends very critically upon the absolute wavelength measurements, it is necessary to make all observations with a proper juxtaposition of good calibration standards. Traditionally, the Pfund iron arc was used for this purpose, but as more complex spectra were encountered it was found that the lines from this arc were neither sharp enough nor sufficiently numerous.

Iron hollow cathode sources have been used to improve the sharpness of the iron lines,[61] and, more recently, electrodeless lamps containing thorium have been extensively used[62] (see Section 4.1.1.2.3). These latter emit a very rich sharp spectrum and a fair number of interferometrically measured lines are now available,[139] except in the vacuum UV where standards are at present fewer and less accurate.[140,141] The photographic plate is still preferred for highest-precision wavelength measurements. Adequate precision can certainly be achieved with

---

[139] Report of Commission 14, *Trans. Intern. Astron. Union* 11A, 97 (1962); 12A (1964) (in press).

[140] J. C. Boyce, *Revs. Modern Phys.* 13, 1 (1941).

[141] B. Edlén, *Repts. Progr. in Phys.* 26, 181 (1963).

photoelectric instruments. However, the desired precision is of the order of 10^{-3} Å, and the observations usually cover approximately 10^4 Å, or 10^7 intervals total. Furthermore, in order to achieve a high signal-to-noise ratio, the photoelectric amplification usually has a bandwidth of only a few cycles. Scanning the entire spectrum would, therefore, require of the order of 10^6 seconds, a prohibitively long time. The photographic record can also include arc, spark, and calibration exposures in juxtaposition, a feature difficult to achieve photoelectrically.

With modern photoelectrically scanned comparators, settings reproducible to about 1 μ are common. If the dispersion is 1 Å per mm, this then corresponds to an error of 0.001 Å. Differences between different observations on the same line, however, frequently differ by the order of 0.001 to 0.003 Å, even for sharp lines.

The range of observation most easily covered is that from 2000 to 10,000 Å. Fortunately, this range includes most of the lines encountered in the lower ionization of most atoms. However, many important lines, particularly between overlapped configurations, lie beyond 10,000 Å. Unfortunately, photographic plates rapidly become less sensitive in the infrared, and give out completely at about 13,000 Å (see Section 4.1.1.4.1). Beyond this limit only a handful of observations made with PbS detectors* are available. Much more work can and should be done in this region.

At wavelengths shorter than 2000 Å, only transitions involving levels higher than 6 ev are observed. Hence, few neutral atomic transitions are found here, but the higher ionization spectra become increasingly prominent and most transitions for more than triply ionized atoms lie in this region. The instrumentation has been discussed earlier in Section 4.1.1.3.1.6.

By interpolation, the wavelength of each line is determined relative to the calibration standards, usually in an iron or thorium spectrum. Where large numbers of such spectra are measured, the comparator used is generally equipped with a digital output so that the position of each line, both unknown and standard, can be entered on a Hollerith card or on punched tape for a ready transfer to a high-speed computer which is coded to calculate the coefficients a_i of a fifth-degree equation for a least square fit to the observed standards on each photographic plate: $\lambda = \sum_{i=0}^{5} a_i x^i$. The wavelengths of the other lines can then be calculated from this equation.

The positions of the energy levels in an atom are measured in wave numbers: $\sigma = 1/\lambda = \nu/c$, where λ is the wavelength in vacuum, ν is the frequency, and c is the velocity of light. The unit of wave number is

* See Vol. 2, Section 11.1.4.

cm^{-1}. The wave number of a transition is the reciprocal of the wavelength of that transition in the vacuum. The correction for the index of air is generally calculated from the Edlén formula[142]

$$n = 1 + 8342.13 \times 10^{-8} + \frac{2,406,030}{130 \times 10^8 - \sigma^2} + \frac{15,997}{38.9 \times 10^8 - \sigma^2} \quad (4.1.1.27)$$

where σ is the wave number (reciprocal of the wavelength) in cm^{-1}. Tables of this function are also available.[143]

In most spectra, at least a few energy levels are known and, of course, the line list is available. Some of these lines will represent the differences, in wave number units, between known levels and unknown levels of opposite parity. Since, in general, there are a number of lines terminating or originating on each level, it is possible to unravel most of this puzzle, and the development of fast digital computers has rendered even the most complex spectra amenable to analysis.

One method of analysis is illustrated in Fig. 9.[143a] T_1 and T_1' are two known levels of the same parity. If we find in our line list a pair of lines σ_1 and σ_1' whose difference $\Delta\sigma_1$ is equal or very nearly equal to $T_1 - T_1'$ then this coincidence, if it be not pure chance, can be explained by a level of the opposite parity at T_{p1} or T_{p1}^*. If, similarly, the second pair of levels T_2 and T_2' in conjunction with two lines σ_2 and σ_2' predicts the same level T_{p1}, then confidence in that level is increased. In a simple spectrum this may be sufficient to determine the level as real. In a more complex spectrum, two coincidences may be well within the range of chance coincidences expected.

It is this background "noise" of chance coincidences that greatly increases the difficulty of the problem. The number of such chance coincidences is proportional to both the density of observed lines and the uncertainty in their measured values. It is for this reason that it is imperative, particularly in the more complex spectra, to obtain the highest possible precision in the wavelength determination.

A computer code written by Racah performs the same search for energy levels in a somewhat different manner, namely, by adding or subtracting all observed lines from the energy levels of one parity. The operation is systematized in such a manner that all possible sums within a given energy range are obtained at one time and only those sums which occur more than n times within a tolerance δ are retained. The number

[142] B. Edlén, *Metrologia* 2, 12 (1966).

[143] C. D. Coleman, W. R. Bozman, and W. F. Meggers, *Natl. Bur. Standards (U.S.),* *Monograph* 3, Vol. 1, 2000 M to 7000 M; Vol. 2, 7000 M to 1000 M (1960).

[143a] K. G. Kessler, S. B. Prush, and I. A. Stegun, *J. Opt. Soc. Am.* 46, 1043 (1956).

n is chosen to be larger than the statistically predicted number of chance coincidence.

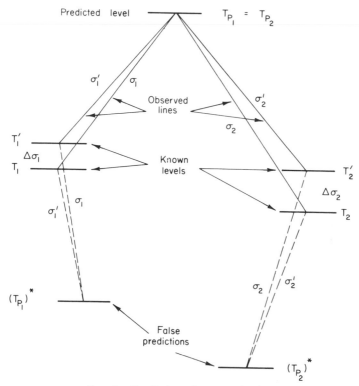

FIG. 9. Prediction of energy levels.

Up to this point the analysis of the spectrum is straightforward and, without machine aid, sheer drudgery. The completion of the task, however, requires a basic understanding of the behavior of atoms and a high degree of imaginative deduction and insight.

First, if at all possible, Zeeman observations (see Section 4.1.1.2.5) should be obtained. To be useful, they must be photographed with the highest possible dispersion and with magnetic fields of between 30,000 and 90,000 oersteds. Completely resolved patterns will confirm the degree of ionization and will give the total angular momentum, j, and the Lande g value for each of the levels involved in the transition. This information, if available, will usually determine the validity of the levels predicted by the computer search and will eliminate most of the accidental coincidence. It is also, of course, invaluable in assigning an L-S designation, if one is valid, to the level. Deviation from the L-S value of the Lande g is one index of the purity of the level.

Second, hyperfine structure observations can yield the j value of one of the levels from the number of components or their spacing, and the term configuration from the magnitude of the splitting. A very widely split pattern usually indicates a configuration with an unpaired s electron.

Third, transitions to the lower-energy state can frequently be identified by noting the self-reversal of the spectrum line. The sources used have a radial temperature distribution, and radiation from the hot center of the plasma must pass out through a cooler region containing a larger population of atoms in the lower-energy states. The reversed line profile which results from absorption at the line center identifies these lines as terminating on one of the lower states or on a metastable state of the atom. The most drastic effect is, of course, observed in transitions to the ground state.

Finally, predictions of level positions and relative energies of the various possible configurations are necessary as a guide to proper assignment of designations to each level. Much can be learned by analogy with isoelectronic or with neighboring atomic spectra. Calculations such as those refined by Racah and others are surprisingly precise, yielding agreements with experiment frequently to within a few dozen wave numbers.

In the foregoing discussion, knowledge of at least a few of the atomic states has been assumed. If no such information is available, a start can be made on the analysis of the spectrum by restricting the line list initially to only those lines that exhibit strong self-reversal and by tabulating differences between all pairs of such lines. From repeating differences it is usually possible to build up a start on the energy structure. Zeeman data and a good understanding of the levels expected, based upon observations in neighboring and isoelectronic spectra, are particularly useful at this stage of the analysis.

4.1.1.5.2. PRECISE MEASUREMENT OF WAVELENGTH. The most precise measurements of wavelength are accomplished with the Fabry–Perot interferometer, generally used in conjunction with a monochromator or a spectrograph. For such measurements it is necessary to observe simultaneously the wavelength to be measured together with several standard lines, one of which should have a precisely known wavelength.

The procedure used is to determine the length of the spacer in terms of the wavelength of the standard line by multiplying the length of the spacer in wavelengths of this line by the known wavelength of the line. The wavelengths of other lines are then obtained by dividing the spacer length by the number of wavelengths of each line in the length of the spacer. Further correction for the dispersion of phase change upon reflection at the interferometer surfaces is also necessary if the lines observed cover an appreciable range of the spectrum.

The determination of n, the length of the interferometer in units of $\lambda/2$, is derived from the equation

$$n\lambda = 2d \cos \theta, \tag{4.1.1.28}$$

which reduces to $n\lambda = 2d$ at the center (see Section 4.1.1.3.2.2). The central order is, in general, equal to an integer plus a fraction, and it is the fractional order that is determined from measurement of the ring diameters. Since the successive rings differ by one order, it is possible from the measurement of two ring diameters to extrapolate back to the fractional order at the center. Generally, however, more than two diameters are measured and the fractional order is determined by a least square fit to the data.[133]

These calculations assume that $\cos \theta \simeq 1 - \theta^2/2$. This approximation is valid for small θ, that is, for interferometers whose length is large compared to the wavelength of the radiation. If $\delta\epsilon$ is the maximum fractional order error which can be tolerated, then we must have $d/\lambda > 2\delta\epsilon$. If we expect to measure to 10^{-3} orders at a wavelength of 5000 Å, then the approximation is valid for any interferometer spacer length, d, greater than 0.25 mm. This is several orders of magnitude smaller than that normally used.

Benoit's method of exact fractions determines the length of the spacer from the measurements on several standard lines. Measurements on the ring patterns yield for each line the fractional order at the center. Only the whole order number to which this fraction must be added is unknown. A first approximation to the whole order number is obtained by dividing the measured length of the spacer by the wavelength of one of the standards. Whatever fractional order is obtained by this division is replaced by the observed fractional order. A second approximation to the spacer length is then obtained by multiplying this corrected order number by the known wavelength. Order numbers for the remaining lines are then obtained by dividing the spacer length by each wavelength.

If the spacer length used is the correct one, then all calculated fractional orders for the known lines will agree with the measured fractions within the error limits of the measurement. If they do not, the calculation is repeated assuming an order number for the first line differing from the previous by a small integer until the above condition is satisfied. The length of spacer so obtained is then used to determine the exact wavelength of each of the observed lines in terms of the standard.

The whole order number for each line is obtained by dividing the spacer length by the best known wavelength for that line. The measured fractional order is then substituted for the calculated, and the wavelength is then obtained by dividing the spacer length by this order number. This method leads to precise and unambiguous values for the wavelength of each line provided that the wavelength is already known with sufficient precision to unambiguously assign the whole order number. If this is not so, then intermediate values for the wavelength must be calculated by using shorter spacers.

The above method assumes that the optical path between plates is independent of the wavelength. If air or some other dispersive medium is used, then the number calculated in each case is not the physical length of the spacer, but rather the optical length: the physical length times the index of air. The calculation is most readily performed for this case if air rather than vacuum wavelengths are used, in which case the procedure is exactly the same as for the vacuum case outlined above.

Even in a vacuum interferometer, however, the effective optical path will be a function of wavelength as the result of the phase shift on reflection at the surface of each plate. In the case of dielectric films, this phase shift will be a very strong function of wavelength. This phase shift can be thought of as a variable penetration of the radiation into the surface of the plate. This effective penetration will be a constant at a particular wavelength, and the apparent effect on the measured wavelength will be a function of the spacer length, becoming negligible for very long spacers. It can, however, be evaluated by measuring the same wavelengths with several different spacers. If δ is the added length due to phase change, then

$$\lambda_n = \lambda_\infty + \delta\,(1/n) \tag{4.1.1.29}$$

where λ_n is the observed wavelength at order n, λ_∞ is the true wavelength, and δ is the phase shift. The slope of a plot of $1/n$ vs. λ_n will then yield the phase shift constant. Note that we can determine only the phase shift relative to that at our standard line, but this is all that is needed to determine other wavelengths. For work of less accuracy absolute wavelengths of several standards can be used to determine phase dispersion as a function of wavelength.

The correction for phase change can be performed quite precisely as outlined above for most interferometry problems. It should be noted, however, that the assumption of a phase shift independent of plate separation is valid only for plane interferometer plates, and then only when the phase shift due to diffraction is small. This latter phase shift becomes important only for very severely stopped-down lasers.

In many problems the absolute wavelength is of less importance than the relative wavelengths of two or more neighboring components. This is relatively easy to determine if we note that the position of the fringe pattern is a function of wavelength. If we observe the nth fringe at wavelength λ, this fringe coincides exactly with the $(n - 1)$ fringe of wavelength $(\lambda + \lambda^2/(2\epsilon d))$. This expression is simpler in wave number units, in which case the wave number difference between adjacent orders is $1/(2\epsilon d)$, where ϵ is the index of the medium and d is the plate separation. If two components are observed separated by the rth part of a fringe, then their separation in wave numbers will be $(i + r)/2\epsilon d$, where i is an integer or zero which must be determined either from previous information or by observations on two or more spacers.

4.1.1.5.3. MEASUREMENT OF NUCLEAR PROPERTIES. By virtue of its resultant moments or its finite size and mass, the atomic nucleus can interact with its optical electrons and thereby alter its atomic spectrum. The study of these spectra, therefore, is a valuable tool in the study of nuclear properties.[19] If the nucleus has a nonzero spin, most of its atomic energy levels and, hence, most of the observed spectrum lines will be split into a number of hyperfine structure components. From measurements of the spacing of these components, the spin, magnetic dipole, and electric quadrupole moments of the nucleus can be determined. Furthermore, if the element under study is composed of a mixture of isotopes, a multiplicity of closely spaced lines will appear in the spectrum, each corresponding to a slightly different nuclear mass.

Since both hyperfine structure and isotope shift splitting usually involve very close line components, sources for their study must be designed to yield very sharp lines and the dispersing instrument must have a very high resolving power.

Except for a few abnormally wide split lines, sources such as the Pfund arc and condensed sparks yield spectrum lines with so much Doppler, pressure, and Stark broadening that their hyperfine structure is completely unresolved. Discharges such as the electrodeless discharges or the ring discharge (Section 4.1.1.2.2) operated at pressures of a few millimeters yield moderately sharp lines, characteristic of Doppler widths at room temperatures.

Further sharpening can be achieved by using hollow cathode discharges (Section 4.1.1.2.3) at liquid nitrogen temperatures. With such a source, Doppler widths corresponding to $80°K$ can be achieved. The sources producing the sharpest lines are the atomic beams, either in emission or absorption (Section 4.1.1.2.3). With these, line widths of the order of 0.001 cm^{-1} or less can be obtained.

Most elements occur naturally as mixtures of a number of isotopes. In order to simplify the interpretation of the observed hyperfine structure, it is usually desirable and sometimes necessary to use mixtures enriched in one or more isotopes in the light source. If highly concentrated isotopes are not available, satisfactory analysis can generally be performed with a variety of mixtures, each having a different isotopic ratio.

If the enriched isotopes are at all valuable, it is advisable to use either electrodeless lamps or a cooled hollow cathode source. Both operate for many hours on a milligram of material. The electrodeless lamps, being simple and completely sealed, are especially well-suited to the study of radioactive isotopes.

Although a few hyperfine structure analyses have been performed with high resolving power grating spectrographs or echelles, nearly all of this type of work is done with the Fabry–Perot interferometer (Section 4.1.1.3.2.2). With the Fabry–Perot, the resolving power is limited only by the width of the spectrum line and by the confusion of overlapping orders.

Either photographic or photoelectric recording is applicable. Photoelectric techniques yield better intensity information and higher-precision fringe setting; however, where the quantity of material in the source is limited, the photographic method is preferred since a large number of lines can be recorded simultaneously.

4.1.1.5.3.1. *Nuclear Properties.* Atomic nuclei containing an odd number of protons or neutrons have a spin angular momentum vector, $\mathbf{I}$, usually measured in units of $h/2\pi$. The magnitude of this vector is half integer for odd mass numbers and integer for even mass numbers. The nucleus has a nuclear magnetic dipole moment vector

$$\mathbf{\mu} = g_I \mathbf{I} \tag{4.1.1.30}$$

measured in units of nuclear magnetons, where the nuclear magneton is equal to

$$\frac{eh}{4\pi Mc} = 5.0504 \times 10^{-24} \text{ erg gauss}^{-1} \tag{4.1.1.31}$$

and g_I is the nuclear g factor.

In cases where the spin I is greater than $\frac{1}{2}$, the nucleus is no longer spherically symmetric, and will therefore have a nuclear quadrupole moment Q usually measured in units of barns (10^{-24} cm^2), where e is the electronic charge. A magnetic octupole moment also exists for nuclei having I greater than 1, but since observations on octupole moments have been only marginally confirmed they will not be discussed here.

Nuclear properties are observed in atomic spectra as the result of the coupling of the nuclear moment with the resultant total angular momentum, J, of the electronic shells. The nuclear spin vector, $\mathbf{I}$, is coupled with the vector $\mathbf{J}$ to give the resultant vector $\mathbf{F}$. This coupling produces a splitting in the energy of the fine structure levels. The energy of these hyperfine multiplets is given by:

$$W_F = W_J + \frac{AC}{2} + B\,\frac{3C(C+1) - 4I(I+1)\,J(J+1)}{8I(2I-1)\,J(2J-1)} \quad (4.1.1.32)$$

where $C = F(F+1) - I(I+1) - J(J+1)$, W_J is the fine structure energy, and A and B are the magnetic dipole and electric quadrupole interaction constants, defined as:

$$A = \frac{\mu \overline{H(0)}}{IJ} \quad (4.1.1.33)$$

$$B = eQ\,\overline{\varphi_{jj}(0)}. \quad (4.1.1.34)$$

$\overline{H(0)}$ is the magnetic field of the electrons measured at the nucleus and $\varphi_{jj}(0)$ is the second derivative in the J direction of the electric potential due to the orbital electrons, evaluated at the nucleus.

For adjacent levels F and $(F+1)$ in the same fine structure level,

and
$$\begin{aligned} C_1 &= F(F+1) - I(I+1) - J(J+1) \\ C_2 &= (F+1)(F+2) - I(I+1) - J(J+1) \end{aligned} \quad (4.1.1.35)$$

and

$$W_{F+1} - W_F = A(F+1) + 3B\,\frac{C_2(C_2+1) - C_1(C_1+1)}{8I(2I-1)J(2J+1)}. \quad (4.1.1.36)$$

4.1.1.5.3.2. *Nuclear Spin Angular Momentum.* For fine structure levels for which $J > I$, the number of hyperfine structure levels is $2I + 1$, corresponding to the $2I + 1$ projections of I on J. In this case, I can be determined by counting the number of levels. If $J < I$, the number of levels will be equal to $2J + 1$. In this latter case, and also in cases where the hyperfine structure pattern is incompletely resolved, the value of I must be determined from a measurement of the interval ratios.

If we neglect quadrupole effects, then

$$W_{F+1} - W_F = A(F+1), \quad (4.1.1.37)$$

that is, the ratio of the intervals will be as the ratios of the upper F value for each interval (for $J = \frac{1}{2}, I = 3/2$, the intervals would be $1 : 2$; for $J = \frac{1}{2}, I = 5/2$, the intervals would be $2 : 3$). The correct value of F and hence I is readily determined.

The observations on atomic spectra yield transitions between energy levels rather than the levels proper. If the transition is such that one of the fine structure levels has a much larger hyperfine structure splitting than the other, then the observed line splitting will correspond closely to the level splitting. Fortunately, in most spectra, certain levels, particularly those involving an unpaired s electron, have a much larger splitting factor than others, such as those involving a p electron.

In cases where the splitting factors for the two levels involved in the transition are comparable, the resulting hyperfine structure in the observed line will reflect the structure of both states. The structure of the individual levels can be sorted out of the observations by a technique of graphical analysis suggested by Fisher and Goudsmit.[144]

4.1.1.5.3.3. *Nuclear Magnetic Dipole Moment.* The dipole splitting factor can be evaluated from the observed level splitting by fitting the level positions to Eq. (4.1.1.32). For single electron spectra, the constant represents the interaction between the nuclear magnetic dipole moment, μ, and the magnetic field due to the electrons. This interaction is taken into account, with however a fair degree of uncertainty, by a formula by Goudsmit,[145] with corrections for configuration interaction dn_a/dn by Fermi–Segre,[146] relativistic corrections, $F_r(j, Z_i)$ and $H_r(l, Z_i)$, the Breit–Crawford–Schawlow corrections[147] $(1 - \delta)$, and the Bohr–Weisskopf corrections[148] $(1 - \epsilon)$ which take into account the finite size of the nucleus.

For s electrons

$$A_s = \frac{8}{3} R\alpha^2 \frac{Z_i Z_a^2}{n_a^3} \frac{dn_a}{dn} F_r(j, Z_i)(1 - \delta)(1 - \epsilon) \frac{m}{m_p} \frac{\mu_I}{I}. \quad (4.1.1.38)$$

For non s electrons

$$A_{lj} = \frac{l(l + 1)}{j(j + 1)} \frac{\zeta}{Z_i} \frac{F_r(j, Z_i)}{H_r(l, Z_i)} \frac{m}{m_p} \frac{\mu_I}{I}. \quad (4.1.1.39)$$

Z_i and Z_a are the effective values of the nuclear charge near to and far from the nucleus, respectively. For s electrons Z_i is taken equal to Z; for p electrons, $Z_i = Z - 4$. Z_a is 1 for neutral and 2 for singly ionized atoms. n_a is the effective total quantum number, R is the Rydberg constant, α is the fine structure constant, m/m_p is the ratio of electron to proton mass, ζ is the spin-orbit parameter, and the doublet splitting parameter $\delta = (l + \frac{1}{2})\zeta$. μ_I is measured in units of nuclear magnetons.

[144] R. A. Fisher and S. A. Goudsmit, *Phys. Rev.* **37**, 1057 (1931).

[145] S. Goudsmit, *Phys. Rev.* **43**, 636 (1933).

[146] E. Fermi and E. Segre, *Z. Physik* **82**, 729 (1933).

[147] M. F. Crawford and A. L. Schawlow, *Phys. Rev.* **76**, 1310 (1949).

[148] A. Bohr and V. F. Weisskopf, *Phys. Rev.* **77**, 94 (1950).

The relativistic corrections are

$$F_r(j, Z) = \frac{4j(j + 1/2)(j + 1)}{\rho(4\rho^2 - 1)},$$

$$\rho = \sqrt{(j + 1/2)^2 - \alpha^2 Z^2};$$

(4.1.1.40)

$$H_r(j, Z) = \frac{2l(l + 1)}{\alpha^2 Z^2} \rho',$$

$$\rho' = \sqrt{(l + 1)^2 - \alpha^2 Z^2} - \sqrt{1 - \alpha^2 Z^2} - 1.$$

(4.1.1.41)

In atoms involving more than a single electron, the coupling constant A is a linear combination of the coupling constants a for the individual electrons. The details of this will be found in Kopfermann.[19] The coupling constant A can be evaluated from the experimental data to a fair precision. The uncertainty in evaluating the individual a's from A and the further uncertainty in evaluating μ from the a's is considerably greater. Calculations of the magnetic moment taken from optical spectra cannot compete, within several orders of magnitude, with values for these constants derived from magnetic resonance atomic beam techniques. They are, however, valuable in supplying data where the atomic beam techniques are difficult to apply.

It should be noted that, for isotopes of the same element, the electronic configurations are very nearly the same, and therefore the ratios of magnetic moments for such isotopes can be calculated to a fair precision.

4.1.1.5.3.4. *Nuclear Electric Quadrupole Moments.* The existence of a nuclear electric quadrupole moment results in the deviation of the hyperfine intervals from the simple $(F + 1)$ interval rule mentioned above. The quadrupole coupling constant, B, can be evaluated from Eq. (0). The calculation of the quadrupole moment, Q, from B requires the evaluation of $\overline{\varphi_{jj}(0)}$. This has been done by Casimir[149]:

$$\overline{\varphi_{jj}(0)} = -e \left(\frac{3 \cos^2 \theta - 1}{r^3} \right)_{jj}.$$

(4.1.1.42)

Evaluations of $\overline{\varphi_{jj}(0)}$ for a number of cases are given by Kopfermann.[19]

Since the measurement of B involves a second difference, and since this difference is generally small, it is usually known to considerably less accuracy than A. In addition, $\varphi_{jj}(0)$ is generally only approximately known. As a result, the uncertainty in the value of Q is frequently in the first significant figure. These measurements are, however, of con-

[149] H. Casimir, *Teyler's Tweede Genootschap, Haarlem* 11 (1936).

siderable importance since methods for direct measurement are not available at present.

4.1.1.5.3.5. *Isotope Shifts in Atomic Spectra.* The energy levels in isotopes of the same element are shifted with respect to each other by two effects: (1) the mass effect due to the difference in mass of the two nuclei and (2) the volume effect due to the difference in the volume occupied by the two nuclei. The observed effects are usually ascribable to a combination of the two, the mass effect predominating in the lighter elements, the volume effect in the heavier.

The mass effect, in hydrogenlike spectra, is simply the effect of correcting for the reduced mass of the nucleus-electron mass distribution:

$$T_n = T_{n\infty} \left(1 - \frac{m}{m_p A} \right) \qquad (4.1.1.43)$$

where $T_{n\infty}$ is the level value for infinite nuclear mass, m is the electron mass, m_p is the proton mass, and A is the atomic mass number. For several electron spectra, appropriate couplings must be taken. Some of these are discussed by Kopfermann.[19]

The shift in energy level due to the volume effect on an s electron can be expressed as

$$\delta T_s = \frac{\pi a_0^3}{Z} \Psi_s^2(0) \frac{12(\rho + 1)R}{(2\rho + 1)(2\rho + 3)\Gamma^2(2\rho + 1)} \left(\frac{2Zr_0}{a_0} \right)^{2\rho} \frac{\delta r_0}{r_0} \quad (4.1.1.44)$$

where $\rho = \sqrt{1 - \alpha^2 Z^2}$, α is the fine structure constant, ρ is the nonrelativistic probability density of an s electron at the nucleus, a_0 is the radius of the first Bohr orbit, R is the Rydberg constant, Z is the atomic number, and the radius of the nucleus, r_0, is approximated by $r_0 = R_0 A^{1/3}$. A is the mass of the nucleus in atomic mass units and R_0 as determined from scattering data is approximately 1.2×10^{-13} cm.

The observed isotope shifts depart, frequently severely, from this simplified picture which does not allow for nonuniform charge distribution or for perturbations. Equation (4.1.44) consists of two parts, one depending upon the electrons only, the other depending on the nucleus only. The nuclear part is usually written:

$$C_{TH} = \frac{4R(\rho + 1)}{(2\rho + 1)(2\rho + 3)\Gamma^2(2\rho + 1)} \left(\frac{2Zr_0}{a_0} \right)^{2\rho} \frac{\delta A}{A}$$

and is frequently compared with the experimental value given by

$$C_{EXP} = \frac{\delta T_{EXP} Z}{\pi a_0^3 \Psi_s^2(0)} .$$

4.1.2. Radio-Frequency and Microwave Spectroscopy*†

4.1.2.1. Introduction. Atomic hyperfine structure and Zeeman effects show up in optical spectra as small splittings of the spectral lines into several components. The splittings are difficult to measure accurately because they are seldom larger than a few tenths of a wave number, which is comparable with the line widths themselves. The techniques of radio-frequency and microwave spectroscopy are better suited to such measurements. Rather than observe optical transitions between widely separated electronic energy levels, one observes long wavelength transitions within the hyperfine structure or Zeeman sublevel structure of a single electronic level. The spectral widths of these transitions are much smaller than the optical line widths, especially if the energy level concerned is the ground level of the atom; spectral widths smaller than 10^{-7} cm^{-1} are not uncommon. Indeed, the frequencies of certain microwave spectral lines are measurable with such precision that they can be used as primary standards of time.

In the radio-frequency and microwave region of the electromagnetic spectrum (hereafter called, for brevity, the "radio spectrum")—wavelengths extending from a few kilometers down to approximately 1 mm—spectroscopic methods bear little resemblance to their optical counterparts. Vacuum tube oscillators replace the arcs and discharge tubes of optical spectroscopy as sources of radiation. The electromagnetic energy is guided along wires or inside metal pipes rather than focused and collimated by lenses and apertures. The need for a dispersive element— the prism or diffraction grating of an optical spectroscope—is removed by the monochromatic nature of vacuum tube oscillators. Finally, the simple photographic plate or photocell gives way to complex and often indirect detection schemes, which usually involve a great deal of electronic apparatus.

The overriding experimental problem in radio spectroscopy is that of detection. The energy content, and thus the detectability, of even the shortest wavelength radio photon is several orders of magnitude smaller than that of an optical photon. To a large extent, the several experimental methods of radio spectroscopy differ only in the way the detection problem has been solved. These methods, all of which have been developed in the past quarter century, fall into three main categories: atomic beam resonance, microwave absorption, and radio-optical resonance. Each is discussed briefly below, and more fully in later sections. Specialized techniques for measuring atomic fine structure are described separately in Section 4.1.2.4.

---

* Section 4.1.2 is by H. E. Radford.
† See also Vol. 3, Chapter 2.1, and Vol. 5B, Section 2.4.1.3.

Radio spectroscopy began with the molecular beam resonance experiments of Rabi and co-workers in 1938[1]; 2 years later Kusch, Millman and Rabi,[2] extended the method to beams of neutral atoms. The beam resonance method is a lineal descendant of beam deflection experiments performed by Stern and co-workers in the early thirties.[3] Rabi, continuing these experiments, found that the deflection of a molecular beam in an inhomogeneous magnetic field could be changed by subjecting the beam to an oscillatory magnetic field, provided the frequency of oscillation was correct. This was spectroscopy of a new kind. Rather than detect a resonant emission or absorption of electromagnetic energy, Rabi detected a change in the physical properties of the beam particles themselves. This is the salient feature of the beam resonance method, both in this original work and in later applications. Side-stepping the problem of detecting long-wavelength photons, the experimenter concentrates instead on the simpler problem of measuring changes in beam trajectories.

The beam resonance method dominated the field of long-wavelength spectroscopy until 1946 when, fathered by wartime radar developments, the microwave absorption method grew rapidly to prominence. Here the problem of detecting long-wavelength photons is attacked directly, rather than circumvented as in the beam resonance method. Success depends on the use of the relatively noise-free klystron oscillator as a source of radiation, together with extremely sensitive microwave detection systems. With even the best electronic techniques, however, absorption spectra are difficult to detect at wavelengths longer than about 10 cm. Restricted further by the necessity for a gaseous absorption sample, microwave absorption studies have been confined chiefly to the rotational spectra of stable molecular gases, although Beringer[4] and others have applied the paramagnetic resonance technique, a variant of the microwave absorption method which employs a strong magnetic field, to the study of atomic vapors. The magnetic field, via the Zeeman effect, shifts the low-frequency atomic transitions to a conveniently high microwave range, and also allows the long absorption cell of conventional microwave absorption work to be replaced by a small resonant cavity, within which it is easier to maintain concentrated atomic vapors.

A third general technique for performing long-wavelength spectroscopy, a hybrid of radio and optical methods, has been developed

---

[1] I. I. Rabi, J. R. Zacharias, S. Millman, and P. Kusch, *Phys. Rev.* **53**, 318 (1938).

[2] P. Kusch, S. Millman, and I. I. Rabi, *Phys. Rev.* **57**, 765 (1940).

[3] Two books by R. G. J. Fraser describe the early beam deflection experiments: "Molecular Rays." Cambridge Univ. Press, London and New York, 1931, and "Molecular Beams." Methuen, London, 1937.

[4] R. Beringer, *Ann. N. Y. Acad. Sci.* **55**, 814 (1952).

intensively in recent years, starting from the "double resonance" experiments of Brossel and Bitter[5] in 1952. As in the beam resonance method, no attempt is made to detect directly the absorption or emission of long-wavelength photons; instead, radio-frequency transitions are detected by consequent changes in the optical absorption or emission properties of the atomic beam or vapor. Effectively, one converts a radio photon to an optical photon before detecting it, and realizes thereby a manyfold increase in detection sensitivity. One of the major advantages of this radio-optical resonance technique is that it provides a systematic way to measure radio spectra in excited atomic states; early experiments were entirely of this type. Later work showed that radio-optical methods were also applicable to atomic ground states, and that this method of radio spectroscopy, called "optical pumping," had in certain cases great advantages in precision and sensitivity over the atomic beam and micro-wave absorption methods of investigating atomic ground states.

4.1.2.2. Practical Theory of Radio Spectra. The photographic plate, which detects light of all wavelengths simultaneously, has no analog in the radio-frequency region. To find a new radio spectrum, one must search for it, scanning slowly over the range of wavelengths within which one expects the spectrum to lie. Because of this search problem, the radio spectroscopist often finds it necessary to be able to predict, as well as measure, the position and intensity of a radio line. This involves calculations of energy levels and transition probabilities, some common examples of which are described in this section. Detailed theoretical discussions may be found in the books of Condon and Shortley,[6] Ramsey,[7] and Kopfermann,[8] and in the original papers cited below.

4.1.2.2.1. ENERGY CLASSIFICATION. To a good approximation, an atom can be considered to be an isolated collection of point masses subject only to mutual electromagnetic interactions. Multipole moments are assigned to the individual particles in accordance with experimental results and certain theoretical restrictions. Thus an atomic electron has an electric monopole amount $-e$ and a magnetic dipole moment $\mu_s = 1.0011596\,\mu_0$ (where μ_0 is the Bohr magneton, equal to $e\hbar/2mc$); the atomic nucleus has an electric monopole moment $+Ze$ and, depending on the nucleus, may also have magnetic dipole, electric quadrupole, and higher-order moments. The electromagnetic inter-

[5] J. Brossel and F. Bitter, *Phys. Rev.* **86**, 308 (1952).

[6] E. U. Condon and G. H. Shortley, "The Theory of Atomic Spectra." Cambridge Univ. Press, London and New York, 1935.

[7] N. F. Ramsey, "Molecular Beams." Oxford Univ. Press, London and New York, 1956.

[8] H. Kopfermann, "Nuclear Moments" (translated by E. E. Schneider). Academic Press, New York, 1958.

actions of these multipole moments with each other and with external fields may be represented by a Hamiltonian of the form

$$\mathscr{H} = \mathscr{H}_{en} + \mathscr{H}_{ee} + \mathscr{H}_{fs} + \mathscr{H}_{hfs} + \mathscr{H}_{z} \qquad (4.1.2.1)$$

whose eigenvalues are the discrete energy levels of the atom. The terms are defined as follows: $\mathscr{H}_{en}$ and $\mathscr{H}_{ee}$ are the electric monopole terms, respectively due to the electrostatic attraction of electrons by the nucleus and to the electrostatic repulsion of electrons by each other. $\mathscr{H}_{fs}$ is the fine structure term, and includes the electron magnetic dipole inter-actions (spin-orbit, spin-spin interactions), the magnetic interactions of electrons through their orbital motions (orbit-orbit interaction), and that part of the interaction with the radiation field responsible for electromagnetic level shifts (Lamb shifts). $\mathscr{H}_{hfs}$ is the hyperfine structure term and includes the magnetic dipole, electric quadrupole, and higher-order interactions of the nucleus with the atomic electrons. $\mathscr{H}_{z}$ is the Zeeman term, which represents the magnetic dipole inter-action of electrons and nucleus with an external static magnetic field; a similar Stark term, representing the electric dipole interaction of the atom with an external static electric field, could be added to (4.1.2.1), but it is rarely needed. Unlike molecules, with their asymmetric charge distributions, an atom can have no permanent electric dipole moment. Consequently (except for special cases to be discussed later) the stark effect in atomic spectra is negligible in comparison with the Zeeman effect, and it may be ignored in a general discussion.[9]

In all but the heaviest atoms the electrostatic interactions $\mathscr{H}_{en}$ and $\mathscr{H}_{ee}$ are dominant, and set the overall pattern of energy levels. Groups of levels can be correlated with various electron *configurations*, which have widely different electrostatic energies. A configuration is specified by listing the occupied one-electron orbitals of the atom and indicating the occupation numbers by superscripts. The ground configuration of sodium, for instance, is $(1s)^2 (2s)^2 (2p)^6 3s$. The filled inner orbitals constitute the electron "core," and often are not written down explicitly. In this abbreviated notation the ground configuration of sodium would be written $3s$ (or, for the alkalies in general, ns).

On closer examination one finds that the grouping of levels by

---

[9] The terminology comes from the early days of optical spectroscopy, where "fine structure" and "hyperfine structure" were used to describe the splitting patterns which emerged in optical lines as the resolving power of spectroscopes was progressively increased, and "Zeeman effect" and "Stark effect" referred to the further line splittings observed when the optical emission source was placed in a strong magnetic or electric field. Through a tacit and nearly universal convention, the same names are applied nowadays to the underlying physical interactions and energy level shifts as well.

configurations, although useful, is not exact. Rather than belong to a single configuration, a given level may belong *mostly* to that configuration, but also partly to others. The reason is that the notion of discrete configurations, each with its own group of energy levels, applies strictly only in the central field approximation, where each electron is considered to move independently of all the others. In reality, part of the interaction between electrons is noncentral in character, and this causes *configuration interaction*. From the viewpoint of the perturbation theory, configuration interaction may be described as the admixture of foreign configurations into the parent configuration of the level in question, caused by interactions between electrons.

The effects of configuration interaction can be quite troublesome in the analysis of optical spectra, where transitions involve changes in the electrostatic energy of the atom. This is not so for radio spectra, where ordinarily only changes in the atomic angular momentum are involved; the over-all angular momentum properties of an atomic energy level are very difficult to disturb. Configuration interaction does, however, affect the distribution of angular momentum among the atomic electrons. In this aspect, configuration interaction is called *core polarization* because it transfers angular momentum from the valence electrons to the electron core, which would otherwise have none.[10] Core polarization does not interfere with the analysis of a radio spectrum, the process of deriving atomic constants from the spectral positions of lines, but it always must be considered in the subsequent interpretation of these constants.

The electrostatic repulsion term $\mathscr{H}_{ee}$, together with the remaining interaction terms of the Hamiltonian (4.1.2.1), accounts for the energy separations of levels within a configuration. The pattern of levels depends on the relative magnitudes of the several interaction energies, and only one special case will be mentioned here. This is the important Russell–Saunders case, where the electrostatic repulsion energy is much larger than the fine structure energy, which in turn is much larger than the hyperfine structure and Zeeman energies; i.e., $W_{ee} \gg W_{fs} \gg (W_{hfs} + W_z)$ where W_{ee} is a characteristic energy of the interaction $\mathscr{H}_{ee}$, etc. Perturbation theory can be applied successively in the calculation of energy levels, and one thereby establishes the following hierarchy of energy level splittings. Starting with a given configuration, electrostatic repulsion causes a splitting into Russell–Saunders *terms* (e.g., the ^3P, ^1D, and ^1S terms of a $(2p)^4$ configuration). The fine structure interaction then splits each term into *fine structure levels* (e.g., the $^3P_0$, $^3P_1$, and $^3P_2$ levels of the ^3P term). In zero external field, the magnetic dipole hyper-

[10] R. Sternheimer, *Phys. Rev.* **84**, 244 (1951).

fine structure interaction further splits each fine structure level into *hyperfine structure levels* (e.g., the $F = 1/2$ and $F = 3/2$ hyperfine structure levels of the $^3P_1$ level, when the nuclear spin in $1/2$). Finally, the Zeeman effect splits each hyperfine structure level into *magnetic sublevels* (e.g., the $M_F = +1/2$ and $M_F = -1/2$ magnetic sublevels of the $F = 1/2$ hyperfine structure level). At this point the splitting process is complete; all energy degeneracy has been removed. Additional interactions, such as an electric quadrupole hyperfine structure interaction, only shift the energies of existing sublevels.

Most atoms in their low-lying energy levels deviate only slightly from the pure Russell–Saunders case, and in these atoms the energy level genealogy given above is unambiguous. In highly excited or very heavy atoms, where the fine structure energy becomes comparable with the electrostatic repulsion energy, the perturbation theory approach breaks down, and the energy level calculation becomes complex and specialized. The conceptual framework of the Russell–Saunders case is still useful, however, since an "intermediate coupling" state can always be represented as a specific mixture of Russell–Saunders states.

4.1.2.2.2. ANGULAR MOMENTUM. Atomic energy levels differ in their angular momentum properties as well as their positions on an energy scale. Indeed, the splitting of the levels by magnetic dipole interactions is a *consequence* of atomic angular momentum. The connecting links are the magnetomechanical relations

$$\boldsymbol{\mu}_N = -g_N\mu_0\mathbf{N} \tag{4.1.2.2}$$

where $\mathbf{N}$ represents any one of the several internal angular momenta of the atom, measured in units of $\hbar$, and $\boldsymbol{\mu}_N$ is the associated magnetic dipole moment. The dimensionless constants g_N are called *g factors*, while μ_0 is the fundamental unit of magnetism, the Bohr magneton. Radio-frequency transitions almost invariably involve changes in the magnetic dipole interaction energies of an atom and hence, through Eq. (4.1.2.2), changes in angular momentum. For this reason angular momentum calculations are highly important in the interpretation of radio spectra; usually, in fact, they give a complete prediction of the spectrum.

Angular momentum calculations are always simplified, sometimes even made trivial, if one or more of the angular momentum vectors $\mathbf{N}$ are known to be conserved, that is, to remain constant in magnitude. For such an angular momentum the quantum number N, defined as the maximum projection of $\mathbf{N}$ on an axis fixed in space, is a "sharp" (i.e., unique) quantum number, and the unvarying magnitude of $\mathbf{N}$ is equal to $\sqrt{N(N+1)}$. The identification of sharp or nearly sharp quantum numbers, an important first step in any radio spectrum calculation, is facilitated by the following general rules:

(1) The nuclear spin I is conserved always, at least as far as atomic spectra are concerned, and the quantum number I is sharp.

(2) In the absence of external fields, the total atomic angular momentum F is conserved. The corresponding quantum number F is sharp, as well as the projection quantum number m_F. The allowed values of m_F are $F, F-1, F-2, ..., -F$.

(3) In the absence of nuclear spin and of external fields, the total *electronic* angular momentum J is conserved, with sharp quantum numbers J and m_J, where $m_J = J, J-1, ..., -J$.

(4) In an axially symmetric magnetic field, the projection quantum number m_F (or m_J) remains sharp, although F (or J) does not.

These four rules apply quite generally to situations met in the laboratory. In addition, the following rules for limiting cases are useful for determining which angular momentum quantum numbers are "good" (i.e., nearly sharp) in a given laboratory situation. Actual deviations from these limiting cases may be negligible in comparison with errors of measurement, in which case the distinction between "good" and "sharp" disappears. In other situations, these limiting cases provide starting points for more accurate energy calculations.

(5) The Russell–Saunders limit ($W_{fs}/W_{ee} \to 0$, $W_{hfs} = W_z = 0$): The electronic angular momentum J may be resolved into an orbital part and a spin part, each of which is conserved. Quantitatively,

$$\mathbf{J} = \mathbf{L} + \mathbf{S}$$

$$\mathbf{L} = \sum_i \mathbf{l}_i$$

$$\mathbf{S} = \sum_i \mathbf{s}_i$$

where $\mathbf{l}_i$ and $\mathbf{s}_i$ are the orbital and spin angular momentum of a single electron, and the sums are taken over all electrons. Sharp quantum numbers are L, S, J, and m_J. This limiting case is often called pure $L - S$ coupling.

(6) The $j - j$ coupling limit ($W_{ee}/W_{fs} \to 0$, $W_{hfs} = W_z = 0$): The total electronic angular moment J is again conserved, and can be decomposed as follows:

$$\mathbf{J} = \sum_i \mathbf{j}_i$$

$$\mathbf{j}_i = \mathbf{l}_i + \mathbf{s}_i$$

where j_i is the conserved angular momentum of a single electron, and the sum is again taken over all electrons. Sharp quantum numbers are J and m_J, as well as j_i for each electron.

(7) The weak field limit of hyperfine structure ($W_z/W_{hfs} \to 0$, $W_{hfs}/W_{fs} \to 0$): This is an extension of rule (3) to include nuclear spin and an external field, for cases where the resulting hyperfine structure and Zeeman interactions have only a vanishingly small effect on the magnitude of **J**. Sharp quantum numbers are L, S, J, I, F, and m_F.

(8) The Back–Goudsmit limit ($W_{hfs}/W_z \to 0$, $W_z/W_{fs} \to 0$): This is simultaneously the strong field limit of hyperfine structure and the weak field limit of fine structure; **J** and **I** are conserved, but **F** is not. Sharp quantum numbers are L, S, J, I, m_J, and m_I.

(9) The Paschen–Back limit ($W_{hfs}/W_z \to 0$, $W_{fs}/W_z \to 0$): This is the strong field limit of fine structure. In the Russell–Saunders case, **L** and **S** are conserved but **J** is not. Sharp quantum numbers are L, S, I, m_L, m_S, and m_I.

Of these five limiting cases, (5), (7), and (8) have the widest application in radio spectroscopy. The Paschen–Back limit, but for a few exceptional cases, is approached only in much stronger magnetic fields than are commonly available in the laboratory.

4.1.2.2.3. ENERGY FORMULAS. The above limiting cases each define an angular momentum *representation*, a set of base functions labeled by the sharp angular momentum quantum numbers of the limiting case. The characteristic energy calculation of radio spectroscopy is the diagonalization of the perturbation matrix of $(\mathscr{H}_{hfs} + \mathscr{H}_z)$ in the representation that fits most closely the atom and the experimental conditions at hand. In most cases the perturbation is not strong enough to affect seriously the magnitude of **J**, and one therefore restricts attention to only that part of the perturbation matrix which is diagonal in J. In this approximation the perturbation Hamiltonian for an atom in a magnetic field of strength H is

$$\mathscr{H}_{hfs} + \mathscr{H}_z = hA\mathbf{I} \cdot \mathbf{J} + \frac{hB}{2I(2I-1)J(2J-1)}$$

$$\times [3(\mathbf{I} \cdot \mathbf{J})^2 + \tfrac{3}{2}(\mathbf{I} \cdot \mathbf{J}) - I(I+1)J(J+1)] + \mu_0(g_J\mathbf{J} + g_I\mathbf{I}) \cdot \mathbf{H}$$

$$(4.1.2.3)$$

where A and B are coupling constants of, respectively, the magnetic dipole and electric quadrupole hyperfine structure interactions, and g_J and g_I are the atomic and nuclear g factors as defined by Eq. (4.1.2.2). In a few atoms the magnetic octupole hyperfine structure interaction is large enough to be detected with present techniques, and for such atoms it is necessary to add an octupole term to (4.1.2.3).[11]

The hyperfine structure coupling constants A and B depend critically on the radial distribution of the atomic electrons, as well as on the size of the nuclear moments and on the angular momentum quantum numbers. Relativistic effects and core polarization may affect them strongly.[12] For these reasons the measured values of A and B, determined by comparing the energies calculated from (4.1.2.3) with observed spectra, offer a great deal of information on atomic structure. Conversely, the experimental spectroscopist, faced with the problem of predicting or identifying a radio spectrum, may have real difficulty in estimating the coupling constants. For atoms with either a single valence electron or a single valence "hole" (a closed electron shell minus one electron) the following formulas[13] are useful for estimating A and B to within 10 % or so.

For $^2S_{1/2}$ levels ($S = \frac{1}{2}, L = 0$):

$$hA = -(16\pi/3)g_I\mu_0^2\,\Psi^2(0),$$

$$hB = 0 \text{ (identically)}.$$

(4.1.2.4)

For ^2L terms ($S = \frac{1}{2}, L = 1, 2, ..., J = L \pm \frac{1}{2}$):

$$hA = -\frac{2L(L+1)}{J(J+1)}\,g_I\mu_0^2\langle r^{-3}\rangle,$$

$$hB = -\frac{2L}{2L+3}\,e^2Q\langle r^{-3}\rangle.$$

(4.1.2.5)

In these formulas, $(-g_I\mu_0)$ and Q are the nuclear magnetic dipole and electric quadrupole moments, $\Psi^2(0)$ is the density of unpaired electrons at the nucleus, and the expectation value $\langle r^{-3}\rangle$ is taken for the radius vector of the valence electron or hole. A rough estimate of $\Psi^2(0)$ may be had from simple Slater-type wavefunctions,[14] and $\langle r^{-3}\rangle$ can be estimated from the observed fine structure doublet splitting, δ, according to

$$\langle r^{-3}\rangle \simeq \frac{h\delta}{(2L+1)\mu_0^2Z_i}$$

(4.1.2.6)

where Z_i is an effective nuclear charge number, somewhat smaller than

[11] V. Jaccarino, J. G. King, R. A. Satten, and H. H. Stroke, *Phys. Rev.* **94**, 1798 (1954).
[12] C. Schwartz, *Phys. Rev.* **97**, 380 (1955); **105**, 173 (1957).
[13] H. B. G. Casimir, "On the Interaction Between Atomic Nuclei and Electrons." Teyler's Tweede Genootschap, Haarlem, 1936.
[14] J. C. Slater, *Phys. Rev.* **36**, 57 (1930).

the true charge number ($Z_i \simeq Z - 4$ for p electrons). When self-consistent field calculations of $\Psi^2(0)$ and $\langle r^{-3} \rangle$ are available they are much to be preferred over these rough estimates.

In contrast with the difficulty of predicting hyperfine structure accurately, the Zeeman effect is easy to predict within a few tenths of a per cent, provided only that one knows the angular momentum quantum numbers. In $L - S$ coupling, for instance, the atomic g factor is given by the Landé formula

$$
g_J = g_l \frac{J(J + 1) + L(L + 1) - S(S + 1)}{2J(J + 1)}
$$

$$
+ g_s \frac{J(J + 1) + S(S + 1) - L(L + 1)}{2J(J + 1)} \tag{4.1.2.7}
$$

where g_l and g_s are the electron orbital and spin g factors, equal, respectively, to $+ 1$ and $+ 2(1.0011596)$. Deviations from $L - S$ coupling are small for most atoms, and have little effect on the g factors. When more accurate theoretical g factors are required for the interpretation of precise measurements of the Zeeman effect, the Landé factors can be corrected for deviations from $L - S$ coupling and for relativistic and diamagnetic effects.[15,16] In light atoms these corrections have a relative magnitude of a few parts in 10^4. This is also the approximate magnitude of the nuclear g factor, g_I, relative to the atomic g factor.

For certain special cases, the energy calculation with the perturbation Hamiltonian (4.1.2.3) can be done once and for all. One such case is the weak field limit, for which the calculation yields

$$
W(F, m_F) - W_0 = \tfrac{1}{2}hAC + \frac{hB}{I(2I - 1)J(2J - 1)}
$$

$$
\times [\tfrac{3}{8}C(C + 1) - \tfrac{1}{2}I(I + 1)J(J + 1)] + g_F m_F \mu_0 H \tag{4.1.2.8}
$$

where C is written for $[F(F + 1) - I(I + 1) - J(J + 1)]$ and

$$
g_F = g_J \frac{F(F + 1) + J(J + 1) - I(I + 1)}{2F(F + 1)}
$$

$$
+ g_I \frac{F(F + 1) + I(I + 1) - J(J + 1)}{2F(F + 1)}.
$$

This gives the energies of all the hyperfine structure levels, labeled by F, and magnetic sublevels, labeled by m_F, relative to W_0, the energy of the

[15] W. Perl. *Phys. Rev.* **91**, 852 (1953).

[16] A. Abragam and J. H. Van Vleck, *Phys. Rev.* **92**, 1448 (1953).

original unsplit fine structure level. The values of F range from $I + J$ to $|I - J|$, the values of m_F from $+ F$ to $-F$, both by integral steps. If either I or J is $\frac{1}{2}$ the quadrupole interaction vanishes and the second term should be stricken from (4.1.2.8). The last term illustrates a *linear Zeeman effect*: the magnetic sublevels, $2F + 1$ in number, diverge linearly with increasing magnetic field strength, H. The energy difference between neighboring sublevels, expressed in frequency units, is $g_F\mu_0 H/h$ and is called the Larmor frequency. It is the frequency at which a classical bar magnet, of magnetic moment $g_F\mu_0$, would execute precessional motion in a magnetic field of strength H.

Energies calculated in the weak field limit begin to fail as the field strength is raised appreciably from zero, and eventually, at a field strength which depends on the accuracy required, they become unusable. At this point (4.1.2.8) can be patched up by a second-order perturbation calculation to last to somewhat larger field strengths. This calculation adds terms to (4.1.2.8) proportional to H^2; hence these terms represent a *quadratic Zeeman effect*. The range of field strengths between zero and the point where the second-order calculation becomes unusable is called *weak fields*. Although higher field strengths can be handled in principle by extending the perturbation calculation to higher order, it is usually more practical to start afresh, and perform an accurate energy calculation for *intermediate fields*. Usually an analytic solution is not possible, and a numerical diagonalization of the perturbation matrix must be performed. There is, however, one important special case for which a simple analytic energy solution exists: this is the case when either J or I is equal to $\frac{1}{2}$. The quadrupole interaction vanishes for this case, and the secular equation is quadratic. The energy solution for $J = \frac{1}{2}$, with I arbitrary, is

$$W(F, m_F) - W_0 = - \frac{\varDelta W}{2(2I + 1)} + g_I m_F \mu_0 H \pm \frac{\varDelta W}{2} \sqrt{1 + \frac{4m_F}{2I + 1} x + x^2},$$

$$(4.1.2.9)$$

where

$$\varDelta W = (2I + 1)hA/2,$$

$$x = (g_J - g_I)\mu_0 H / \varDelta W,$$

and the plus sign is used for the hyperfine structure level $F = I + \frac{1}{2}$ and the minus sign for the other hyperfine structure level, $F = I - \frac{1}{2}$. This is the well-known Breit–Rabi formula[17]; it is correct for all field strengths. The *hyperfine structure interval*, $\varDelta W$, is the separation between the two hyperfine structure levels at zero field; when expressed in frequency

[17] G. Breit and I. I. Rabi, *Phys. Rev.* **38**, 2082 (1931).

units it is written $\Delta\nu$, which is equal to $|\Delta W|/h$. By interchanging J and I throughout (4.1.2.9), one gets a second energy solution valid for the case $I = \frac{1}{2}$, with J arbitrary.

At field strengths high enough to approach the Back–Goudsmit limit the energy calculation again becomes simple, and gives a general formula for the sublevel energies:

$$W(m_J m_I) - W_0 = g_J m_J \mu_0 H + g_I m_I \mu_0 H + hA m_I m_J$$

$$+ \frac{hB}{4I(2I-1)J(2J-1)} [3m_J{}^2 - J(J+1)][3m_I{}^2 - I(I+1)] \qquad (4.1.2.10)$$

where, as before, the electric quadrupole term vanishes if either J or I is $\frac{1}{2}$. In any practical case, (4.1.2.10) may be useful over a wide or narrow range of field strengths, depending on the accuracy desired. As in the weak field case, the range of usefulness can always be extended, this time to lower field strengths, by a second-order perturbation calculation. This adds correction terms to (4.1.2.10) of order $(hA)^2/\mu_0 H$, $h^2 AB/\mu_0 H$, and $(hB)^2/\mu_0 H$. At still lower fields strengths these second-order hyperfine structure corrections also become inadequate, and the point where this happens is called the lower limit of *strong fields*. Below this breakdown point one again enters the intermediate field region, where the perturbation theory becomes too cumbersome to use, and the sublevel energies are better calculated in a form such as (4.1.2.9).

The division of magnetic field strengths into weak, intermediate, and strong categories provides a convenient way to discuss experiments, but it should be remembered that what these terms really refer to is the type of energy calculation required to interpret a given experiment, and not the absolute field strength measured in gauss or some other fixed unit. A field strength of 1000 gauss, say, may be "weak" for one experiment, "intermediate" for another, and "strong" for a third. The dimensionless parameter x defined in (4.1.2.9) is a convenient measure of field strength in this relative sense; for a typical experiment of moderate precision, values of x less than $1/10$ might be weak fields, values of x greater than 10 might be strong fields, and intermediate fields would fall between. The parameter x is also useful in plotting graphs which show qualitatively the splitting of the magnetic sublevels as a function of magnetic field strength. These are helpful in the identification and rough analysis of a complex radio spectrum, especially a spectrum observed under intermediate field conditions. Figure 1 shows such a graph, a plot of (4.1.2.9) for the case $I = \frac{3}{2}$, $J = \frac{1}{2}$. This is a universal plot, not restricted to any one atom, since both x and the energy ordinate $(W - W_0)/\Delta W$ are dimensionless. Similar plots can be drawn for any values of I and J; Fig. 2 illustrates the case $I = 3/2$, $J = 3/2$. The

Breit–Rabi formula (4.1.2.9) does not apply here (neither I nor J is $\frac{1}{2}$), and the intermediate field behavior of the energy sublevels in Fig. 2 was computed by numerical methods. The solid curves give the results for values of the magnetic field parameter up to 6. The dashed extensions connect these curves smoothly to the high field energies (4.1.2.10) computed at a value of 10 for the field parameter. At zero field there are four hyperfine structure levels (in general there are $2I + 1$ or $2J + 1$, whichever is smaller), with three corresponding values of ΔW (or $\Delta \nu$).

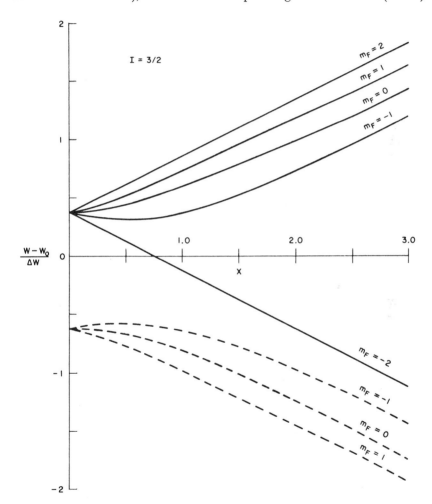

Fig. 1. The magnetic field dependence of energy sublevels for an atom with electronic angular momentum $J = \frac{1}{2}$ and nuclear spin $I = \frac{3}{2}$. The full curves are for $F = I + J = 2$; the dotted curves are for $F = I - J = 1$. The field parameter x is equal to $(g_J - g_I)\mu_0 H/\Delta W$.

Consequently, the dimensionless coordinates of Fig. 1 are not applicable to Fig. 2, and they have been replaced by $(W - W_0)/hA$ for the energy ordinate and by $g_J\mu_0H/hA$ for the magnetic field parameter. Strictly speaking, Fig. 2 is not, like Fig. 1, a universal energy plot, since it is drawn for a specific value of the electric quadrupole coupling constant, B, relative to the magnetic dipole coupling constant, A. In such cases, where both I and J are greater than $\frac{1}{2}$ and the electric quadrupole hyperfine structure interaction is nonvanishing, a universal energy plot would have to be three-dimensional.

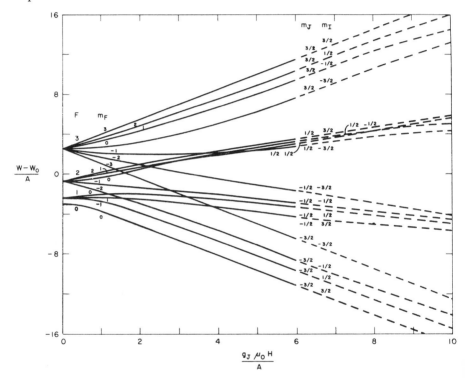

FIG. 2. The magnetic field dependence of energy sublevels for Ga^{69} in its $^2P_{3/2}$ level. For values of $g_J\mu_0H/A$ up to 6, the sublevels were computed by numerical methods. At $g_J\mu_0H/A = 10$, the calculation was made for a strong field approximation, and the dotted curves join the two solutions smoothly.

The sublevel energy formulas (4.1.2.8), (4.1.2.9), and (4.1.2.10), although adequate for most purposes, may fail to fit radio spectra measured with extreme precision. The reason is inherent in the form of the Hamiltonian (4.1.2.3) from which these energies were calculated. As written, the Hamiltonian is diagonal in J; it has no matrix elements which connect neighboring fine structure levels. This of course is an approximation, albeit a good one, since both the hyperfine structure and Zeeman interactions actually do possess matrix elements off-diagonal in J. The Zeeman interaction between fine structure levels, when exaggerated by extremely strong fields, produces the Paschen–Back effect. The hyperfine structure interaction between fine structure levels is less familiar, but at the relatively low field strengths employed in radio spectroscopy it may be quite comparable in magnitude with the "incipient" Paschen–Back effect at these field strengths.

Corrections to the Breit–Rabi formula (4.1.2.9) for both types of off-diagonal interaction have been calculated by Clendenin.[18] Similar corrections to the weak field and strong field energy formulas, (4.1.2.8) and (4.1.2.10), may be calculated as second-order perturbation terms. The energy corrections are, in order of magnitude, $(hA)^2/\delta$ for the weak field case and $(\mu_0 H)^2/\delta$ for the strong field case, where δ is the separation of the perturbing fine structure levels. The relative size of these second-order terms is typically less than 0.1 %.

4.1.2.2.4. TRANSITION PROBABILITIES AND INTENSITIES. In contrast with the optical spectrum, where spontaneous radiation is the rule, atoms do not emit radio-frequency radiation spontaneously.[19] Rather, the characteristic radiative processes of the radio spectrum are absorption and its inverse, stimulated emission. The transition probabilities for upward (absorption) and downward (stimulated emission) transitions, excited by a radio-frequency field of given frequency and intensity, are identical. *Hence the radio-frequency resonance condition always tends to equalize the populations of the two energy levels concerned.* Unless there is a population difference to begin with, the resonance condition will, in general, have no detectable effect either on the material system or on the electromagnetic field. Since Nature does not ordinarily provide large population differences between closely spaced energy levels, it is usually necessary for the experimenter to produce them artificially, through the use of "state selection" techniques. Only for energy level separations in the upper microwave range, or for dense atomic systems, does the natural Boltzmann distribution provide population differences large enough for spectroscopic work.

4.1.2.2.4.1. *Line Shapes.* The highly monochromatic nature of vacuum tube oscillators as spectroscopic sources makes it possible to measure accurately the widths and detailed shapes of radio lines as well as their positions. Line shapes may be studied for the information they offer on atomic velocities, collision cross sections, and radiative lifetimes;

[18] W. W. Clendenin, *Phys. Rev.* **94**, 1590 (1954).

[19] Only in the tenuous gas of interstellar space, where an atom may remain undisturbed by collisions for years at a time, has spontaneous radio line emission by atoms (hydrogen) been observed.

frequently also an understanding of the line shape is necessary before one can measure the true center frequency of a radio line. The principal sources of line broadening are as follows.

(1) Transit Time Broadening. In a atomic beam resonance apparatus, atoms pass rapidly through the radio-frequency exciter, and experience the transition-inducing field for only a brief time. If this time interval is Δt, an application of the Heisenberg uncertainty principle indicates that the minimum resonance line width will be of order $(\Delta t)^{-1}$ cps.

(2) Natural Line Breadth. Unstable atoms, such as those in optically excited states, are also limited in the time interval over which they can interact with a radio-frequency field. The corresponding line width will be of order τ^{-1} cps, where τ is the mean lifetime of the unstable atom. This mean lifetime is ordinarily a characteristic property of the atom, and hence the term "natural" line breadth.

(3) Collision Broadening. Inelastic collisions of an atom with other gas particles or with the walls of a container can broaden a radio line, since the lifetime of an atom in a given energy level or sublevel is thereby shortened. Elastic collisions, which change only the phase of the atomic wave function, can also have a broadening influence. If the mean time interval between collisions is T, the minimum line breadth will be of order T^{-1}. The value of T will depend on experimental variables such as gas constitution, temperature, and wall conditions, and especially on the gas pressure.

(4) Saturation Broadening. Whatever the mechanism by which population differences are set up—state selection in an atomic beam, thermal relaxation or selective excitation in an atomic vapor—that mechanism will be limited in its ability to maintain the population difference in competition with the equalizing influence of radio-frequency transitions. Consequently, as the transition probability is increased by a gradual increase of the radio-frequency field strength, the detectable resonance signal will not increase proportionately, but will gradually "saturate" instead. Since the transition probability varies over the contour of the resonance line, being largest at the center, saturation will depress the peak of the line relative to its sides. The line width, measured customarily between the two half-intensity points, will thus increase. Saturation broadening is an experimental effect, and can always be eliminated by reducing the radio-frequency field strength.

(5) Field Inhomogeneity Broadening and Modulation Broadening. These are two more experimental sources of broadening which, at least in principle, can always be eliminated. Field inhomogeneity broadening occurs in Zeeman spectra, when different parts of the atomic sample find themselves in slightly different magnetic field strengths, and thus

have slightly different resonance frequencies. Modulation broadening can occur when, in order to use ac detection methods, the resonance condition is modulated in one way or another, for example, by modulating the frequency of the radio-frequency oscillator. If either the modulation frequency or its amplitude (measured in equivalent frequency units), is comparable in magnitude with the true spectral line width, an artificial broadening of the detected line shape will result.

Significant by its omission from this list is the Doppler effect. Although it is a major source of line breadth in optical spectra, Doppler broadening is almost always negligible in atomic radio spectra. In gaseous absorption work, because of the long wavelength and fixed field distribution of the radiation usually employed, a moving atom experiences a nearly uniform electromagnetic field over its path of interaction with the field, and under these circumstances the normal Doppler width is reduced approximately by the ratio L/λ, where L is the mean free path between collisions and λ is the wavelength.[20] In atomic beam work, Doppler effects can be made very small by keeping the interaction region short and by orienting the radio-frequency field so that it is perpendicular to the beam direction. In radio-optical work on excited atomic states, Doppler broadening is usually insignificant in comparison with the natural line width.

To aid in analyzing experimental line shapes there are several idealized line shape formulas to compare them with. These formulas are obtained by computing, for certain well-defined experimental conditions, the theoretical transition probability as a function of frequency. For example, transitions excited by a sinusoidally varying field of angular frequency ω, between two isolated states a and b of atoms in a monoenergetic beam, have a probability $P_{ab}(\omega)$ given by

$$P_{ab}(\omega) = \frac{|2V_{ab}|^2}{(\omega_0 - \omega)^2 + |2V_{ab}|^2} \sin^2\{\tfrac{1}{2}[(\omega_0 - \omega)^2 + |2V_{ab}|^2]^{1/2}t\}, \quad (4.1.2.11)$$

where t is elapsed time since the atom entered the radio-frequency field, ω_0 is the resonance frequency $|W_a - W_b|/\hbar$, and V_{ab} is the matrix element of the interaction between atom and radio-frequency field, assumed to be constant for the time interval t and zero immediately before. If the interaction is magnetic, as is usually the case, V_{ab} is the matrix element $(a \mid \mathbf{\mu} \cdot \mathbf{H}_1 \mid b)/\hbar$, where $\mathbf{\mu}$ is the magnetic moment of the atom and $\mathbf{H}_1$ is the radio-frequency magnetic field. The shape function (4.1.2.11) includes the effects of both transit time broadening and saturation broadening. The dimensionless product $|2V_{ab}|\Delta t$, where Δt is the total time required for an atom to pass through the radio-frequency field, measures both of these broadening effects, and provides a useful

[20] R. H. Dicke, *Phys. Rev.* **89**, 472 (1953).

parameter for the calculation of representative line shapes. The dashed curve in Fig. 3 shows such a calculated line shape for the case $|2V_{ab}|\,\Delta t = \pi$. This is the optimum signal case; the transition probability becomes unity at $\omega = \omega_0$. In physical terms, this means that every atom that enters the radio-frequency field in state a will have achieved a transition to state b by the time it leaves the field.

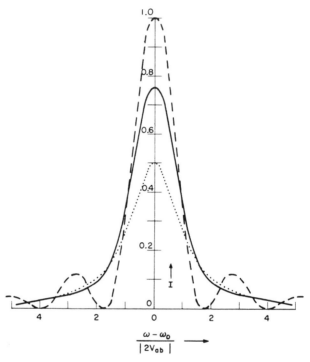

FIG. 3.   Theoretical line shapes for an atomic beam apparatus. The intensity I is plotted against the frequency parameter $(\omega - \omega_0)/|\,2V_{ab}|$. The dashed curve is for a uniform velocity and optimum perturbation ($|\,2V_{ab}|\,\Delta t = \pi$). The full curve is the result of averaging over a Maxwellian velocity distribution, again with optimum perturbation ($|\,2V_{ab}|\,\overline{\Delta t} = 1.200\pi$, where $\overline{\Delta t}$ is the most probable interaction time). The dotted curve shows the effect of extreme power saturation for a Maxwellian beam ($|\,2V_{ab}|\,\overline{\Delta t} \gg \pi$).

If the atomic beam is not monoenergetic, the interaction time Δt will not have a unique value, and the line shape function must be averaged over the actual velocity distribution in the beam. The solid curve in Fig. 3 shows the result of averaging (4.1.2.11) over a Maxwellian beam velocity distribution for conditions that maximize the line amplitude at resonance. This new optimum signal case is given by $|\,2V_{ab}|\overline{\Delta t} = 1.200\pi$, where $\overline{\Delta t}$ is the most probable interaction time. The full width of the line at half intensity is $1.072/\overline{\Delta t}$ cps for this case. Saturation effects in a

Maxwellian beam are represented by the dotted curve in Fig. 3, which is calculated for the limiting case $|\ 2V_{ab}\ |\ \Delta t \gg \pi$. Atoms passing through such a strong radio-frequency field will shuttle back and forth many times between the two states a and b. An atom entering the field in one state will have a 50 % chance of leaving the field in the same state, and the detectable resonance signal is only half its maximum value.

By lengthening the radio-frequency field, and hence increasing the interaction time Δt, one can reduce the transit time broadening of an atomic beam resonance line to any desired degree. A practical limit is reached when some other source of broadening becomes important; this limiting width usually comes from unavoidable magnetic field inhomogeneities over an extended interaction region. A very powerful experimental technique devised by Ramsey[21] will eliminate this inhomogeneity broadening if very narrow resonance lines are desired. This technique, which has become standard in precision beam spectroscopy, uses two (or more) separate radio-frequency exciters. Beam atoms pass through one radio-frequency exciter as they enter a long dc magnetic field region, and pass through a second radiofrequency exciter as they leave the field. If both exciters are fed from the same oscillator, so that there is a definite phase relation between the two radio-frequency fields, the resonance line shape will be modified by interference effects. If the two fields are in phase, the central part of the line will show the fringelike structure illustrated by Fig. 4. The central peak of this structure can be used to locate the resonant frequency with great precision, since its width is determined by the transit time between the two radio-frequency fields, and this width is independent of inhomogeneities in the intervening region of magnetic field. Ramsey's technique is valuable also for high-frequency work, where it allows the radio-frequency excitation regions to be made short in comparison with the wavelength. This is necessary to prevent Doppler broadening and distortion of the resonance line shape.

A second example of a calculable line shape is that encountered in radio-frequency experiments on excited atoms. Here one or both of the two excited levels involved is subject to rapid radiative decay, and natural broadening is the chief source of line width. The transition probability near resonance, calculated from first-order time-dependent perturbation theory, is given by

$$P_{ab}(\omega) = \frac{(\Gamma_a + \Gamma_b)|\ V_{ab}\ |^2}{(\omega_0 - \omega)^2 + \frac{1}{4}(\Gamma_a + \Gamma_b)^2}\ , \qquad (4.1.2.12)$$

where Γ_a and Γ_b are the optical decay rates of the two levels and V_{ab} is again the matrix element of the interaction with the radio-frequency

[21] N. F. Ramsey, *Phys. Rev.* **78**, 695 (1950).

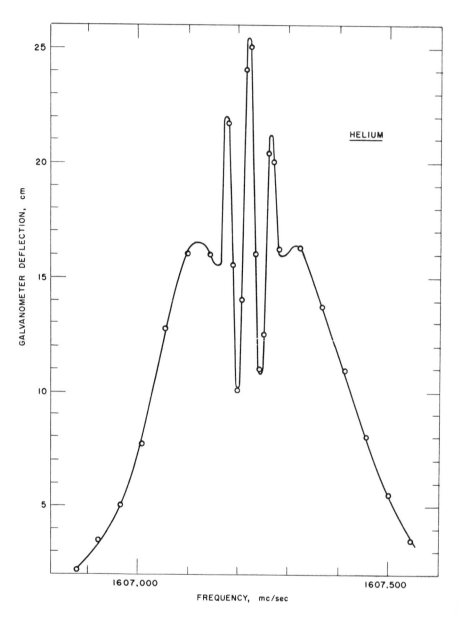

FIG. 4.   An experimental line shape observed with separated radio-frequency fields in an atomic beam experiment on metastable helium.

field. Saturation effects are not included, and so (4.1.2.12) is valid only as long as the microwave transition rate is much smaller than either optical decay rate (i.e., $| V_{ab} | \ll \Gamma_a, \Gamma_b$). Typical decay rates of excited atomic levels range between 10^8 and 10^9 second^{-1}, and radio-frequency power levels of several watts or tens of watts may be required to produce even the beginnings of saturation effects. The shape function (4.1.2.12) is of the familiar Lorentzian type, and has a half-width at half-maximum of $\Delta \nu = (\Gamma_a + \Gamma_b)/4\pi$ cps, which is usually in the range 10–100 Mc/sec. The actual line width observed in a radio-optical experiment may be somewhat smaller than this because of radiation imprisonment effects. Line shapes other than (4.1.2.12) are encountered in excited state work, and are discussed in a review article by Series.[22]

A third important experimental situation for which line shapes may be calculated with some precision is that of microwave absorption experiments on ground state atoms. Because of the relatively high gas densities required in these experiments, collision broadening is frequently the major source of line width. For such cases the first-order transition probability in the neighborhood of resonance is given by

$$P_{ab}(\omega) = \frac{2T^{-1} | V_{ab} |^2}{(\omega_0 - \omega)^2 + T^{-2}}, \qquad (4.1.2.13)$$

in which T is the mean time between line-broadening collisions. The line shape is again Lorentzian, and has a half-width at half-maximum of $\Delta \nu = (2\pi T)^{-1}$ cps. The effects of saturation and of nonresonant absorption on the shape of collision-broadened lines have been calculated,[23] and can be included in (4.1.2.13) when necessary.

4.1.2.2.4.2. *Polarizations and Relative Intensities of Zeeman Components.* The various transitions $a \leftrightarrow b$ between magnetic sublevels of fine or hyperfine structure levels are more or less probable according to the square of the interaction matrix element, $| V_{ab} |^2$. For dipole transitions (electric or magnetic) between fine structure sublevels, the relative magnitudes of these squared matrix elements are[6]:

$$| V_{J,m_J \leftrightarrow J,m_J} |^2 = P m_J{}^2$$
$$| V_{J,m_J \leftrightarrow J,m_J \pm 1} |^2 = \tfrac{1}{2}P(J \mp m_J)(J \pm m_J + 1)$$
$$| V_{J,m_J \leftrightarrow J+1,m_J} |^2 = Q[(J + 1)^2 - m_J{}^2]$$
$$| V_{J,m_J \leftrightarrow J+1,m_J \pm 1} |^2 = \tfrac{1}{2}Q(J \pm m_J + 1)(J \pm m_J + 2) \qquad (4.1.2.14)$$
$$| V_{J,m_J \leftrightarrow J-1,m_J} |^2 = Q(J^2 - m_J{}^2)$$
$$| V_{J,m_J \leftrightarrow J-1,m_J \pm 1} |^2 = \tfrac{1}{2}Q(J \mp m_J)(J \mp m_J - 1),$$

[22] G. W. Series, *Repts. Progr. in Phys.* **22**, 280 (1959).
[23] C. H. Townes and A. L. Schawlow, "Microwave Spectroscopy." McGraw-Hill, New York, 1955.

where P and Q are independent of J and m_J. The same formulas apply to transitions between hyperfine structure sublevels, when F and m_F are substituted throughout for J and m_J. Relative transition probabilities computed from (4.1.2.14) are strictly correct only in the weak field limit, where J (or F) is a sharp quantum number. For intermediate field conditions, exact transition probability formulas may be calculated from (4.1.2.14) and wavefunctions written as linear combinations of J, m_J (or F, m_F) eigenfunctions.

Transitions between Zeeman sublevels are called π (for *parallel*) transitions when the radiation absorbed or emitted is linearly polarized with its electric vector parallel to the magnetic field; they are called σ (for *senkrecht*) transitions when the radiation is polarized with its electric vector in a plane perpendicular to the magnetic field. Radiation which is π-polarized can cause electric dipole transitions of the type $\Delta m = 0$ only, while radiation which is σ-polarized can cause electric dipole transitions of the type $\Delta m = \pm 1$ only. Right-hand circularly polarized (σ^+) radiation causes absorption in $\Delta m = +1$ transitions and stimulated emission in $\Delta m = -1$ transitions; left-hand circularly polarized (σ^-) radiation causes absorption in $\Delta m = -1$ transitions and stimulated emission in $\Delta m = +1$ transitions. Linearly polarized σ radiation, which can be regarded as an equal intensity mixture of σ^+ and σ^- radiation, is equally effective in causing $\Delta m = +1$ or $\Delta m = -1$ transitions.

This π and σ terminology provides a convenient shorthand for describing optical Zeeman spectra (this was its original purpose), which are almost universally of the electric dipole type, but it becomes awkward when applied to radio Zeeman spectra, which may be of either the electric or magnetic dipole type, usually the latter. The reason is that the magnetic vector of electromagnetic radiation is perpendicular to the electric vector, and this makes it possible to speak of π transitions as being excited by σ-polarized radiation and so on. Confusion can be avoided by specifying a transition according to the change in magnetic quantum number that is involved, and by specifying the polarization according to the projections of the electric and magnetic vectors along the coordinate axes.

Equations (4.1.2.14) are correct as written for spontaneous emission and for absorption and stimulated emission in an unpolarized electromagnetic field. Radio-frequency fields are often highly polarized, however, and this polarization must be considered in computing the relative probabilities of inducing $\Delta m = 0$ and $\Delta m = \pm 1$ transitions. In such cases, the quantities P and Q will depend on both the intensity and the polarization of the radio-frequency fields.

In experiments where polarized light is involved in the detection of radio-frequency resonance, another aspect of polarized radiation becomes important. This is the different spatial distribution of the π and σ dipole radiation emitted by atoms in a magnetic field, whereby π radiation is emitted mostly perpendicular to the field direction and σ radiation is emitted mostly parallel to the field direction. Letting I_π, $I_\sigma{}^+$, and $I_\sigma{}^-$ represent the maximum intensities of π, σ^+, and σ^- radiation emitted in any direction, one finds that the total intensity emitted in a direction perpendicular to the field direction is $I_\pi + \frac{1}{2}(I_\sigma{}^+ + I_\sigma{}^-)$, while the total intensity emitted along the field direction is $I_\sigma{}^+ + I_\sigma{}^-$. Observed at any intermediate angle, φ, with respect to the field direction, the intensity is

$$I(\varphi) = I\left[\frac{3(100 - P\cos^2\varphi)}{300 - P}\right], \qquad (4.1.2.15)$$

where $4\pi\bar{I}$ is the total intensity, integrated over all angles, and

$$P = \frac{100[I_\pi - \frac{1}{2}(I_\sigma{}^+ + I_\sigma{}^-)]}{I_\pi + \frac{1}{2}(I_\sigma{}^+ + I_\sigma{}^-)} \qquad (4.1.2.16)$$

is the "percentage polarization" of the radiation. Equation (4.1.2.15) shows that a change in the polarization of the light will be accompanied by a change in the intensity, as measured by a polarization-insensitive detector oriented at any angle (except 0° or 180°) with respect to the field direction.

4.1.2.3. Radio Spectroscopic Apparatus. Certain elements of apparatus are common to the various methods of radio spectroscopy. These include the elements that generate and control radio-frequency or microwave power, measure its frequency, and transmit it to the region where the interaction with the atoms under study take place. Through the rapid development of communication technology over the past two decades, most of these elements—oscillators and transmission line components—are now commercially available for the entire range of frequencies up to 120 Gc (kMc). The theory and use of this apparatus is discussed in several books, and will not be dwelt upon here; among the best general references for the experimental spectroscopist are the MIT Radiation Laboratory Series[24] (especially Volumes 7, 8, 10, and 11), the Radio Research Laboratory volumes,[25] and the textbook by Reich et al.[26] Shorter but more specialized treatments are given in the

[24] "Massachusetts Institute of Technology Radiation Laboratory Series." McGraw-Hill, New York, 1946-1951.

[25] "Very High-Frequency Techniques" (H. J. Reich, ed.), 2 vols. McGraw-Hill, New York, 1947.

[26] H. J. Reich, P. F. Ordung, H. J. Krauss, and J. G. Skalnik, "Microwave Theory and Techniques." Van Nostrand, Princeton, New Jersey, 1953.

microwave spectroscopy books of Townes and Schawlow,[23] Gordy *et al.*,[27] and Ingram.[28] The major news in communications apparatus since these books were written has been the rapid development of ferrite devices. Applications of these one-way transmission line components—load isolators, circulators, and switches—are discussed in a recent book by Clarricoats.[29]*

Other pieces of apparatus that find wide use in radio spectroscopy are the precision magnet, the nuclear resonance magnetometer, the electronic frequency counter, and the lock-in amplifier. All of these have become commercial items in the past few years, largely in response to the burgeoning interest in paramagnetic resonance investigations of solids. The experimental problems solved by the use of magnets and lock-in amplifiers are so characteristic of radio spectroscopy in general, however, that fuller discussion is warranted.

4.1.2.3.1. MAGNETS.[†] Atoms that have radio spectra also have, in general, magnetic dipole moments (cf. Section 4.1.2.2). By placing such atoms between the poles of a laboratory magnet one may measure the Zeeman effect of their radio spectra, i.e., the splitting of the lines caused by the interaction between atomic moment and magnetic field, and thereby measure the size of the atomic moments.

Magnets are also used in other more utilitarian ways in radio spectroscopy. The components of a line that has been split by the field clearly may be *shifted* by a further increase or decrease of the field strength. Thus one may "scan" a radio line, or indeed an entire spectrum, by varying the magnetic field strength, leaving the frequency of the source oscillator fixed. This technique is widely practiced, for it removes one of the most vexing problems of radio spectroscopy: the problem of maintaining a radio-frequency field reasonably constant in amplitude while varying its frequency. When a wide range of frequencies must be covered, this is made difficult, if not impossible, by the frequency-dependent characteristics of all the apparatus used to generate, transport, and detect radio-frequency power. As an extreme example of this undesirable frequency dependence, the curve of output power vs. frequency for a vacuum tube oscillator may possess "holes," frequency regions where the oscillator refuses to work at all. Erratic behavior of this sort is at times a nuisance that must be borne, for instance in searches

[27] W. Gordy, W. V. Smith, and R. F. Trambarulo, "Microwave Spectroscopy." Wiley, New York, 1953.

[28] D. J. E. Ingram, "Spectroscopy at Radio and Microwave Frequencies." Butterworth, London and Washington, D.C., 1955.

[29] P. J. B. Clarricoats, "Microwave Ferrites." Wiley, New York, 1961.

* See also different parts of Vol. 2, particularly Part 10.

† See also Vol. 1, Chapter 9.2.

for the absorption spectra of diamagnetic gases, but it is a nuisance that can be got around whenever the technique of magnetic scanning is applicable.

Magnetic scanning requires a field that may be varied in strength over a wide range, and one that is sufficiently homogeneous over the experimental volume to prevent artificial broadening of the spectral lines. These requirements are met by the "precision" electromagnet, so-called because of the great care taken during its construction to make the field in its air gap as homogeneous as possible. The iron yoke is massive, structurally rigid, and usually symmetric in form. The pole caps are made of the highest quality iron or special alloys, with surfaces ground flat to optical precision. Highly regulated electronic power supplies, or in some cases storage cells, provide current to the magnet coils. Early work in radio spectroscopy was done with precision electromagnets which were constructed on the spot, but now, much to the convenience of the experimenter, there are several commercial versions available. The most efficient and trouble-free of these employ low-impedance coils, energized by automatic solid state power supplies.

Another practical use for magnets in radio spectroscopy is peculiar to the atomic beam method where, through the magnetic deflection properties of the beam, they serve as state selectors. Since the deflecting force exerted on a dipole by a magnetic field is proportional to the gradient of the field strength, the magnet must in this application produce as inhomogeneous a field as possible, but one that at the same time has a constant gradient over the region occupied by the beam. The classic example of such a magnetic field is the two-wire field, produced by two parallel conductors carrying a heavy current close alongside the beam path. A similar field distribution can be produced with less electrical power by an electromagnet with appropriately shaped poles. Permanent magnets with shaped poles are sometimes used in special purpose beam apparatus, such as the cesium frequency standard, where variable deflecting fields are not necessary.

4.1.2.3.2. LOCK-IN AMPLIFIERS.* The detectors used in radio spectroscopy—microwave crystals, photoelectric devices, ionization detectors—produce small electrical signals which must be amplified before they can actuate recording instruments. Electrical noise which originates in the detector and in the first amplifier stage is amplified along with the signal, and this noise sets a limit to the usable gain of the amplifier. The usable gain or, what is equivalent, the signal-to-noise ratio, may often be increased by modulating the radio line at some arbitrary frequency and then passing the resulting ac signal through

* See also Vol. 2, Chapter 6.2.

a narrow-band amplifier tuned to the modulation frequency. The noise power, which is proportional to the amplifier bandwidth, is thereby reduced at no cost, or at most small cost, to the signal power. Noise sometimes may be reduced still further by choosing the modulation frequency in a range where the detector happens to have a low noise output. Microwave crystals, for example, have a noise spectrum which varies in intensity nearly as the reciprocal of the frequency. Clearly, for this case, a high modulation frequency is desirable. Frequencies as high as one-tenth the radio line width can be employed without appreciable distortion of the line shape.

A narrow-band amplifier followed by a lock-in detector (also called a synchronous detector, or phase-sensitive detector) constitutes a lock-in amplifier. The lock-in detector is a circuit which responds selectively to that part of the incoming signal which is coherent with (i.e., has the same frequency and phase as) a reference signal derived from the modulation oscillator. Several versions of the basic lock-in detector circuit have been devised, all of which operate in the same general way. A particularly simple version consists of two identical half-wave rectifiers, connected as shown in Fig. 5. In the absence of a signal, the

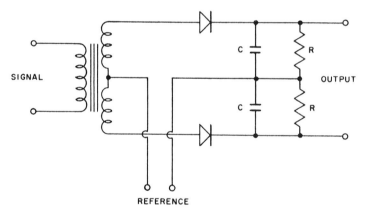

FIG. 5.   A lock-in detector circuit that uses diode rectifiers.

rectifiers work in tandem on the reference voltage, and their output voltages buck to zero. If now a coherent signal is applied to the circuit, the balance condition will be upset, since signal and reference voltages will add on one rectifier and subtract on the other. Signals (and noise) at other frequencies will tend to cause fluctuations in the balance condition, but these fluctuations will be smoothed out by the RC filter network. The RC time constant can be made arbitrarily long, and hence the lock-in detector can be made to have an arbitrarily narrow bandwidth, always centered exactly at the reference frequency. A second interesting feature of the circuit is its phase sensitivity: the magnitude and sign of the net output voltage varies according to the cosine of the phase angle between the signal and reference voltages. This is the reason for the characteristic dispersionlike shape of radio lines drawn out on recorder charts by lock-in detectors.

4.1.2.4. Fine Structure. A major success of the Dirac relativistic theory of the electron, new in 1928, was its ability to predict correctly the fine structure in the optical spectra of one-electron atoms. The spectrum of atomic hydrogen, measured repeatedly and with increasing precision over the years prior to World War II, failed to show any significant departure from the Dirac theory, although there was some inconclusive evidence for a very small energy difference, approximately 0.03 cm^{-1}, between two levels which, according to the theory, should be exactly degenerate. Shortly after the war Lamb and Retherford, seeking to exploit the new spectroscopic tools made available in the development of military radar, set out to measure the hydrogen fine structure directly, using an ingenious radio-frequency resonance method. The experiment succeeded, and the radio spectrum showed immediately that, as hinted by the earlier optical measurements, there was indeed a small level splitting where none should be. In seeming contradiction with the Dirac theory, the two first-excited levels, $2^2S_{1/2}$ and $2^2P_{1/2}$, were found to be separated by about 1000 Mc (0.033 cm^{-1}). This "Lamb shift" was eventually reconciled with the Dirac theory by considering the interaction of the atom with the quantized electromagnetic radiation field, and a theoretical calculation of the shift was the first important task carried out with the modern theory of quantum electrodynamics. By thus simultaneously putting a new theory on its feet and establishing a new branch of atomic spectroscopy, the Lamb–Retherford experiment became one of the most celebrated experiments of postwar physics.

In the years since 1947, the Lamb–Retherford experiment has been refined to the highest degree, both in technique and interpretation. Experiments similar in aim but somewhat different in method have also been performed on singly ionized helium. In a review article[30] Lamb discusses the historical antecedents of the Lamb–Retherford experiment, describes experimental methods, and gives the results obtained for the first-excited levels ($n = 2$) of hydrogen, deuterium, and singly ionized helium prior to 1951. In more recent years, radio spectroscopic measurements of Lamb shifts have been made on the second-excited levels ($n = 3$) of hydrogen and deuterium, and preliminary observations have been reported on the $n = 4$ levels of singly ionized helium.[31] Some of

[30] W. E. Lamb, Jr., *Repts. Progr. in Phys.* **14**, 19 (1951).
[31] G. W. Series and W. N. Fox, *J. phys., radium* **19**, 850 (1958).

these results, together with recent optical observations of Lamb shifts, are discussed in a monograph by Series,[32] which is an excellent and readable introduction to the complexities of the hydrogen atom.

Precise fine structure measurements on atoms with more than one electron are harder to interpret, chiefly because of the difficulty of including electron-electron interactions in the relativistic theory of fine structure. The simplest test case for the study of such interactions is the two-electron system, represented by the neutral helium atom or, even more simply, by the positronium atom, the transitory "hydrogen" atom in which the role of the proton is taken by a positron. These are the only two multielectron atoms on which radio spectroscopic measurements of fine structure have been made to date, although the experimental methods developed for the helium atom could probably be extended to other light atoms and ions.

TABLE I.   Atomic Fine Structure Separations Measured by Radio Spectroscopy

Atom	Principal quantum number	Fine structure levels	Experimental value (Mc)[a]	Reference
H	2	$^2S_{1/2}-^2P_{1/2}$	1057.77(10)	TRI-53
	3	$^2S_{1/2}-^2P_{1/2}$	313.6(57)	KLE-61
D	2	$^2S_{1/2}-^2P_{1/2}$	1059.00(10)	TRI-53
		$^2P_{3/2}-^2S_{1/2}$	9912.59(10)	DAY-53
	3	$^2S_{1/2}-^2P_{1/2}$	315.30(80)	WIL-60
		$^2P_{3/2}-^2P_{1/2}$	3250.7(20)	
		$^2P_{3/2}-^2D_{3/2}$	5.0(10)	
	4	$^2S_{1/2}-^2P_{1/2}$	133.0(10)	WIL-60
He$^+$	2	$^2S_{1/2}-^2P_{1/2}$	14040.2(45)	LIP-57
He	2	$^3P_1-^3P_2$	2291.56(9)	COL-59
		$^3P_0-^3P_1$	29650(280)	
	3	$^3P_1-^3P_2$	658.55(15)	WIE-57
		$^3P_0-^3P_1$	8113.78(22)	
Positronium	1	$^3S_1-^1S_0$	203.33(4) $\times 10^3$	HUG-57

[a] Error estimates in parentheses apply to last figure of quoted value.

COL-59   F. D. Colgrove, P. A. Franken, R. R. Lewis, and R. H. Sands, *Phys. Rev. Letters* **3**, 420 (1959).

DAY-53   E. S. Dayhoff, S. Triebwasser, and W. E. Lamb, Jr., *Phys. Rev.* **89**, 106 (1953).

HUG-57   V. W. Hughes, S. Marder, and C. S. Wu, *Phys. Rev.* **106**, 934 (1957).

KLE-61   H. Kleinpoppen, *Z. Physik* **164**, 174 (1961).

LIP-57   E. Lipworth and R. Novick, *Phys. Rev.* **108**, 1434 (1957).

TRI-53   S. Triebwasser, E. S. Dayhoff, and W. E. Lamb, Jr., *Phys. Rev.* **89**, 98 (1953).

WIE-57   I. Wieder and W. E. Lamb, Jr., *Phys. Rev.* **107**, 125 (1957).

WIL-60   L. R. Wilcox and W. E. Lamb, Jr., *Phys. Rev.* **119**, 1915 (1960).

[32] G. W. Series, "Spectrum of Atomic Hydrogen." Oxford Univ. Press, London and New York, 1957.

Table I gives a complete list of the atomic fine structure intervals that have been measured by radio-frequency methods, together with latest numerical results (as of mid-1963).

4.1.2.4.1. HYDROGEN; DEUTERIUM, $n = 2$. The Lamb–Retherford[33,34] experiment depends on a special property of the $2^2S_{1/2}$ level, which is its metastability toward radiative decay. Once formed in the $2^2S_{1/2}$ level, a free hydrogen atom can survive for a considerable fraction of a second, and travel large distances, before finally giving up its excitation energy of 10.2 ev in a spontaneous radiative transition to the ground $1^2S_{1/2}$ level. If, however, a beam of such atoms is intercepted by a metal target a short distance from its starting point, de-excitation may occur by means of an Auger process, in which an electron is simultaneously ejected from the metal surface. Collected and measured by an electrometer, the current of ejected electrons is a sensitive indicator of changes in the flux of metastable atoms striking the target.

One way to change the flux of metastable atoms is to apply a radio-frequency electromagnetic field to the beam as it crosses the space between source and target. When its frequency is correct, the field transfers metastable beam atoms to one of the nearby 2^2P levels, from which they immediately decay in radiative transitions to the ground $1^2S_{1/2}$ level (the radiative half-life of the 2^2P levels is approximately 10^{-9} second). Thus the radio-frequency resonance condition removes metastable atoms from the beam—it "quenches" the beam—and this causes a dip in the current of electrons ejected from the metal target. By tuning the radio-frequency oscillator, it should be possible to trace out the complete radio-frequency quenching spectrum—the spectrum of all possible transitions between the $2^2S_{1/2}$ level and the $2^2P_{1/2}$ and $2^2P_{3/2}$ levels. In practice, because of the usual difficulties in tuning a radio-frequency system smoothly, Lamb and Retherford found it simpler to place their apparatus between the poles of an electromagnet, and use magnetic scanning at a fixed radio frequency. This made necessary an accurate calculation of the Zeeman effect of the quenching spectrum.

The Zeeman splitting pattern of the $n = 2$ fine structure levels, calculated by Lamb and Retherford, is illustrated by Fig. 6. The Lamb shift has been included, and is evident as a separation of the $2^2S_{1/2}$ and $2^2P_{1/2}$ levels at zero field. The curvature of the sublevels b, c, e, and f (the nomenclature is arbitrary, but has become standard in Lamb shift experiments) demonstrates a phenomenon mentioned earlier, the incipient Paschen–Back effect caused by the Zeeman interaction between fine structure levels. The effect occurs at relatively low field strengths

---

[33] W. E. Lamb, Jr., and R. C. Retherford, *Phys. Rev.* **79**, 549 (1950); **81**, 222 (1951); **86**, 1014 (1952).

[34] S. Triebwasser, E. S. Dayhoff, and W. E. Lamb, Jr., *Phys. Rev.* **89**, 98 (1953).

here because of the small fine structure splitting ($\sim$10 Gc) of the $2^2P_{1/2}$ and $2^2P_{3/2}$ levels. Hyperfine structure splittings are too small to be shown in Fig. 6, although they were readily detectable in the observed quenching spectrum. In the accurate energy calculations required for the analysis of the spectrum, intermediate field effects had to be considered, as they affected both fine structure and hyperfine structure.[35]

4.1.2.4.1.1. *Electrostatic Quenching.* In designing their experiment, Lamb and Retherford had to guard against a second, nonresonant quenching of the metastable beam, which could be caused by stray electrostatic fields along its path. Because the $2^2S_{1/2}$ and $2^2P_{1/2}$ levels are nearly degenerate and are connected by electric dipole matrix elements, the Stark effect in a weak electric field will cause an appreciable mixing of the two levels, with a consequent reduction of the $2^2S_{1/2}$ lifetime. Even a small amount of this electrostatic quenching would be objectionable if it caused erratic changes in the flux of metastable atoms at the beam target. At worst, the metastable beam might even be quenched completely by stray fields before it could reach the detector target.

To estimate their chances of success in the face of electrostatic quenching, and to aid in the design of their apparatus, Lamb and Retherford calculated the Stark effect of the $2^2S_{1/2}$ level as a function of its separation from the $2^2P_{1/2}$ level. They found that if the two levels were indeed degenerate, as predicted by the Dirac theory, stray fields larger than $\frac{1}{3}$ volt/cm would quench nearly all the metastable atoms in a beam length of a few centimeters. Fortunately, as the successful experiment showed, the two levels are not degenerate. For a separation of 1000 Mc, the Stark effect is reduced to the point where stray fields as high as 7 volts/cm can be tolerated. As a restriction on the allowable buildup of static charges near the metastable beam, this was still a difficult, but not impossible, criterion to satisfy.

4.1.2.4.1.2. *Production of a Metastable Beam.* The beam originated in a tungsten furnace, fed with hydrogen gas and heated electrically to a temperature sufficient to dissociate a large fraction of the hydrogen molecules. Hydrogen atoms and molecules effused from a slit in the side of the furnace, passed through a second beam-defining slit, and then through an electron bombarder, a simple triode electron gun oriented transverse to the hydrogen beam. The bombarder was designed for maximum stability and freedom from electrostatic quenching effects rather than for maximum bombardment efficiency; Lamb and Retherford estimated that only one beam atom out of forty million was excited to the metastable level as it passed through the bombardment region.

[35] W. E. Lamb, Jr., *Phys. Rev.* **85**, 259 (1951).

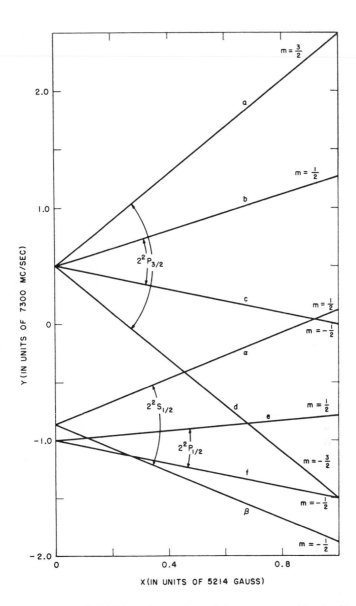

Fig. 6. The magnetic field dependence of $n = 2$ fine structure sublevels of hydrogen. The Lamb shift is indicated by the small separation, at zero field, of the levels $2^2S_{1/2}$ and $2^2P_{1/2}$.

Thus the "metastable beam" was really a beam of ground state hydrogen atoms, with a small percentage of hydrogen molecules and, every now and then, a metastable atom. The experiment could not have succeeded without a metastable atom detector that was capable of discriminating against the enormous background flux of unwanted atoms and molecules; one of the beautiful simplicities of the experiment was that such a detector was nothing but a plain tungsten disc.

Before settling on this two-stage method of producing metastable atoms, Lamb and Retherford considered several other possible methods. The simplest beam source of metastable atoms would be a hydrogen discharge tube with a small opening, from which the discharge products could effuse into the vacuum in the general direction of the detector. This method was rejected at the start because of the unlikelihood that metastable atoms could survive the escape through the opening, subject to the electric quenching effect of ions simultaneously escaping, and also because of the large amount of ultraviolet light emitted by an electric discharge. Other methods of producing metastable atoms, such as the optical excitation of a beam of ground state atoms or the bombardment of molecular hydrogen with electrons, were rejected largely because they would also produce an objectionable amount of ultraviolet light. This energetic light, falling on the beam target, would eject electrons by the photoelectric effect and cause an unwanted background current at the electrometer. The direct current detection method employed throughout the Lamb–Retherford experiment offered no way to distinguish between a fluctuating background current and the true signal caused by radio-frequency quenching of the metastable beam, and so it was necessary to eliminate as far as possible all sources of background current. The two-stage "metastabilizer," which accomplished its task with no energy to spare, reduced the incidental ultraviolet light to a minimum.

4.1.2.4.1.3. *Magnetic Quenching.* There are several points in Fig. 6 where magnetic sublevels of the 2^2S level cross magnetic sublevels of the 2^2P levels. For magnetic field strengths in the vicinity of one of these crossing points, atoms in the corresponding 2^2S sublevel can be quenched much more readily by static electric fields than can atoms in the other 2^2S sublevel. Degeneracy alone does not suffice to cause this differential quenching effect, however, since the dipole selection rules $\Delta m = 0$ or ± 1 must also be satisfied if the two crossed sublevels are to be mixed by the electric field.[36] Examination of Fig. 6 shows that an

---

[36] Actually, sublevels that satisfy the dipole selection rules do not cross, but rather approach each other closely, exchange identities, and veer away again. At the point of closest approach, the state functions of the two sublevels are 50-50 hybrids, and are equally susceptible to electrostatic quenching.

electric field perpendicular to the direction of the magnetic field will quench the β sublevel at the 575-gauss crossing point and also the α sublevel at the 4700-gauss crossing point, while an electric field parallel to the magnetic field will quench the β sublevel at the 1190-gauss crossing point.

Although Lamb and Retherford took care to eliminate stray electrostatic fields from their apparatus as far possible, there was one quenching field that they had to tolerate; this was the motional electric field $(\mathbf{v} \times \mathbf{H})/c$ experienced by a beam atom as it passed through the field of the electromagnet. This electric field is perpendicular to the magnetic field, and at 575 gauss and a typical velocity of 8×10^5 cm/sec it amounts to 4.5 volts/cm. Thus the β sublevel will be completely quenched at the 575-gauss crossing point. At higher magnetic field strengths the motional electric field becomes stronger and keeps the β sublevel partially quenched even though the crossing point is past. Above 4000 gauss, both α and β sublevels are quenched so strongly that no metastable atoms reach the beam target. It is evident that, over a broad range of field strengths, a uniform magnetic field will orient the metastable fraction of the beam through its preferential quenching of atoms in the β sublevel. A short distance within the field, the magnetic moments of the surviving metastable beam atoms will nearly all point antiparallel to the magnetic field. The orientation at field strengths above 575 gauss can be enhanced, if desired, by placing a pair of condenser plates between the magnet poles, one on each side of the beam, and deliberately applying a small electrostatic quenching field parallel to the magnetic field direction, thereby bringing into play the βf crossing point at 1190 gauss.

4.1.2.4.1.4. *The Radio-Frequency Quenching Spectrum.* Because atoms in the β sublevel are quenched on entering the magnetic field, the subsequent radio-frequency quenching can work only on the remaining atoms in the α sublevel. Limited further by the selection rule $\Delta m = 0$ or ± 1, the fine structure transitions observable in the radio-frequency quenching spectrum will therefore be (see Fig. 6) αb and αe in π excitation $(\Delta m = 0)$ and αa, αc, and αf in σ excitation $(\Delta m = \pm 1)$. Also because of motional quenching of the β sublevel, it is possible to observe the direct $\alpha\beta$ Zeeman transition in σ excitation. This transition has a natural width of only a few megacycles, because of the residual metastability of the β sublevel, and it can serve to calibrate the magnetic field strength for the much wider fine structure transitions.

The transitions αe and αf can be observed conveniently at frequencies in the neighborhood of 2 Gc; their measured positions, extrapolated to zero magnetic field, give directly the value of the Lamb shift. A recording of this low-frequency spectrum in hydrogen is shown by Fig. 7; hyperfine structure is evident as a clear splitting of the αf resonance and as a broadening of the αe resonance. In deuterium the hyperfine structure is much smaller, as expected from the relative sizes of the nuclear g factors, and the widths of the deuterium resonances are only slightly greater than the natural radiative width of 100 Mc. To observe the transitions αa, αb, and αc requires frequencies higher than 7000 Mc. Their measured positions determine the quantity $\Delta E - S$, where ΔE is the separation of the $2^2P_{1/2}$ and $2^2P_{3/2}$ levels and S is the Lamb shift. The value of ΔE can be calculated with great precision from the Dirac theory, in terms of the fine structure constant $\alpha(= e^2/hc)$. Thus measurements on the high-frequency transitions, combined with the experimental value of S, afford a way of determining the fundamental atomic

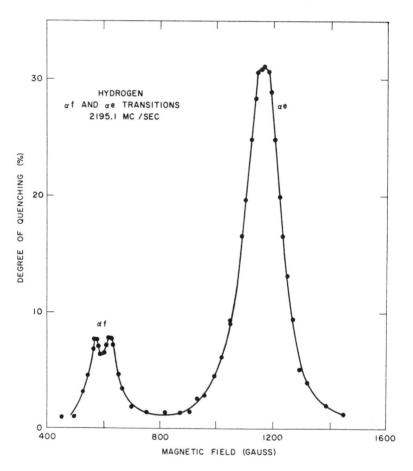

FIG. 7.   The $n = 2$ radio-frequency quenching spectrum of hydrogen at a frequency of 2195.1 Mc. The splitting of the αf line is hyperfine structure.

constant α. These measurements, on deuterium,[37] yielded finally the result $\alpha = 1/(137.0388 \pm 0.0012)$.

4.1.2.4.2. SINGLY IONIZED HELIUM $n = 2$. After the successful measurement of the Lamb shift in hydrogen, similar experiments were attempted on ionized helium, the one-electron atom of next larger charge number ($Z = 2$). The new quantum electrodynamical theory that had been developed to explain the Lamb shift exhibited an interesting logarithmic Z dependence, one that differed appreciably from the Z^4 dependence of the normal (Dirac) fine structure. It was important to check this Z dependence, particularly in view of a small residual discrepancy between theory and experiment for hydrogen.

The beam resonance method developed for hydrogen is not suited to ionized helium, even though the 2^2S state is again metastable, with a lifetime considerably longer than the transit time in a typical beam apparatus. A surface detector of the type used for metastable hydrogen could not be used because ground state ions, of which the beam would consist chiefly, are also capable of ejecting electrons from a metal surface. The corresponding background current would swamp the minute signal due to metastable ions.

For these reasons, Lamb and Skinner, in their initial work,[38] tried a new experimental method, one which, however, still depended on the metastability of the 2^2S level. They bombarded helium gas with electrons of several hundred volts energy, and monitored the intensity of the resulting collision light with a photoelectric detector that was sensitive to ultraviolet light (a plain copper disc). On applying a radio-frequency field to the gaseous sample, they detected a resonant increase in the amount of ultraviolet light emanating from the collision region. The resonant frequency was approximately 14 Gc, in agreement with the predicted value of the Lamb shift in ionized helium.

How the Lamb–Skinner experiment worked may be understood with the help of Fig. 8, which shows some of the energy levels of helium. The debris of the relatively high-energy electron bombardment will include a few He^+ ions in the $n = 2$ state at 65.39 ev. In the radiative decay of these ions to the ground 1^2S state of He^+, ultraviolet photons of energy 41 ev are emitted, and are recorded by the photoelectric detector. This radiative decay takes place from the 2^2P fine structure levels (shown in expanded scale at the right of Fig. 8). The 2^2S level is metastable, and its population builds up to a fairly large steady state

[37] E. S. Dayhoff, S. Triebwasser, and W. E. Lamb, Jr., *Phys. Rev.* **89**, 106 (1953). See W. E. Cleland, J. M. Bailey, M. Eckhause, V. W. Hughes, R. M. Mobley, R. Prepost, and J. E. Rothberg, *Phys. Rev. Letters* **13**, 202 (1964) for the corrected value of α quoted above.

[38] W. E. Lamb, Jr., and M. Skinner, *Phys. Rev.* **78**, 539 (1950).

value during the bombardment. If now a radio-frequency resonance is established between the 2^2S level and one of the 2^2P levels, the metastable ions will be quenched—transferred to the 2^2P level—and will then contribute to the 41-ev radiation. By varying the strength of a steady magnetic field and recording the output of the photoelectric detector, the radio-frequency quenching spectrum may be measured, just as was done in the experiment on hydrogen.

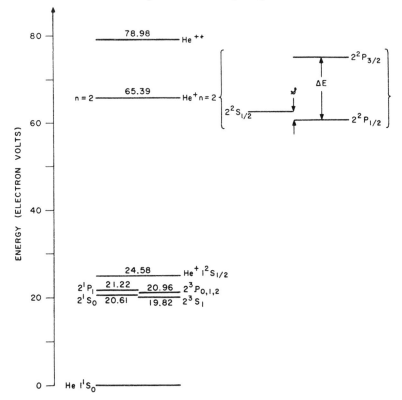

FIG. 8.   Energy levels of neutral and ionized helium.

The main experimental problem was again that of distinguishing between the desired signal, in this case the 41-ev radiation due to radio-frequency quenching, and extraneous background. Ions and metastable atoms could be kept away from the detector by a suitable membrane, but it was more difficult to screen out unwanted radiation, such as the 20-ev ultraviolet light emitted in the dacay of excited neutral helium atoms to their ground state. The most troublesome background signal, however, was the large amount of 41-ev radiation coming from the decay of helium ions which had been excited directly to the 2^2P

levels. To make precise measurements on the radio-frequency quenching spectrum, it was necessary to find a detection method that would discriminate against this background signal.

4.1.2.4.2.1. *Pulse Detection.* In Lamb and Skinner's work the helium gas was bombarded with electrons continuously, the radio-frequency quenching oscillator operated continuously, and collision light was detected continuously. The subsequent experiment by Novick, Lipworth, and Yergin[39] was much more complex; bombardment, quenching, and detection were all pulsed repetitively in a carefully timed sequence. The reason was as follows. The desired quenching signal comes entirely from ions in the long-lived 2^2S level, while the interfering background signal comes from atoms and ions in short-lived (10^{-9}–10^{-10} second) levels. A very short time after a bombardment pulse, these short-lived levels will have been emptied by radiative decay, and the background will have subsided. If then the radio-frequency quenching field is pulsed on, the remaining metastable ions will be transferred to a now empty 2^2P level, and the photodetector, pulsed on at the same time, will respond to the resulting 41-ev signal radiation. After a time interval comparable with the mean lifetime of the metastable ions, the radio-frequency field and the photodetector may be pulsed off and the cycle repeated.

To ensure that every 41-ev signal photon would be recorded, Novick, Lipworth, and Yergin substituted a photomultiplier detector for the simple copper disc detector used by Lamb and Skinner. They fed the photomultiplier output, in the form of pulses, to a pulse processing and counting circuit with two counting channels, one to record an "undelayed" count during the electron bombardment period, the other to record a "delayed" count during the radio-frequency quenching period (both periods were about 1 μsec). A master timing circuit, which also pulsed the electron gun and the radio-frequency oscillator, gated the two channels on and off. The undelayed count was used to normalize the delayed count, so as to correct for changes in detection efficiency, helium pressure, bombarding current, and counting intervals. To trace out the radio-frequency quenching spectrum, counts were taken for fixed time intervals, while varying the magnetic field strength in a point-by-point way. Natural line breadth, which amounted to 1600 Mc, was the most serious limitation on precision, and, as in the hydrogen work, a careful interpretation of the observed line shapes was necessary.

4.1.2.4.2.2. *Lock-in Detection.* Although the "bombard-wait-detect" pulse scheme gave a thirtyfold increase in the signal-to-background ratio over the continuous detection method, it was not an unqualified

[39] R. Novick, E. Lipworth, and P. F. Yergin, *Phys. Rev.* **100**, 1153 (1955).

success. The inherent complexity of the apparatus made it difficult to use, and prevented the accumulation of enough data for a study of systematic experimental errors. Within a few years after Novick, Lipworth, and Yergin completed their experiment, the advantages of the lock-in detection method began to be fully appreciated by radio spectroscopists, and it became apparent that this detection method, applied to the ionized helium experiment, would allow the apparatus to be simplified considerably. The aim of the pulse scheme had been to eliminate the large background signal, but it became clear that this was not really necessary. Provided that one could modulate the small radio-frequency quenching signal without at the same time modulating the background signal, a lock-in detector would respond only to the desired quenching signal. Thus one could return, in principle at least, to the very simple apparatus of Lamb and Skinner, add a lock-in detector, and equal or better the sensitivity of the pulse apparatus.

Essentially, Lipworth and Novick[40] did this in their remeasurement of the Lamb shift in ionized helium. Rather than discard the existing pulse-counting detection system, however, they modified it to function as a lock-in system. They bombarded helium gas continuously with electrons, and modulated the radio-frequency quenching oscillator on and off with a 500-cps square wave. The same square wave gated the two channels of the pulse-counting circuit on and off, much as in the conventional lock-in detector of Fig. 5 where the reference signal switches the diodes into and out of conduction. During the half of the modulation cycle when the radio-frequency power was off, one channel counted background alone; during the half of the modulation cycle when the radio-frequency power was on, the other channel counted background plus signal. Counts were allowed to accumulate in the two channels over many modulation cycles, after which the net signal count was found by subtracting one total from the other. This accumulating and sub-tracting process is analogous in function with the RC output filtering provided by the circuit in Fig. 5. By averaging out fluctuations that do not occur at the modulating frequency, it narrowed the "bandwidth" of the counting system.

4.1.2.4.3. HYDROGEN; DEUTERIUM, $n = 3$. The Lamb shift theory contained, in addition to the $1/n^3$ factor of normal fine structure, a further small dependence on the principal quantum number in its peculiar logarithmic factor. With the logarithmic Z dependence already verified by the experiments on first-excited hydrogen and ionized helium, the next important task was to check this predicted n dependence by measuring Lamb shifts in more highly excited states of the same

[40] E. Lipworth and R. Novick, *Phys. Rev.* **108**, 1434 (1957).

atoms. The prospects of success would at first glance seem poor, since the 3^2S level is not metastable (it decays readily to the 2^2P levels) and it was the metastability of the 2^2S level that made the earlier experiments possible. Or so it appeared at the time. Actually, the pertinent question was not "Is one of the levels metastable?" but rather "Is it possible to maintain a population difference between the two levels?" In a low-pressure gas bombarded with electrons, the population of an excited atomic level will depend not only on its radiative lifetime but also on its excitation cross section, the probability that atoms will be placed in that level by the bombardment process. In general, neither the radiative lifetime nor the excitation cross section of an n^2S level will be the same as those of an n^2P level, and so it could be expected that the experimental method that worked for first-excited ionized helium might also work for higher excited levels of hydrogen and helium. The experiment of Lamb and Sanders[41] showed this expectation to be correct.

From calculated values of radiative lifetimes and rough estimates of excitation cross sections, Lamb and Sanders found that the steady state population of the hydrogen 3^2S level, excited by the electron bombardment of molecular hydrogen, should be about an order of magnitude larger than the populations of the 3^2P levels. The radio-frequency resonance condition thus should have an appreciable effect on the intensity of radiations from the 3^2S and 3^2P levels: one would expect a decrease in the red H_α radiation of the 3^2S level and an increase in the ultraviolet L_β radiation of the 3^2P levels. The H_α line was the natural choice as a resonance indicator. Allowing for the contributions of 3^2P and 3^2D levels to the H_α line, Lamb and Sanders estimated that the radio-frequency resonance condition could decrease the H_α emission by approximately 7 %. This would be easily detectable, especially if the effects of changes in the background signal were reduced by the lock-in detection method.

A schematic picture of the apparatus used in early measurements of the deuterium fine structure is shown in Fig. 9. The electron bombarder is enclosed in a glass envelope which contains deuterium gas at a pressure of a few microns Hg. The Helmholtz coils generate a magnetic scanning field of up to 600 gauss, and also serve to focus the electron beam. The wishbonelike structure is a pair of radio-frequency electrodes, oriented to give a quenching field mostly perpendicular to the Helmholtz field. A lens system collects light from the bombardment region and focuses it on the photomultiplier detector which, being disturbed easily by magnetic fields, must be kept well away from the Helmholtz coils. Background light at the photomultiplier is reduced by a narrow-band

[41] W. E. Lamb, Jr., and T. M. Sanders, Jr., *Phys. Rev.* **103**, 313 (1956).

interference filter and by designing the electron gun structure so as to minimize leakage of the red filament light. A standard lock-in detector records the radio-frequency quenching signal on a strip chart recorder; the quenching is modulated by a 500-cps on-off modulation of the radio-frequency oscillator, which for most of the work was an S-band (10 cm) klystron. During the course of the fine structure measurements the electron bombarder tube was rebuilt, with improvements, several times. In the later work of Wilcox and Lamb[42] the light collection efficiency was improved by substituting an elliptical reflector for the lens system of Fig. 9. It was then possible to detect resonances in the $n = 4$ levels, but with insufficient intensity for accurate measurements.

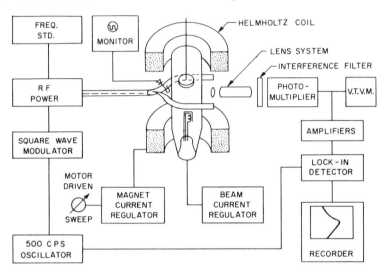

FIG. 9.   Schematic diagram of apparatus used to measure the $n = 3$ fine structure of deuterium.

Electrostatic quenching effects were large, because of the small Lamb shift ($\sim$300 Mc) of the $n = 3$ levels, and unpredictable, because of the uncertain electrical environment of an atom in the electron bombardment region. Possible Stark shifts of the energy levels, another aspect of the electrostatic perturbation, were large enough to become the major source of uncertainty in the experimental results. For higher excited states, electrostatic perturbations would become progressively more serious as the fine structure separations decreased; thus it appears that there would be little profit in extending the experimental method of Lamb and Sanders to higher excited states of hydrogen and deuterium,

[42] L. R. Wilcox and W. E. Lamb, Jr., *Phys. Rev.* **119**, 1915 (1960).

except possibly as a means of investigating the electrostatic perturbations themselves.

In a recent experiment, Kleinpoppen[43] has demonstrated a second means of measuring the $n = 3$ fine structure, which has the advantage that electrostatic perturbations may be kept under better control. This was an atomic beam experiment, quite similar to the original Lamb–Retherford experiment except that the place of the electron bombarder is taken by a hydrogen discharge lamp. The L_β radiation of this lamp excites ground state beam atoms to the 3^2P levels, from which some decay to the metastable 2^2S level. These metastable atoms are detected when the beam strikes a metal target. A radio-frequency field tuned to one of the $3^2P \leftrightarrow 3^2S$ transitions is applied to the beam in the optical excitation region; the resonance condition transfers atoms from the 3^2P level to the 3^2S level before they can decay to the 2^2S level, thus decreasing the number of metastable atoms which go on to strike the target. A lock-in detector separates the rather weak radio-frequency quenching signal from the background current of the metastable atom detector.

4.1.2.4.4. TWO-ELECTRON ATOMS. The S and P levels of multielectron atoms are widely separated in energy by the electrostatic interaction between electrons, and there is no opportunity for radio-frequency measurements of Lamb shifts in these atoms. The fine structure separations that are small enough to measure with radio waves are those caused by the magnetic interactions of electrons, the spin-orbit, spin-spin, spin–other orbit, and orbit-orbit interactions. Transitions between the corresponding magnetic fine structure levels are of the magnetic dipole type, and require much larger radio-frequency field strengths than the electric dipole transitions observed in the Lamb shift experiments. A second point of difference is that, whereas the levels involved in Lamb shift experiments have quite different radiative lifetimes, magnetic fine structure levels have, in general, equal radiative lifetimes. To maintain the population differences necessary for radio spectroscopy, one therefore must devise some method of exciting atoms to certain fine structure levels or sublevels in preference to other levels or sublevels which lie at practically the same energy. In their measurement of the neutral helium fine structure, Lamb and Maiman[44] found that the electron bombardment process could be made to yield this high degree of selective excitation, provided it was carried out under carefully controlled conditions.

4.1.2.4.4.1. *Neutral Helium.* Lamb and Maiman exploited the long-

[43] H. Kleinpoppen, *Z. Physik* **164**, 174 (1961).
[44] W. E. Lamb, Jr., and T. H. Maiman, *Phys. Rev.* **105**, 573 (1957).

known phenomenon of the polarization of collision light. Atoms bombarded by electrons emit partially polarized light when the electron energy is raised just over one of the characteristic excitation thresholds of the atom. This is a consequence of the conservation of angular momentum in the electron-atom collision, as explained by Lamb[45] for the following simplified case. In the head-on collision of an electron with an S state atom, the component of orbital angular momentum (spin is disregarded) along the direction of motion of the incoming electron, call it the Z direction, is zero. If the electron is stopped by the collision, it cannot carry off angular momentum. Thus after such a collision, which corresponds to excitation at threshold, the atom still can have no component of angular momentum along the Z direction; it must be in an $m_L = 0$ sublevel of the excited atomic state. Other sublevels of the excited state, $m_L = \pm 1$, for example, cannot be populated. The subsequent radiative decay of the atom to the ground S state will of necessity be a $\Delta m_L = 0$ transition, and so the emitted light will be π-polarized along the Z direction. The effects of spin angular momentum and the finite energy spread of real electron beams reduce the expected amount of polarization, but do not alter the basic argument. Bombardment experiments show fairly good agreement with detailed calculations of the polarization, although there remain some unexplained discrepancies.[46]

Radio-frequency resonance transitions between sublevels of the atomic level excited by electron bombardment would tend to equalize their populations, and hence would have a depolarizing effect on the particular optical line emitted in the decay of that level. Rather than detect this depolarization directly, Lamb and Maiman chose to detect the accompanying change [see Eq. (4.1.2.15)] in directional light intensity. Radiofrequency transitions within the 2^3P fine structure levels are detectable by the intensity change (or depolarization) of the 10830 Å infrared line, while similar transitions within the 3^3P fine structure levels are detectable by corresponding changes in the 3889 Å blue line. Lamb and Maiman made their initial measurements on the $J = 1 \leftrightarrow J = 2$ transitions of the 3^3P term, both because the blue line was easier to detect with existing photomultiplier tubes and because the radio-frequency power requirements were easier to meet for the lowest-frequency transitions. When the experimental method had proved successful, Wieder and Lamb[47]

[45] W. E. Lamb, Jr., *Phys. Rev.* **105**, 559 (1957).

[46] Recent work by R. H. McFarland [*Phys. Rev. Letters* **10**, 397 (1963)] indicates that the most unsettling of these discrepancies, the tendency of the polarization to approach zero rather than a maximum at threshold, is an experimental effect, caused by poor energy resolution in the electron beam.

[47] I. Wieder and W. E. Lamb, Jr., *Phys. Rev.* **107**, 125 (1957).

went on to measure the higher-frequency $J = 0 \leftrightarrow J = 1$ transitions in the same 3^3P term, as well as (using the infrared line) the $J = 1 \leftrightarrow J = 2$ transitions in the 2^3P term. To measure the remaining fine structure interval, $2^3P_0\text{--}2^3P_1$, would have required a high-power oscillator at 1 cm wavelength, which was not then available.

Radio-frequency magnetic field strengths of several gauss were required to excite the helium fine structure transitions, and were provided by resonators such as that shown in Fig. 10. This is a half-wave

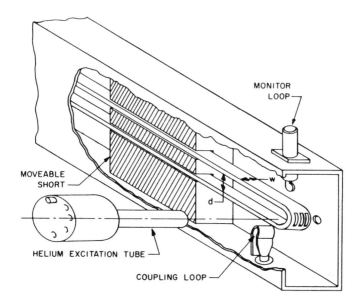

FIG. 10.   Radio-frequency resonator used in measurements of the fine structure of neutral helium. The dimensions d and w are 3/8 inch and 1/2 inch, respectively.

parallel-line resonator, tuned by a movable short circuit. The helium excitation tube is inserted, as shown, close to the other shorted end of the resonant line, where the radio-frequency magnetic field is most intense. Slots cut in the line permit the collision light to be viewed in a direction perpendicular to the electron beam. A section of S band ($1\frac{1}{2}$ inch × 3 inch) wave guide tubing provides electromagnetic shielding. The resonator of Fig. 10, driven at its resonant frequency of about 900 Mc by a radar jammer transmitter, was used in early measurements of the smallest fine structure separation, $3^3P_1\text{--}3^3P_2$. Other resonators and radio-frequency power sources were required for the later measurements of the larger fine structure intervals. The techniques of magnetic scanning and lock-in detection were used throughout, the experimental setup being much like that of Fig. 9.

The helium fine structure has been remeasured recently by Colegrove, Franken, Lewis, and Sands,[48] using a new, simpler experimental technique which they call "level crossing." The method depends on the change in the spatial distribution of optical resonance radiation when sublevels of the excited atomic state are brought into coincidence by an external magnetic field, and is discussed further in Section 4.1.2.5.4 below. Although not strictly radio spectroscopy at all, since no radio-frequency transitions are involved, level crossing experiments are performed in much the same spirit (and yield just as precise results) as experiments in which atomic energy levels are measured with vacuum tube oscillators, and are included here for that reason.

4.1.2.4.4.2. *Positronium.* A slow positron and electron may, upon meeting, join in a temporary electrostatic bond before annihilating each other. The lifetime and the mode of annihilation of this "positronium atom" depend on whether positron and electron join with spins parallel or antiparallel. In the former case (*ortho*-positronium), conservation of energy and angular momentum require that annihilation take place with the emission of at least three gamma rays, whose energy distribution is continuous up to mc^2. In the latter case (*para*-positronium), annihilation can take place by a more probable process in which two gamma rays, each of energy mc^2, are emitted in opposite directions. The gamma ray spectrum of positronium therefore consists of a two-quantum peak at mc^2, superposed on the continuous three-quantum spectrum. Changes in the relative numbers of *ortho*- and *para*-positronium atoms in, say, a gas being bombarded with positrons may be detected from changes in the shape of the gamma ray spectrum.

The $^3S_1$ ground level of *ortho*-positronium lies above the $^1S_0$ ground level of *para*-positronium by approximately 7 cm^{-1}, due jointly to the spin-spin interaction and to the virtual annihilation interaction between electron and positron. This fine structure interval (or hyperfine structure interval, depending on one's point of view) provided an ideal test for the new quantum electrodynamical theory, which was a theory of electrons and photons, since the positronium atom contained no particles foreign to the theory. Exploratory experiments by Deutsch and Brown[49] showed that it was possible to make radio-frequency measurements of the positronium fine structure, despite the necessarily very small concentrations of such atoms that were available. A precise theoretical calculation of the fine structure was then made, and was followed by

[48] F. D. Colgrove, P. A. Franken, R. R. Lewis, and R. H. Sands, *Phys. Rev. Letters* **3**, 420 (1959).

[49] M. Deutsch and S. C. Brown, *Phys. Rev.* **85**, 848 (1952).

two independent and equally precise radio-frequency measurements[50,50a] of the $^3S_1-{}^1S_0$ interval.

In a manner reminiscent of the Lamb shift experiments, radio-frequency transitions can "quench" those positronium atoms that happen to occupy the relatively long-lived ($\sim 10^{-7}$ second) $^3S_1$ level by transferring them to the short-lived ($\sim 10^{-10}$ second) $^1S_0$ level. These radio-frequency transitions are detectable by a change in the shape of the gamma ray spectrum—an intensification of the two-quantum peak relative to the three-quantum background. The actual experiments were somewhat less straightforward than this. The direct fine structure transition would require a radio-frequency field strength of several gauss at a frequency of 200 Gc, which would have been impossible to achieve with existing oscillators. To avoid this problem, the experimenters applied a magnetic field to the positronium atoms, and observed low-frequency transitions among the Zeeman sublevels of the $^3S_1$ level alone.

The Zeeman effect of positronium is given by the Breit–Rabi formula (Eq. 4.1.2.9), with I and J replaced throughout by S_+ and S_-, the spin quantum numbers of positron and electron. Because the spin g factors of the two particles are equal but opposite in sign, positronium has no permanent magnetic moment, and consequently there is no linear Zeeman effect at weak fields. Intermediate field strengths cause a mixing of the $m = 0$ sublevels of the $^3S_1$ and $^1S_0$ levels, and these two sublevels separate with increasing field strength, as shown in Fig. 11. The magnetic mixing causes the $^3S_1$, $m = 0$ sublevel to take on partially the properties of the $^1S_0$, $m = 0$ sublevel, including in particular the ability to decay by two-quantum annihilation. This is an essential feature of the experiment, since otherwise radio-frequency transitions within the $^3S_1$ level would have no effect on the shape of the gamma ray spectrum. By adjustment of the magnetic field strength, the transition $m = 0 \leftrightarrow m = \pm 1$ indicated in Fig. 11 can be made to occur at any convenient frequency. A field strength of 8 kilogauss places the transition frequency at about 2.5 Gc, a frequency for which high-power oscillators are readily available.

Hughes, Marder, and Wu[50a] describe their experiment in detail. They placed a positron-emitting sample of Cu^{64} inside a gas-filled cavity resonator, tuned to 2.5 Gc, which was located between the poles of a precision electromagnet. Gamma rays emitted in the annihilation of positronium atoms within the cavity were monitored outside the cavity by a scintillation detector and twenty-channel pulse height analyzer, which measured the ratio of two-quantum to three-quantum decays.

[50] R. Weinstein, M. Deutsch, and S. C. Brown, ibid. 94, 758(A) (1954); 98, 223(A) (1955).

[50a] V. W. Hughes, S. Marder, and C. S. Wu, Phys. Rev. 106, 934 (1957).

The radio-frequency resonance line was traced out by recording counts during a step-by-step scan of the magnetic field strength; the peak height of the line, i.e., the enhancement of two-quantum decays at resonance, was typically 10 %. The zero-field fine structure separation was then calculated from the theoretical Zeeman effect (the Breit–Rabi formula) and measured values of the frequency and magnetic field strength at resonance.

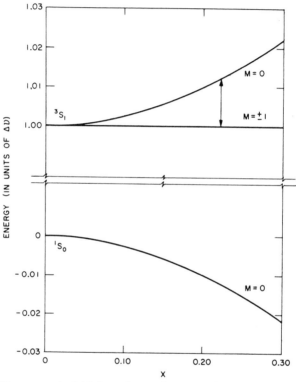

FIG. 11. The magnetic field dependence of energy sublevels for positronium in its $^3S_1$ and $^1S_0$ levels.

4.1.2.5. Hyperfine Structure. In contrast with atomic fine structure, where energy separations are so large that radio spectroscopy can barely get a toehold, atomic hyperfine structure intervals fall comfortably within the radio-frequency and low microwave range, where they are accessible to all three of the highly developed general methods of radio spectroscopy—atomic beam resonance, microwave absorption, and radio-optical resonance. There have been made a great many measurements of atomic hyperfine structure, most of which differ significantly in some aspect or other of experimental method. It is neither possible nor, because of the excellent books and review articles available, necessary to discuss all of these experiments here. Rather, an attempt will be made to illustrate the major experimental methods through descriptions of a few representative experiments.

The aim of any such experiment is to measure and interpret, for one or more levels of a particular atom, the magnetic dipole and electric quadrupole hyperfine structure coupling constants, the quantities called A and B in Section 4.1.2.2.3. Occasionally, when hyperfine structure interactions are both large and carefully measured, it is possible to find values of magnetic octupole coupling constants. All of these constants depend on the spin (I) of the atomic nucleus, on the size of the nuclear multipole moments (magnetic dipole, electric quadrupole, magnetic octupole), and on the distribution of atomic electrons near the nucleus. The nuclear spin, which can take only integral or half-integral values, is easily determined from a glance at the radio spectrum. Thus, if one knows the distribution of atomic electrons, knows, that is, the electronic wave function, the measured coupling constants will yield values for the nuclear multipole moments. Conversely, prior knowledge of the nuclear multipole moments, gotten, say, from nuclear resonance experiments, allows one to deduce from the coupling constants certain characteristics of the electronic wave function, such as angular momentum quantum numbers and the value of the radial integral $\langle 1/r^3 \rangle$. By comparing measurements on different isotopes of the same element, furthermore, one may study the small effect of the finite size of the nucleus on hyperfine structure, the so-called "hyperfine structure anomaly." Finally, for those atoms simple enough to allow a complete theoretical prediction of their hyperfine structure, experimental measurements of the coupling constants can afford, and have afforded, several extremely precise tests of present-day quantum theory.

4.1.2.5.1. HYPERFINE STRUCTURE TRANSITIONS. A complete hyperfine structure measurement yields $2J + 1$ or $2I + 1$ (whichever is smaller) separate values of $\varDelta\nu_{F,F-1}$, the hyperfine structure intervals at zero magnetic field. The coupling constants A and B are then derivable from the formula

$$\varDelta\nu_{F,F-1} = \frac{W(F) - W(F-1)}{h}$$

$$= F\left[A + \frac{3}{4}B\,\frac{2F^2 + 1 - 2I(I+1) - 2J(J+1)}{I(2I-1)J(2J-1)}\right], \quad (4.1.2.17)$$

which comes out of (4.1.2.8) when H is set equal to zero. Since A is usually much larger than B, the values of $\varDelta\nu_{F,F-1}$ are approximately proportional to F; this is the well-known "interval rule" of hyperfine structure. An electric quadrupole interaction makes its presence known by causing deviations from the interval rule, according to the second term of (4.1.2.17). Other deviations from the interval rule, usually very small, may be caused by a magnetic octupole interaction, or by the magnetic dipole hyperfine structure interaction between fine structure levels.[51]

A radio spectrum measured under zero-field conditions would yield the $\Delta\nu$ values directly, since they are just the frequencies of the allowed $\Delta F = \pm 1$ magnetic dipole transitions. For a number of practical reasons, one of them being the omnipresent magnetic field of the earth, this is rarely done; instead, $\Delta\nu$ values are found by measuring the Zeeman spectrum of the hyperfine structure and then, with energy formulas such as (4.1.2.8), (4.1.2.9), and (4.1.2.10), extrapolating the results to zero field. Several different types of transitions are allowed by the Zeeman selection rules, and their special properties are discussed below.

(1) Weak Field $\Delta F = \pm 1$ Transitions. The linear Zeeman effect splits each zero-field hyperfine structure line into a number of equally spaced components, the resonance frequencies of which may be calculated from (4.1.2.8). For the special case of a ^2S state ($J = \frac{1}{2}$, $g_J \simeq 2$) the frequencies of $\Delta m_F = \pm 1$ transitions are

$$\nu = \Delta\nu + \frac{2m_F \pm 1}{I + \frac{1}{2}} \frac{\mu_0 H}{h} \qquad (4.1.2.18)$$

and the frequencies of $\Delta m_F = 0$ transitions are

$$\nu = \Delta\nu + \frac{2m_F}{I + \frac{1}{2}} \frac{\mu_0 H}{h} . \qquad (4.1.2.19)$$

In these expressions, m_F takes integral steps from $I + \frac{1}{2}$ to $-(I + \frac{1}{2})$. Hence the Zeeman pattern is symmetrical about $\Delta\nu$, and the value of $\Delta\nu$ follows from suitable averages of the observed resonance frequencies.

(2) Weak Field $\Delta F = 0$ Transitions. The low-frequency transitions $\Delta m_F = \pm 1$ within a single hyperfine structure level clearly offer no information on $\Delta\nu$, but they do provide a fast way to measure an unknown nuclear spin. A convenient transition, used often in radioactive beam measurements, is the $m_F = -(I - \frac{1}{2}) \leftrightarrow m_F = -(I + \frac{1}{2})$ transition of a $J = \frac{1}{2}$, $F = I + \frac{1}{2}$ level, whose frequency is, from (4.1.2.8),

$$\nu = (\tfrac{1}{2}g_J + Ig_I) \frac{\mu_0 H}{h(I + \frac{1}{2})} \simeq \frac{g_J \mu_0 H}{(2I + 1)h} . \qquad (4.1.2.20)$$

[51] T. G. Eck and P. Kusch, *Phys. Rev.* 106, 958 (1957).

For each possible value of I, this transition occurs at a characteristic frequency, which is easily calculated from the above expression. The particular one of these frequencies at which resonance is observed determines immediately the nuclear spin.

(3) Intermediate Field $\Delta F = \pm 1$ Transitions. At intermediate magnetic field strengths the Zeeman patterns of hyperfine structure lines become asymmetric, and values of $\Delta \nu$ cannot be found from simple averages of line frequencies. Individual Zeeman lines can still be fitted to an energy formula such as (4.1.2.9), but the values of $\Delta \nu$ derived therefrom suffer in precision from the difficulty of making accurate measurements of the magnetic field strength, as well as from the broadening and distortion of line shapes caused by field inhomogeneities. The best values of $\Delta \nu$ clearly are to be found from those transitions whose frequencies are least sensitive to changes in the magnetic field strength, which may be identified from energy plots like Fig. 1. For certain of these field-insensitive transitions, values of $\Delta \nu$ can be found simply by varying the field and measuring the maximum frequency which the transition attains. Details of this technique, which requires no magnetic field measurements at all, are given in a paper by Kusch and Taub.[52]

(4) Strong Field $\Delta m_J = 0$ Transitions. Symmetry and simplicity return to the Zeeman spectrum at strong fields. For the $J = \frac{1}{2}$ case, (4.1.2.10) shows that the spectrum of all $\Delta m_J = 0$, $\Delta m_I = \pm 1$ transitions will consist of two lines, with frequencies

$$\nu = \Delta \nu/(2I + 1) \pm g_I \mu_0 H/h. \qquad (4.1.2.21)$$

Since g_I is small, these lines appear as a closely spaced doublet. The mean position of the doublet, which is field-independent, yields the value of $\Delta \nu$, and the doublet splitting yields the nuclear g factor. These strong field transitions are advantageous for measurements of large $\Delta \nu$'s, since they allow the measurements to be made with the much lower frequencies $\Delta \nu/(2I + 1)$, which are often easier to work with.

(5) Strong Field $\Delta m_J = \pm 1$ Transitions. These transitions, being extremely field-dependent, are seldom used in measurements of hyperfine structure. For the case $I = \frac{1}{2}$, the frequencies of the transitions $\Delta m_J = \pm 1$, $\Delta m_I = 0$ are, from (4.1.2.10),

$$\nu = g_J \mu_0 H/h \pm \Delta \nu/(2I + 1), \qquad (4.1.2.22)$$

which is similar to (4.1.2.21) except for the fact that g_J is several thousand times larger than g . The chief use of $\Delta m_J = \pm 1$ transitions is for measurements of atomic g factors, which are discussed in Section 4.1.2.6.

[52] P. Kusch and H. Taub, *Phys. Rev.* **75**, 1477 (1949).

4.1.2.5.2. ATOMIC BEAM RESONANCE. The method of detecting radio-frequency resonance by changes in beam trajectories is illustrated by Fig. 12, which is a schematic drawing of an atomic beam magnetic resonance apparatus. The beam is formed by atoms that effuse from the source within a small acceptance solid angle, defined by a slit and baffle system. A typical trajectory is indicated by the heavy line, with deflections much exaggerated for clarity. The principle of the beam resonance method may be understood by following the progress of three atoms with angular moment a $J = \frac{1}{2}, I = 0$, which start out along this trajectory.

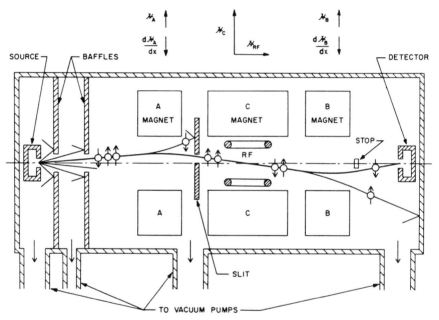

FIG. 12. A simplified view of an atomic beam resonance apparatus.

On entering the A magnet, two of the atoms are presumed to be oriented parallel to the field, the other oriented antiparallel to the field; in other words, two atoms are in the $m_J = + \frac{1}{2}$ sublevel and one in the $m_J = - \frac{1}{2}$ sublevel, the axis of quantization being determined by the field direction. The A magnet generates a strong inhomogeneous field, which deflects the atoms as shown. The atom in the $m_J = - \frac{1}{2}$ sublevel is deflected out of the beam, and is lost. Thus the A magnet performs as a state selector; the atoms that survive it are oriented in a particular way. This orientation-by-selection process is different for different trajectories and, in particular, will have opposite senses for two trajectories that are mirror images of each other about the symmetry plane of the apparatus. Accordingly, atoms in the two halves of the ribbon-shaped beam, coming out of the *A* magnet, will be oppositely oriented. It is possible, and sometimes necessary, to intercept one half of the beam with a suitably placed obstacle, thereby leaving a net orientation of the remaining beam atoms. This is necessary in the hypothetical experiment of Fig. 12, where only two magnetic sublevels are available, and is done pictorially by displacing the slit to one side.

Progressing along the sample trajectory, the two surviving beam atoms enter the *C* magnet, which has between its poles the radio-frequency exciter. The *C* magnet, which generates a homogeneous field, has three functions: (1) it preserves the axis of quantization of the beam atoms in the region between the *A* and *B* magnets; (2) it develops the Zeeman effect to the degree desired for the experiment; (3) it provides for magnetic scanning of the resonance spectrum. The radio-frequency exciter is, archetypically, a hairpin-shaped loop of wire, which carries a radio-frequency current close to and parallel to the beam. In high-frequency work the "hairpin" may be a cavity resonator or transmission line, situated so that the beam, in passing through, encounters a strong radio-frequency magnetic field. The Ramsey method of excitation requires two (or more) radio-frequency exciters, separated along the beam path and fed by the same oscillator. Whatever its form, the purpose of the radio-frequency exciter is to induce transitions in the beam atoms, and thereby to undo, at least partially, the orienting effect of the *A* magnet. This it will accomplish if the radio-frequency magnetic field magnetic field is strong enough and has the correct frequency and direction. In the simplified case under discussion there is only the one $\Delta m_J = -\frac{1}{2}$ transition available, and so the radio-frequency field must be perpendicular to the direction of the *C* field. In Fig. 12 the radio-frequency field has been assumed to have the correct frequency, $g_J \mu_0 H/h$, and to be strong enough to completely disorient the beam; leaving the *C* magnet, one atom is in the $m_J = +\frac{1}{2}$ sublevel and the other is in the $m_J = -\frac{1}{2}$ sublevel.

On their continuing flight through the apparatus, the beam atoms now enter the *B* magnet, a second deflecting magnet. To preserve the axis of quantization, the direction of the field generated by this magnet must be the same as that of the *A* and *C* magnets. However, the direction of the field *gradient*, and hence the direction of the deflecting force exerted on a magnetic dipole, may be either parallel or antiparallel to the gradient of the *A* field. The schematic apparatus of Fig. 12 illustrates the parallel, or "flop-in" case: the beam atom that has undergone a transition in the *C* field is deflected *into* the detector. In the antiparallel, or "flop-out" case, the beam atom that had undergone a transition would be deflected *out of* the detector. In either arrangement,

TABLE II. Atomic Hyperfine Structure Intervals Measured by the Atomic Beam Magnetic Resonance Method

Isotope	I	Atomic term	J	F	$\Delta\nu_{F,F-1}(\text{Mc})^a$	Reference
H	$\frac{1}{2}$	^2S	$\frac{1}{2}$	1	1420.405751800(28)	CRA-63
	$\frac{1}{2}$	$2s\ ^2S$	$\frac{1}{2}$	1	177.55686(5)	HEB-56
He³⁺	$\frac{1}{2}$	^2S	$\frac{1}{2}$	1	1083.35499(20)	NOV-58
He³	$\frac{1}{2}$	$1s2s\ ^3S$	1	$\frac{3}{2}$	6739.7013(4)	WHI-59
Li⁶	1	^2S	$\frac{1}{2}$	$\frac{3}{2}$	228.208(5)	KUS-49
Li⁷	$\frac{3}{2}$	^2S	$\frac{1}{2}$	2	803.512(15)	KUS-49
B¹⁰	3	^2P	$\frac{1}{2}$	$\frac{7}{2}$	429.048(3)	LEW-60
B¹¹	$\frac{3}{2}$	^2P	$\frac{1}{2}$	2	732.153(3)	LEW-60
Ne²¹	$\frac{3}{2}$	$2p^5\ 3s\ ^3P$	2	$\frac{7}{2}$	1034.48(10)	GRO-58
				$\frac{5}{2}$	599.44(10)	
				$\frac{3}{2}$	303.93(10)	
Mg²⁵	$\frac{5}{2}$	$3s\ 3p\ ^3P$	2	$\frac{9}{2}$	567.291(10)	LUR-62
				$\frac{7}{2}$	452.338(10)	
				$\frac{5}{2}$	329.044(10)	
				$\frac{3}{2}$	199.82(4)	
			1	$\frac{7}{2}$	516.140(10)	
				$\frac{5}{2}$	349.987(10)	
K³⁹	$\frac{3}{2}$	^2S	$\frac{1}{2}$	2	461.71971(15)	KUS-49
K⁴¹	$\frac{3}{2}$	^2S	$\frac{1}{2}$	2	254.018(6)	KUS-49
K⁴³	$\frac{3}{2}$	^2S	$\frac{1}{2}$	2	192.64(5)	PET-59
Sc⁴⁵	$\frac{7}{2}$	^2D	$\frac{5}{2}$	6	635.003(50)	FRI-59b
				5	543.841(50)	
				4	444.652(50)	
				3	339.095(60)^b	
				2	228.748(50)^b	
			$\frac{3}{2}$	5	1328.96(10)	
				4	1085.772(15)	
				3	827.515(75)^b	
Sc⁴⁶	4	^2D	$\frac{5}{2}$	$\frac{13}{2}$	405.84(6)	FRI-59b
				$\frac{11}{2}$	336.19(2)	
				$\frac{9}{2}$	270.14(3)	
				$\frac{7}{2}$	207.05(3)	
				$\frac{5}{2}$	146.25(3)	
			$\frac{3}{2}$	$\frac{11}{2}$	838.06(11)	
				$\frac{9}{2}$	674.12(6)	
				$\frac{7}{2}$	517.13(10)	

TABLE II (*continued*)

Isotope	I	Atomic term	J	F	$\Delta\nu_{F,F-1}(Mc)^a$	Reference
Mn⁵⁵	$\frac{5}{2}$	^6S	$\frac{5}{2}$	5	362.123(10)	WOO-57
				4	289.676(10)	
				3	217.260(15)	
				2	144.844(10)^b	
				1	72.422(10)^b	
Mn⁵⁶	3	^6S	$\frac{5}{2}$	$\frac{11}{2}$	310.173(15)	CHI-61
				$\frac{9}{2}$	253.766(10)	
				$\frac{7}{2}$	197.375(8)	
				$\frac{5}{2}$	140.981(10)^b	
				$\frac{3}{2}$	84.589(10)^b	
Co⁵⁹	$\frac{7}{2}$	^4F	$\frac{9}{2}$	8	3655.470(200)	EHR-61
				7	3169.440(50)	
				6	2695.056(100)	
				5	2230.638(50)	
				4	1774.548(50)	
				3	1325.087(120)^b	
				2	880.621(90)^b	
Zn⁶⁷	$\frac{5}{2}$	$4s\,4p\,{}^3P$	2	$\frac{9}{2}$	2418.111(25)	LUR-62
				$\frac{7}{2}$	1855.690(15)	
				$\frac{5}{2}$	1312.065(15)	
				$\frac{3}{2}$	781.865(15)	
Ga⁶⁸	1	^2P	$\frac{3}{2}$	$\frac{5}{2}$	−8.695(33)	EHL-62
				$\frac{3}{2}$	25.611(41)	
			$\frac{1}{2}$	$\frac{3}{2}$	17.574(15)	
As⁷⁶	2	^4S	$\frac{3}{2}$	$\frac{7}{2}$	117(4)	CHR-61
				$\frac{5}{2}$	69(16)	
				$\frac{3}{2}$	25(30)^b	
Br⁷⁶	1	^2P	$\frac{3}{2}$	$\frac{5}{2}$	1256.47(5)	LIP-60a
				$\frac{3}{2}$	189.11(5)	
Br⁸²	5	^2P	$\frac{3}{2}$	$\frac{13}{2}$	766.82(60)	GAR-59
				$\frac{11}{2}$	1287.32(43)	
				$\frac{9}{2}$	1488.6(11)	
Kr⁸³	$\frac{9}{2}$	$4p^5\,5s\,{}^3P$	2	$\frac{13}{2}$	1830.7236(5)	FAU-63
				$\frac{11}{2}$	1341.8217(2)	
				$\frac{9}{2}$	956.5583(2)	
				$\frac{7}{2}$	656.0844(30)	
Rb⁸⁵	$\frac{5}{2}$	^2S	$\frac{1}{2}$	3	3035.732439(5)	PEN-62
Rb⁸⁶	2	^2S	$\frac{1}{2}$	$\frac{5}{2}$	3946.883(2)	BRA-61

TABLE II (*continued*)

Isotope	I	Atomic term	J	F	$\Delta\nu_{F,F-1}(\text{Mc})^a$	Reference
Rb^{87}	$\frac{3}{2}$	^2S	$\frac{1}{2}$	2	6834.682614(1)	PEN-62
Y^{89}	$\frac{1}{2}$	^2D	$\frac{5}{2}$	3	88.63(60)	FRI-59a
			$\frac{3}{2}$	2	114.72(20)	
Y^{90}	2	^2D	$\frac{5}{2}$	$\frac{9}{2}$	403.719(37)	PET-62a
				$\frac{7}{2}$	293.203(22)	
				$\frac{5}{2}$	198.287(24)	
				$\frac{3}{2}$	114.515(19)	
			$\frac{3}{2}$	$\frac{7}{2}$	613.023(34)	
				$\frac{5}{2}$	410.871(24)	
				$\frac{3}{2}$	235.722(26)	
Y^{91}	$\frac{1}{2}$	^2D	$\frac{5}{2}$	3	103.05(4)	PET-62c
			$\frac{3}{2}$	2	136.69(3)	
Ag^{104}	5	^2S	$\frac{1}{2}$	$\frac{11}{2}$	33500(2000)	AME-61
Ag^{104m}	2	^2S	$\frac{1}{2}$	$\frac{5}{2}$	35000(2000)	AME-61
Ag^{105}	$\frac{1}{2}$	^2S	$\frac{1}{2}$	1	1529.057(20)	EWB-63
Ag^{107}	$\frac{1}{2}$	^2S	$\frac{1}{2}$	1	1712.56(4)	WES-53
Cd^{111}	$\frac{1}{2}$	$5s\,5p\,^3P$	2	$\frac{5}{2}$	8232.341(2)	FAU-60
Cd^{113}	$\frac{1}{2}$	$5s\,5p\,^3P$	2	$\frac{5}{2}$	8611.586(4)	FAU-60
In^{113m}	$\frac{1}{2}$	^2P	$\frac{1}{2}$	1	781.084(10)	CHI-60
Sb^{121}	$\frac{5}{2}$	^4S	$\frac{3}{2}$	4	1199.08(1)	FER-60
				3	819.45(1)	
				2	595.12(1)	
Sb^{123}	$\frac{7}{2}$	^4S	$\frac{3}{2}$	4	815.60(1)	FER-60
				3	648.46(1)	
				2	484.02(1)	
I^{131}	$\frac{7}{2}$	^2P	$\frac{3}{2}$	5	3292.99(9)	LIP-60b
				4	2138.22(5)	
				3	1314.24(7)	
Xe^{129}	$\frac{1}{2}$	$5p^5\,6s\,^3P$	2	$\frac{5}{2}$	5961.2577(9)	FAU-61
Xe^{131}	$\frac{3}{2}$	$5p^5\,6s\,^3P$	2	$\frac{7}{2}$	2693.6234(9)	FAU-61
				$\frac{5}{2}$	1608.3475(8)	
				$\frac{3}{2}$	838.7636(4)	
Cs^{127}	$\frac{1}{2}$	^2S	$\frac{1}{2}$	1	8950(200)	NIE-58
Cs^{129}	$\frac{1}{2}$	^2S	$\frac{1}{2}$	1	9200(200)	NIE-58
Cs^{130}	1	^2S	$\frac{1}{2}$	$\frac{3}{2}$	6400(350) or 6800(350)	NIE-58
Cs^{132}	2	^2S	$\frac{1}{2}$	$\frac{5}{2}$	8648(35)	NIE-58

TABLE II (*continued*)

Isotope	I	Atomic term	J	F	$\Delta\nu_{F,F-1}(Mc)^a$	Reference
Cs^{133}	$\frac{7}{2}$	^2S	$\frac{1}{2}$	4	9192.631830(10)	ESS-57
Cs^{134m}	8	^2S	$\frac{1}{2}$	$\frac{17}{2}$	3684.578640(175)	COH-62
Pr^{142}	2	^4I	$\frac{9}{2}$	$\frac{13}{2}$	443(4)^b	CAB-62
				$\frac{11}{2}$	371(3)^b	
				$\frac{9}{2}$	305(3)^b	
				$\frac{7}{2}$	233(3)^b	
Nd^{143}	$\frac{7}{2}$	^5I	4	$\frac{15}{2}$	1418.25(14)	SPA-63
				$\frac{13}{2}$	1257.53(4)	
				$\frac{11}{2}$	1084.70(4)	
				$\frac{9}{2}$	901.47(6)	
				$\frac{7}{2}$	710.0(1)	
				$\frac{5}{2}$	511.7(2)^b	
				$\frac{3}{2}$	308.9(2)^b	
Nd^{145}	$\frac{7}{2}$	^5I	5	$\frac{17}{2}$	789.83(20)	SPA-63
				$\frac{15}{2}$	708.38(20)	
				$\frac{13}{2}$	622.80(15)	
				$\frac{11}{2}$	533.36(20)	
				$\frac{9}{2}$	440.7(2)^b	
				$\frac{7}{2}$	345.5(2)^b	
				$\frac{5}{2}$	248.2(2)^b	
			4	$\frac{15}{2}$	886.25(6)	
				$\frac{13}{2}$	783.08(4)	
				$\frac{11}{2}$	673.49(3)	
				$\frac{9}{2}$	558.27(3)	
				$\frac{7}{2}$	439.10(15)	
				$\frac{5}{2}$	316.0(2)^b	
				$\frac{3}{2}$	190.6(2)^b	
Eu^{151}	$\frac{5}{2}$	^8S	$\frac{7}{2}$	6	120.675(1)	SAN-60
				5	100.286(1)	
				4	80.049(1)	
				3	59.932(2)^b	
				2	39.904(2)^b	
Eu^{153}	$\frac{5}{2}$	^8S	$\frac{7}{2}$	6	54.038(1)	SAN-60
				5	44.329(1)	
				4	35.004(1)	
				3	25.986(2)^b	
				2	17.196(2)^b	
Ho^{165}	$\frac{7}{2}$	^4I	$\frac{15}{2}$	11	8282.20(5)^b	GOO-62

TABLE II (*continued*)

Isotope	I	Atomic term	J	F	$\Delta\nu_{F,F-1}(\text{Mc})^a$	Reference
				10	7767.55(4)^b	
				9	7184.82(3)^b	
				8	6540.82(3)^b	
				7	5842.36(3)^b	
				6	5096.24(3)^b	
				5	4309.27(3)^b	
Tm^{169}	$\frac{1}{2}$	^2F	$\frac{7}{2}$	4	1496.555(10)	RIT-62b
Tm^{170}	1	^2F	$\frac{7}{2}$	$\frac{9}{2}$	1874(30)^b	CAB-60
				$\frac{7}{2}$	$-562(30)^b$	
Lu^{175}	$\frac{7}{2}$	^2D	$\frac{5}{2}$	6	1837.5792(100)	RIT-62a
				5	800.3467(43)	
				4	161.8248(56)	
				3	$-157.7283(51)$	
				2	$-238.0556(40)$	
			$\frac{3}{2}$	5	2051.2305(40)	
				4	345.4974(24)	
				3	$-496.5777(8)$	
Lu^{176}	7	^2D	$\frac{3}{2}$	$\frac{17}{2}$	2486(20)^b	SPA-62
				$\frac{15}{2}$	1307(10)^b	
				$\frac{13}{2}$	$-404(20)^b$	
Lu^{177}	$\frac{7}{2}$	^2D	$\frac{5}{2}$	6	1811.784(95)	PET-62b
				5	800.348(50)	
				4	175.896(50)	
				3	$-138.968(55)$	
				2	$-221.640(45)$	
			$\frac{3}{2}$	5	2021.850(130)	
				4	360.300(85)	
				3	$-463.130(105)$	
Au^{197}	$\frac{3}{2}$	^2S	$\frac{1}{2}$	2	6099.309(10)	REC-60
Hg^{199}	$\frac{1}{2}$	$6s\,6p\;^3P$	2	$\frac{5}{2}$	22666.559(5)	MCD-60
Hg^{201}	$\frac{3}{2}$	$6s\,6p\;^3P$	2	$\frac{7}{2}$	11382.6288(8)	MCD-60
				$\frac{5}{2}$	8629.5218(5)	
				$\frac{3}{2}$	5377.4918(20)	
Bi^{203}	$\frac{9}{2}$	^4S	$\frac{3}{2}$	6	3386(30	LIN-59
				5	2396(15)	
				4	1638(30)^b	
Bi^{204}	6	^4S	$\frac{3}{2}$	$\frac{15}{2}$	2841(25)	LIN-59
				$\frac{13}{2}$	2216(15)	

TABLE II (*continued*)

Isotope	I	Atomic term	J	F	$\Delta\nu_{F,F-1}(\mathrm{Mc})^a$	Reference
				$\frac{11}{2}$	1696(30)^b	
Bi^{205}	$\frac{9}{2}$	^4S	$\frac{3}{2}$	6	~4000	LIN-59
				5	~3000^b	
				4	~2000^b	
Bi^{206}	6	^4S	$\frac{3}{2}$	$\frac{15}{2}$	2914(25)	LIN-59
				$\frac{13}{2}$	2411(20)	
				$\frac{11}{2}$	1957(30)^b	
Bi^{209}	$\frac{9}{2}$	^4S	$\frac{3}{2}$	6	2884.7(2)	TIT-60
				5	2171.5(1)	
				4	1585.7(4)^b	
Bi^{210}	1	^4S	$\frac{3}{2}$	$\frac{5}{2}$	194.93(9)	ALP-62
				$\frac{3}{2}$	220.19(8)	
Po^{205}	$\frac{5}{2}$	—	2	$\frac{9}{2}$	760.4(50)^b	OLS-61
				$\frac{7}{2}$	431.0(20)^b	
				$\frac{5}{2}$	221.9(30)^b	
				$\frac{3}{2}$	98.8(30)^b	
Po^{207}	$\frac{5}{2}$	—	2	$\frac{9}{2}$	884.785(13)	OLS-61
				$\frac{7}{2}$	421.950(8)	
				$\frac{5}{2}$	158.567(12)	
				$\frac{3}{2}$	38.1(2)^b	
Pa^{233}	$\frac{3}{2}$	—	$\frac{11}{2}$	7	2640(400)^b	MAR-61a
				6	3960(200)^b	
				5	4500(350)^b	
Pu^{239}	$\frac{1}{2}$	^7F	1	$\frac{3}{2}$	7.683(60)	HUB-58
Am^{241}	$\frac{5}{2}$	^8S	$\frac{7}{2}$	6	964.96(10)^b	MAR-60
				5	852.78(4)^b	
				4	714.06(5)^b	
				3	554.12(6)^b	
				2	378.26(7)^b	
Am^{242}	1	^8S	$\frac{7}{2}$	$\frac{9}{2}$	112.71(9)^b	MAR-61b
				$\frac{7}{2}$	−51.61(9)^b	

^{a} Error estimates in parentheses apply to last figure of quoted value.
^{b} Calculated from Eq. (4.1.2.17) using values of A and B quoted in the reference.

ALP-62   S. S. Alpert, E. Lipworth, M. B. White, and K. F. Smith, *Phys. Rev.* **125**, 256 (1962).
AME-61   O. Ames, A. M. Bernstein, M. H. Brennan, and D. R. Hamilton, *Phys. Rev.* **123**, 1793 (1961).
BRA-61   N. Braslau, G. O. Brink, and J. M. Khan, *Phys. Rev.* **123**, 1801 (1961).

CAB-60   A. Y. Cabezas and I. Lindgren, *Phys. Rev.* **120**, 920 (1960).
CAB-62   A. Y. Cabezas, I. P. K. Lindgren, R. Marrus, and W. A. Nierenberg, *Phys. Rev.* **126**, 1004 (1962).
CHI-60   W. J. Childs and L. S. Goodman, *Phys. Rev.* **118**, 1578 (1960).
CHI-61   W. J. Childs, L. S. Goodman, and L. J. Kieffer, *Phys. Rev.* **122**, 891 (1961).
CHR-61   R. L. Christensen, D. R. Hamilton, H. G. Bennewitz, J. B. Reynolds, and H. H. Stroke, *Phys. Rev.* **122**, 1302 (1961).
COH-62   V. W. Cohen, T. Moran, and S. Penselin, *Phys. Rev.* **127**, 517 (1962).
CRA-63   S. B. Crampton, D. Kleppner, and N. F. Ramsey, *Phys. Rev. Letters* **11**, 338 (1963).
EHL-62   V. J. Ehlers and H. A. Shugart, *Phys. Rev.* **127**, 529 (1962).
EHR-61   D. von Ehrenstein, *Ann. Physik* [7] **7**, 342 (1961).
ESS-57   L. Essen and J. V. L. Parry, *Phil. Trans. Roy. Soc. London* **A250**, 45 (1957).
EWB-63   W. B. Ewbank and H. A. Shugart, *Phys. Rev.* **129**, 1617 (1963).
FAU-60   W. L. Faust, M. N. McDermott, and W. L. Lichten, *Phys. Rev.* **120**, 469 (1960).
FAU-61   W. L. Faust and M. N. McDermott, *Phys. Rev.* **123**, 198 (1961).
FAU-63   W. L. Faust and L. Y. Chow Chiu, *Phys. Rev.* **129**, 1214 (1963).
FER-60   P. C. B. Fernando, G. D. Rochester, I. J. Spalding, and K. F. Smith, *Phil. Mag.* [8] **5**, 1291 (1960).
FRI-59a   G. Fricke, H. Kopfermann, and S. Penselin, *Z. Physik* **154**, 218 (1959).
FRI-59b   G. Fricke, H. Kopfermann, S. Penselin, and K. Schlüpmann, *Z. Physik* **156**, 416 (1959).
GAR-59   H. L. Garvin, T. M. Green, E. Lipworth, and W. A. Nierenberg, *Phys. Rev.* **116**, 393 (1959).
GOO-62   L. S. Goodman, H. Kopfermann, and K. Schlüpmann, *Naturwissenschaften* **49**, 101 (1962).
GRO-58   G. M. Grosof, P. Buck, W. Lichten, and I. I. Rabi, *Phys. Rev. Letters* **1**, 214 (1958).
HEB-56   J. W. Heberle, H. A. Reich, and P. Kusch, *Phys. Rev.* **101**, 612 (1956).
HUB-58   J. C. Hubbs, R. Marrus, W. A. Nierenberg, and J. L. Worcester, *Phys. Rev.* **109**, 390 (1958).
KUS-49   P. Kusch and H. Taub, *Phys. Rev.* **75**, 1477 (1949).
LEW-60   H. Lew and R. S. Title, *Can. J. Phys.* **38**, 868 (1960).
LIN-59   I. Lindgren and C. M. Johansson, *Arkiv Fysik* **15**, 445 (1959).
LIP-60a   E. Lipworth, T. M. Green, H. L. Garvin, and W. A. Nierenberg, *Phys. Rev.* **119**, 1053 (1960).
LIP-60b   E. Lipworth, H. L. Garvin, and T. M. Green, *Phys. Rev.* **119**, 2022 (1960).
LUR-62   A. Lurio, *Phys. Rev.* **126**, 1768 (1962).
MAR-60   R. Marrus, W. A. Nierenberg, and J. Winocur, *Phys. Rev.* **120**, 1429 (1960).
MAR-61a   R. Marrus, W. A. Nierenberg, and J. Winocur, *Nuclear Phys.* **23**, 90 (1961).
MAR-61b   R. Marrus and J. Winocur, *Phys. Rev.* **124**, 1904 (1961).
MCD-60   M. N. McDermott and W. L. Lichten, *Phys. Rev.* **119**, 134 (1960).
NIE-58   W. A. Nierenberg, H. A. Shugart, H. B. Silsbee, and R. J. Sunderland, *Phys. Rev.* **112**, 186 (1958).
NOV-58   R. Novick and E. D. Commins, *Phys. Rev.* **111**, 822 (1958).
OLS-61   C. M. Olsmats, S. Axensten, and G. Liljegren, *Arkiv Fysik* **19**, 469 (1961).
PEN-62   S. Penselin, T. Moran, V. W. Cohen, and G. Winkler, *Phys. Rev.* **127**, 524 (1962).
PET-59   F. R. Petersen, V. J. Ehlers, W. B. Ewbank, L. L. Marino, and H. A. Shugart, *Phys. Rev.* **116**, 734 (1959).
PET-62a   F. R. Petersen and H. A. Shugart, *Phys. Rev.* **125**, 284 (1962).
PET-62b   F. R. Petersen and H. A. Shugart, *Phys. Rev.* **126**, 252 (1962).

PET-62c   F. R. Petersen and H. A. Shugart, *Phys. Rev.* **128**, 1740 (1962).
REC-60   E. Recknagel, *Z. Physik* **159**, 19 (1960).
RIT-62a   G. J. Ritter, *Phys. Rev.* **126**, 240 (1962).
RIT-62b   G. J. Ritter, *Phys. Rev.* **128**, 2238 (1962).
SAN-60   P. G. H. Sandars and G. K. Woodgate, *Proc. Roy. Soc.* **A257**, 269 (1960).
SPA-62   I. J. Spalding and K. F. Smith, *Proc. Phys. Soc. (London)* **79**, 787 (1962).
SPA-63   I. J. Spalding, *Proc. Phys. Soc. (London)* **81**, 156 (1963).
TIT-60   R. S. Title and K. F. Smith, *Phil. Mag* [8] **5**, 1281 (1960).
WES-53   G. Wessel and H. Lew, *Phys. Rev.* **92**, 641 (1953).
WHI-59   J. A. White, L. Y. Chow, C. Drake, and V. W. Hughes, *Phys. Rev. Letters* **3**, 428 (1959).
WOO-57   G. K. Woodgate and J. S. Martin, *Proc. Phys. Soc. (London)* **A70**, 485 (1957).

the B magnet behaves as a state analyzer, since it sends on to the detector a flux of atoms that depends on the way the beam atoms, coming out of the C magnet, are distributed over their various magnetic sublevels, i.e., their state of orientation.

The sole function of the beam detector is to give a response proportional to the flux of atoms entering or striking it. Any sort of measurable response will do, and the experimenter is free to choose the type of detector best suited to the atom under study. Early work in beam spectroscopy was done mostly with surface ionization detectors and Stern–Pirani detectors; more recently, the "universal" electron bombardment detector and the radioactivity detector have become popular. Detailed descriptions of beam detectors, and beam sources, are contained in other chapters of this volume.*

Further information on atomic beam apparatus and technique may be found in the book by Ramsey[7] and in an encyclopedia article by Kusch and Hughes.[53] The latter contains a tabulation of atomic hyperfine structures measured by the atomic beam resonance method, complete through 1958. Table II extends Kusch and Hughes' tabulation to mid-1963, and includes also a partial listing of earlier measurements.

4.1.2.5.2.1. *Hydrogen.* The hydrogen atom, after yielding up the Lamb shift, kept a second surprise in store. Measuring the hyperfine structure of the 1^2S ground level of hydrogen by the atomic beam resonance method, Nafe, Nelson, and Rabi[54] found that their result was about $\frac{1}{4}\%$ larger than the theoretical value given by the Fermi formula (4.1.2.4). Although this may seem to be a very small discrepancy indeed, it was definite evidence that the Dirac theory of the electron (on which the Fermi formula is based), which had failed to predict the Lamb

---

* See Chapters 1.3 and 2.2.

[53] P. Kusch and V. W. Hughes, *in* "Handbuch der Physik—Encyclopedia of Physics" (S. Flügge, ed.), Vol. 37, Part I, p. 1. Springer, Berlin, 1959.

[54] J. E. Nafe, E. B. Nelson, and I. I. Rabi, *Phys. Rev.* **71**, 914 (1947).

shift, also did not withstand close examination where hyperfine structure was concerned. Breit[55] subsequently pointed out that the discrepancy could be explained by assuming that the electron has a small "intrinsic" magnetic moment, in addition to the spin magnetic moment of one Bohr magneton predicted by the Dirac theory. This intrinsic moment would increase the magnetic dipole hyperfine structure interaction between the electron and proton of the hydrogen atom, and also should show up in the interaction between an electron and an external magnetic field. The correctness of Breit's suggestion was soon demonstrated by measurements of the Zeeman effect in several atoms (including hydrogen), which gave results consistent with the hydrogen hyperfine structure measurements. In a burst of theoretical work stimulated by these measurements, the new methods of quantum electrodynamics were brought to bear on the hydrogen hyperfine structure and Zeeman effect, and were successful in reconciling theory with experiment.

Nafe and Nelson[56] (and later, Prodell and Kusch[57,58]) redid the hyperfine structure experiment, to higher precision, with apparatus much like the schematic drawing of Fig. 12. The source of atomic hydrogen was a Woods discharge tube, fed with hydrogen or deuterium gas, and pierced by a slit that opened into the vacuum space; the detector was of the Stern–Pirani type, which detects beam atoms by macroscopic pressure changes in a beam collection chamber. The pressure-measuring device, like that in the familiar Pirani vacuum gauge, is a heated filament, whose resistance is monitored by a dc bridge and galvanometer. This is a beam detector that has been much used for work with noncondensable gases. It is simple and relatively noise-free, but has the disadvantage of a slow response to changes in beam intensity; the $1/e$ response time of Nafe and Nelson's detector was 20 seconds. In addition to making data collection a time-consuming process, such a response time precludes the use of beam modulation and lock-in detection techniques.

The deflecting magnets were arranged for flop-out detection, i.e., with antiparallel field gradients. This arrangement is usually preferred over the flop-in arrangement, since it simplifies the task of aligning the apparatus, always a problem in beam work. With flop-out detection, the deflecting magnets can be adjusted so that beam atoms in any magnetic sublevel and having any speed are focused on the detector, provided they remain in their original sublevel while passing between the two deflecting fields. Hence the various beam slits and obstacles may be aligned by maximizing the total beam flux at the detector, with

[55] G. Breit, *Phys. Rev.* **72**, 984 (1947).
[56] J. E. Nafe and E. B. Nelson, *Phys. Rev.* **73**, 718 (1948).
[57] A. G. Prodell and P. Kusch, *Phys. Rev.* **88**, 184 (1952).
[58] P. Kusch, *Phys. Rev.* **100**, 1188 (1955).

the radio-frequency field turned off. The radio-frequency resonance condition announces itself by decreasing the focused beam flux.

The two hyperfine structure levels of hydrogen, $F = 0$ and $F = 1$, have only four magnetic sublevels between them (the Zeeman effect is given by (4.1.2.9) with $J = \frac{1}{2}$, $I = \frac{1}{2}$) and the choice of a transition to use for the measurement of $\Delta\nu$ is rather limited. For maximum precision, a field-insensitive transition of the $\Delta F = 1$ type is desirable, and there is only one of these in hydrogen, the $m_F = 0 \leftrightarrow m_F = 0$ transition at zero field strength. Accordingly, Nafe and Nelson made their measurements on this transition, using C field strengths just large enough to resolve the $0 \leftrightarrow 0$ line adequately from the neighboring Zeeman components. At this field strength, approximately 2 gauss, the $0 \leftrightarrow 0$ line was shifted by only a small quadratic Zeeman effect. The shift could be corrected for easily, using the value of the magnetic field strength determined from the separation of the other Zeeman components.

In addition to these measurements on the ground 1^2S level, Heberle, Reich, and Kusch[59] have investigated the hyperfine structure of the metastable 2^2S level—the level that played such an important role in the Lamb shift experiments. The purpose was to measure the ratio $\Delta\nu(2^2S)/\Delta\nu(1^2S)$, which the hyperfine structure theory predicts more accurately than it predicts either of the absolute values of $\Delta\nu$. The experiment was performed on a metastable hydrogen beam, generated by the thermal dissociation and electron bombardment method of Lamb and Retherford. The beam detection method was again that of electron ejection from a metal target, the dc electron current being monitored by an electrometer. Despite these similarities with the Lamb–Retherford experiment, the method of observing radio-frequency resonances was quite different. A precise measurement of the hyperfine structure could be made only under weak field conditions, for the usual reasons connected with magnetic shifts and broadening of the resonance lines, and more particularly because of the quenching effect of strong fields, discussed in Section 4.1.2.4.1.3. Magnetic quenching in the radio-frequency transition region, by its shortening of the metastable lifetime, would broaden the resonance lines severely. Deprived of the automatic state selecting action of magnetic quenching, Heberle, Reich, and Kusch found it necessary to modify the Lamb–Retherford design by adding a separate state selector and analyzer to the beam apparatus. Conventional beam deflection methods might have worked, but there was a much more effective state selection method at hand, the very magnetic quenching effect that had to be avoided in the radio-frequency transition

---

[59] J. W. Heberle, H. A. Reich, and P. Kusch, *Phys. Rev.* **101**, 612 (1956).

region. A uniform magnetic quenching field set at roughly 575 gauss has a very strong orienting effect on the metastable beam atoms. One such field located ahead of the transition region will pass into the radio-frequency field only those metastable atoms that occupy the $\alpha(m_J = + \frac{1}{2})$ sublevels; a second such field located after the transition region will pass on to the detector only those metastable atoms that remain in the α sublevels after being exposed to the radio-frequency field. The radio-frequency resonance condition, to the extent that it depopulates α sublevels, will therefore decrease the flux of metastable atoms reaching the detector. This was the method of state selection and analysis used by Heberle, Reich, and Kusch; its great advantage over the beam deflection method is that wide, intense beams may be used, since the magnetic quenching effect is independent of beam width. Unfortunately, it is a method that applies only to metastable beams.

4.1.2.5.2.2. *Helium*-3. In hyperfine structure, as in fine structure, the next precise tests of the theory were made on the helium atom and the helium ion. Because common He^4 has no nuclear spin, and hence no hyperfine structure, it was necessary to investigate the rare, stable isotope of helium, He^3, and its ion, He^{3+}. Both experiments were beam resonance experiments, but they differed in several important respects, especially in the method of state selection and analysis.

In the work on neutral helium, both the original experiment by Weinreich and Hughes[60] and its later refinement by White, Chow, Drake, and Hughes,[61] conventional magnetic deflection methods were used. The apparatus and experimental technique were similar to those of the hydrogen experiment, except that a recirculating gas handling system was needed to conserve the He^3 gas, and the beam was detected by an electron ejection detector rather than by a Stern–Pirani detector. This detector was chosen because of its sensitivity to the metastable ^3S fraction of the beam, the source of which was a Woods discharge tube. It was necessary to investigate the metastable level because the ^1S ground level of neutral helium, lacking electronic angular momentum, has no hyperfine structure regardless of nuclear spin.

The He^{3+} ion, in an experiment by Novick and Commins,[62] was also studied in its metastable level, not because the ground 1^2S level lacks hyperfine structure (it doesn't, since $J \neq 0$) but rather because there was no practical means of orienting and analyzing a beam of ground state ions. Magnetic deflection methods were out of the question, since the Lorentz force would deflect all the ions completely out of the beam.

[60] G. Weinreich and V. W. Hughes, *Phys. Rev.* **95**, 1451 (1954).
[61] J. A. White, L. Y. Chow, C. W. Drake, and V. W. Hughes, *Phys. Rev. Letters* **3**, 428 (1959).
[62] R. Novick and E. D. Commins, *Phys. Rev.* **111**, 822 (1958).

The metastable 2^2S level of He^{3+} offered two additional state selection methods: the magnetic quenching method, which worked well for hydrogen but was no good here (again because of the Lorentz deflection), and secondly a radio-frequency quenching method, which turned out to be ideally suited to the He^{3+} experiment. Radio-frequency quenching, it will be recalled from the Lamb shift experiments, transfers atoms from the metastable 2^2S level to the nearby $2^2P_{1/2}$ level, from which they are immediately lost by radiative decay. For the common helium ion, He^{4+}, and in the absence of a magnetic field, the quenching spectrum consists of a single line at 14 Gc. For He^{3+} this line is split into two components by the hyperfine structure of the 2^2S level. (The hyperfine structure of the $2^2P_{1/2}$ level is much smaller than the natural width of the lines, and does not cause any further splitting.) By setting the quenching frequency on one of these hyperfine components, it is possible to quench atoms in one hyperfine structure level but not in the other. Because the two hyperfine components of the 14-Gc line overlap to some extent, this differential quenching cannot be made complete, but experiment showed that it was possible to obtain population ratios as high as 3 to 1 between the $F = 0$ and $F = 1$ hyperfine structure levels of the 2^2S level by proper adjustment of the quenching frequency.

Two radio-frequency quenchers, which consisted of sections of wave guide fed by 14-Gc oscillators, were used in the He^{3+} beam experiment. Between them, in the path of the ion beam, was a radio-frequency "hairpin" driven at the hyperfine structure transition frequency of approximately 1 Gc. A weak magnetic field applied to this region separated the Zeeman components of the $F = 0 \leftrightarrow F = 1$ transition. The helium ion beam, produced by an electron bombardment ionizer, accelerating grid, and electrostic focusing electrodes, passed through the three radio-frequency fields on the way to the beam detector, an electron ejection target. Both radio-frequency quenchers were tuned to quench metastable atoms in the $F = 1$ hyperfine structure level. Most of the metastable atoms that reached the beam target were thus in the $F = 0$ level, and resonance transitions between the $F = 0$ and $F = 1$ levels caused a decrease in the ejected electron current. Since the beam consisted mostly of ground state ions, which were also capable of ejecting electrons from the target, it was necessary to extract the signal due to metastable ions from a large background signal. Novick and Commins did this by amplitude modulating the first radio-frequency quencher, and detecting, with a lock-in detector, only the coherent ac component of the ejected electron current.

4.1.2.5.2.3. *Lithium, Potassium.* The conventional atomic beam magnetic resonance method, as it has come to be called, is exemplified by early experiments on alkali beams. Particularly noteworthy, because it prepared the way for many later experiments, is the measurement of the hyperfine structure of lithium and potassium performed by Kusch, Millman, and Rabi,[2] the original experiment of atomic radio spectroscopy. Not by chance were alkali atoms the first to be investigated, but by natural extension from earlier beam deflection experiments, in which methods of producing and detecting beams of alkali atoms had already become well-developed. Alkali metals vaporize readily when heated, and the vapor consists mainly of atoms. Thus a simple electrically heated oven, with a slit opening into the vacuum of the beam apparatus, serves as a beam source. Atoms that succeeded in reaching the other end of the apparatus, after negotiating slits, obstacles, and magnets, can be detected with nearly 100 % efficiency by a surface ionization detector. This type of detector, which consists of a heated tungsten wire, together with an ion collector and current measuring device, is particularly sensitive to alkali atoms because of their low ionization potentials.

Kusch, Millman, and Rabi experimented in the period just prior to World War II, when microwave oscillator tubes were not to be had. Limited to frequencies below 1 Gc, they were able to investigate only the alkali atoms with the smallest hyperfine structure intervals, Li^6, Li^7, K^{39}, and K^{41}. When atomic beam spectroscopy was taken up again after the war, radio-frequency apparatus was available for frequencies up to 10 Gc, and the remaining alkali atoms were covered in short order.

4.1.2.5.2.4. *Silver, Gold.* The surface ionization detector was improved by means such as oxidizing the tungsten wire to increase its work function and by using a mass spectrometer to discriminate against the background ionization current. With these and other improvements the number of different atomic beams detectable by surface ionization increased to a dozen or so, but it was clear that a practical limit was being reached. What was needed was a universal ionizer, a device that would ionize any beam atom, regardless of its ionization potential. Wessel and Lew[63] developed such a device and demonstrated it in a beam resonance experiment on silver and gold, two atoms which were not detectable by surface ionization. This universal ionizer consisted of an electron bombardment chamber, placed so as to intercept the neutral beam atoms as they emerged from the second deflecting magnet of an otherwise conventional beam resonance apparatus. Electrons oscillating back and forth in the chamber, in a direction transverse to the beam, ionized a small fraction (about 1 in 3000) of the entering beam atoms. The ions were drawn off to a mass spectrometer, which deflected them to the slit of an electron multiplier detector. The mass spectrometer was necessary to get rid of undesired background ions, produced by the electron bom-

[63] G. Wessel and H. Lew, *Phys. Rev.* **92**, 641 (1953).

bardment of residual gas in the detector chamber. Wessel and Lew further increased the signal-to-background ratio by chopping the atomic beam with a rotating shutter (thus modulating the resonance signal but not the background ionization current) and feeding the electron multiplier output to a lock-in detector. This increased the detection sensitivity approximately one hundredfold.

4.1.2.5.2.5. *Bromine-82.* As a beam detector the universal ionizer has two major drawbacks: it is complicated and it is inefficient. Because of the low ionization efficiency, high beam intensities and large amounts of starting materials are necessary. In direct contrast stands the radio-active method. The beam detector could hardly be simpler; it is a de-position target, usually a sulfur-coated button, to which the radioactive beam atoms adhere. Nor could the method be more efficient, since every beam atom that strikes (and sticks to) the target is individually detectable by its subsequent radioactive decay. The main disadvantage of radioactive detection, apart from its obvious lack of universality, is its slowness. To record a resonance line one must expose several deposition targets in succession, while varying the radio frequency or the magnetic field strength a small amount between each exposure. The exposed targets are then placed one at a time before an appropriate radioactivity detector, and counts are taken for fixed time intervals, usually for several minutes. Clearly this is a time-consuming way to record a radio spectrum, particularly an unknown spectrum that must first be searched for and located. For this reason, radioactive detection is most effective for quick measurements of nuclear spins, using the low field $\Delta F = 0$ transitions in the way discussed in Section 4.1.2.5.1. Experiments of this sort require only a few exposures to determine uniquely an unknown spin value, and it is possible to work with very small quantities of radioactive material. A measurement of the nuclear spins of four rubidium isotopes by Hobson et al.[64] was done with a beam source that contained fewer than 10^{14} active atoms.

When time and sample size permit, it is feasible to carry out a complete measurement of hyperfine structure, using radioactive detection. An example of such an experiment is that performed by Garvin et al.[65] on radioactive bromine-82. The goal of this experiment, as in most precise measurements of hyperfine structure, was to locate and measure the frequencies of the $\Delta F = \pm 1$ transitions. Because of the slowness of radioactive detection, however, a direct search for these transitions was impractical, and Garvin et al. chose a roundabout, but faster, method.

[64] J. P. Hobson, J. C. Hubbs, W. A. Nierenberg, H. B. Silsbee, and R. J. Sutherland, *Phys. Rev.* **104**, 101 (1956).

[65] H. L. Garvin, T. M. Green, E. Lipworth, and W. A. Nierenberg, *Phys. Rev.* **116**, 393 (1959).

Knowing the nuclear spin and the atomic g factor they could locate immediately a weak field $\Delta F = 0$ transition since its frequency does not depend on hyperfine structure. Guessing at the coupling constants, they then predicted the second-order shift of this line, caused by hyperfine structure, at a somewhat higher field strength. A short search at this field strength located the line again, and gave rough experimental values for the hyperfine structure constants. These were used to predict the line position at a new and higher field strength, the line was located again, and better values of the hyperfine structure constants were derived from its position. Repeating this process several times, the experimenters progressed by steps into the intermediate field region, never losing the $\Delta F = 0$ line for long, until finally they had values of the hyperfine structure constants that were good enough to predict the frequencies of the $\Delta F = \pm 1$ lines with reasonable accuracy. A final short search located these lines, and a precise measurement of their frequencies completed the experiment.

Apart from the detection method, and the special problems of preparing and handling radioactive samples, the experimental techniques of radioactive atomic beam spectroscopy are similar to those of conventional atomic beam spectroscopy.[66] The deflecting magnets of a radioactive beam apparatus are customarily adjusted for the flop-in mode of operation, in which only atoms that have made a radio-frequency transition in the C field are able to reach the detector. This reduces the background level of radioactivity on the deposition target, and thereby shortens the required counting times. The alignment problem that accompanies flop-in operation would be quite troublesome, especially for short-lived isotopes, if the final alignment had to be performed with the radioactive beam itself. Fortunately, this is not necessary. The trajectories of atoms in strong deflecting fields are the same for all isotopes of a given element, since these trajectories are determined by the electronic magnetic moment of the atom. Accordingly, the radioactive beam apparatus can be aligned with a conventional beam detector, which responds to all the isotopic atoms in the beam, including the predominant fraction of stable isotopes. After the alignment is completed, the deposition target is substituted for the conventional detector, and the experiment may begin.

4.1.2.5.3. MICROWAVE ABSORPTION.* The atomic beam resonance apparatus is a precise and versatile instrument for measuring atomic hyperfine structure, but it is not an apparatus whose construction

---

[66] The apparatus and methods of radioactive beam experiments are discussed by W. A. Nierenberg in two review article: *Ann. Rev. Nuclear Sci.* **7**, 349 (1957), and *Proc. Natl. Acad. Sci. U. S.* **45**, 429 (1959).

* See also Vol. 3, Chapter 2.1.

is to be undertaken lightly. For certain atoms the microwave absorption method affords a far simpler, but equally precise, means of measuring hyperfine structure. The apparatus consists of a resonant microwave cavity, coupled to a suitable oscillator and microwave detector. A vapor of atoms fills the cavity, and hyperfine structure transitions are detected by changes in the microwave power transmitted through or reflected from the cavity. Like its first cousin, the paramagnetic resonance method (Section 4.1.2.6.2.), this technique works poorly at frequencies below the microwave range, and it requires relatively dense atomic vapors, which are often difficult to produce. For these reasons, and also perhaps because it was second on a scene already dominated by atomic beams, the microwave absorption method has been little used for hyperfine structure measurements.

The first such experiment was performed on cesium vapor by Roberts, Beers, and Hill[67] in 1946. Cesium was chosen to test the experimental method; its hyperfine structure frequency of 9193 Mc, already known from an atomic beam measurement, was high enough for good sensitivity but not too high for microwave apparatus that was available at the time. The aim of the experiment was to detect the anomalous dispersion of microwaves that accompanied resonant absorption at the hyperfine structure frequency, rather than the absorption itself. This dispersive effect changed the resonant frequency of a microwave cavity full of cesium vapor, and this in turn changed the frequency of an oscillator that was stabilized to the cavity frequency. Through a modulation of the cesium resonance with a weak alternating magnetic field ("Zeeman modulation") the resonance condition was detected as a synchronous frequency modulation of the microwave oscillator.

A few years later, Shimoda and Nishikawa[68] did a similar experiment on sodium vapor, but with an apparatus that detected the resonant absorption of microwave energy directly. The vapor-filled microwave cavity was connected into a transmission line which was terminated by a crystal detector. Hyperfine structure transitions, which occur in sodium at 1772 Mc, were detected as a decrease in the microwave power transmitted through the cavity. Although operating very close to the practical low-frequency limit of microwave absorption, Shimoda and Nishikawa were able to get reasonably good spectra by using Zeeman modulation and lock-in detection. Their measurements confirmed the value of $\Delta \nu$ found earlier by atomic beam measurements under strong field conditions.

In view of the difficulty Shimoda and Nishikawa had in detecting absorption at 1772 Mc in an almost purely atomic vapor, it is somewhat

[67] A. Roberts, Y. Beers, and A. G. Hill, *Phys. Rev.* **70**, 112(A) (1946).

[68] K. Shimoda and T. Nishikawa, *J. Phys. Soc. Japan* **6**, 512 (1951).

startling to consider the next absorption experiment, a remeasurement by Wittke and Dicke[69] of the hyperfine structure of hydrogen. This experiment, which was a successful attempt to improve upon the atomic beam value of this fundamental quantity, detected absorption at 1420 Mc, which is comparable with the sodium frequency, but in a gas that was composed less than 1 % of hydrogen atoms. The gas was molecular hydrogen that had been pumped through an electric discharge tube of the Woods type, and thence into the microwave cavity. Ordinarily one might expect that the inert gas would lower the peak absorption intensities through collision broadening of the absorption lines, but this did not occur. Instead, the inert gas (molecular hydrogen) *narrowed* the lines, making them easier to detect. The reason for this behavior, as shown by Wittke and Dicke's calculation of electron exchange effects, is that collisions between two hydrogen atoms are much more effective in broadening the absorption lines than are collisions between a hydrogen atom and a hydrogen molecule. Consequently, the inert gas acted chiefly as a buffer gas; it narrowed the lines by reducing the broadening effects of Doppler shifts and wall collisions.

The microwave circuit used by Wittke and Dicke was a variant of the hybrid tee impedance bridge, a circuit which has become popular for paramagnetic resonance work and which is described further in Section 4.1.2.6.2. This circuit measures the reflection coefficient of the tuned microwave cavity, a property which is determined partly by the absorptive and dispersive nature of the gas which fills the cavity. The bridge was adjusted to respond only to the absorptive part of the signal caused by hyperfine structure transitions, so as to avoid difficulties in the interpretation of line shapes. By careful design of the experiment, Wittke and Dicke were able to reduce the absorption line width to as little as 3 kc. They used Zeeman modulation and lock-in detection at 30 cps, which was low enough to give no appreciable distortion of the line shape. To avoid the noisiness of crystal microwave detectors at this low frequency, they used barretter detectors instead. A barretter, being a simple resistance thermometer which is heated by the incident microwaves, does not have the excess low-frequency noise characteristic of a crystal detector.

It is no coincidence that the three experiments mentioned above, the only absorption experiments that have been performed under weak field conditions, were each concerned with an atom whose hyperfine structure had already been measured with considerable precision. The reason is the frequency tuning problem; this common problem of radio spectroscopy is especially troublesome in absorption work because

---

[69] J. P. Wittke and R. H. Dicke, *Phys. Rev.* **103**, 620 (1956).

the signal that is being searched for is itself just a fluctuation in the microwave power level. For this reason, searches for new absorption spectra are made by varying the strength of a magnetic field applied to the absorption sample, keeping the microwave frequency fixed. Field strengths of several kilogauss, which are strong fields for most atoms, are commonly used, and the experiments usually give more information about the Zeeman effect of the atom than about its hyperfine structure. Nevertheless, the hyperfine structure separations of several atoms have been measured for the first time by this method. Table III lists these measurements, together with the results of the weak field experiments.

TABLE III. Atomic Hyperfine Structure Intervals Measured by the Microwave Absorption (and Paramagnetic Resonance) Method

Isotope	Nuclear spin	Atomic term	J	F	$\Delta\nu_{F,F-1}(\mathrm{Mc})^a$	Reference
H^1	$\frac{1}{2}$	^2S	$\frac{1}{2}$	1	1420.40580(6)	WIT-56
N^{14}	1	^4S	$\frac{3}{2}$	$\frac{5}{2}$	$26.13(5)^b$	HEA-54
				$\frac{3}{2}$	$15.68(3)^b$	
O^{17}	$\frac{5}{2}$	^3P	2	$\frac{9}{2}$	$991.2(12)^b$	KAM-57
				$\frac{7}{2}$	$763.6(7)^b$	
				$\frac{5}{2}$	$541.6(8)^b$	
				$\frac{3}{2}$	$323.4(6)^b$	
F^{19}	$\frac{1}{2}$	^2P	$\frac{3}{2}$	2	4020.01(2)	RAD-61
Na^{23}	$\frac{3}{2}$	^2S	$\frac{1}{2}$	2	1771.70(15)	SHI-51
P^{31}	$\frac{1}{2}$	^4S	$\frac{3}{2}$	2	$112.4(30)^b$	DEH-55

[a] Error estimates in parentheses apply to last figure of quoted value.

[b] Reference gives values of the coupling constants A and B which have been used to calculate $\Delta\nu$ from Eq. (4.1.2.17).

DEH-55   H. G. Dehmelt, *Phys. Rev.* **99**, 527 (1955).

HEA-54   M. A. Heald and R. Beringer, *Phys. Rev.* **96**, 645 (1954).

KAM-57   R. A. Kamper, K. R. Lea, and C. D. Lustig, *Proc. Phys. Soc. (London)* **B70**, 897 (1957).

RAD-61   H. E. Radford, V. W. Hughes, and V. Beltran-Lopez, *Phys. Rev.* **123**, 153 (1961).

SHI-51   K. Shimoda and T. Nishikawa, *J. Phys. Soc. Japan* **6**, 512 (1951).

WIT-56   J. P. Wittke and R. H. Dicke, *Phys. Rev.* **103**, 620 (1956).

4.1.2.5.4. RADIO-OPTICAL RESONANCE. Light from a sodium lamp, focused on a vessel of sodium vapor, makes the vapor fluoresce with a soft yellow glow. A similar fluorescence, but at different wavelengths, is observable when light from a mercury lamp falls on a vessel of mercury

TABLE IV. Hyperfine Structure Intervals of Excited Atoms Measured
by Radio-Optical Methods

Isotope	Nuclear spin	Atomic term	J	F	$\Delta\nu_{F,F-1}(\text{Mc})^a$	Method[b]	Reference
Na^{23}	$\frac{3}{2}$	$3p\ ^2P$	$\frac{3}{2}$	3	57.8(20)^c	D	DOD-60
				2	34.8(15)^c		
				1	16.2(10)^c		
		$5d\ ^2D$	$\frac{5}{2}$		($A < 0.33$ Mc)	E	ARC-60
K^{39}	$\frac{3}{2}$	$5p\ ^2P$	$\frac{1}{2}$	2	17.98(30)^c	D	FOX-61
K^{40}	4	$5p\ ^2P$	$\frac{3}{2}$	$\frac{11}{2}$	14.375(115)	D	BUC-62a
				$\frac{9}{2}$	9.8(5)^c		
				$\frac{7}{2}$	7.675(300)		
Rb^{85}	$\frac{5}{2}$	$6p\ ^2P$	$\frac{3}{2}$	4	39.275(48)	D	BUC-61a
				3	20.812(61)		
				2	9.824(44)		
Rb^{87}	$\frac{3}{2}$	$6p\ ^2P$	$\frac{3}{2}$	3	87.122(43)	D	BUC-61a
				2	51.418(31)		
				1	23.696(97)		
Sr^{87}	$\frac{9}{2}$	$5s\ 5p\ ^3P$	1	$\frac{11}{2}$	1463.1(1)	D	BUC-62c
				$\frac{9}{2}$	1130.2(1)		
Cd^{111,113}	$\frac{1}{2}$	$5s\ 5p\ ^3P$	1	$\frac{3}{2}$	6540(135)^c	E	GEN-60
Cs^{133}	$\frac{7}{2}$	$7p\ ^2P$	$\frac{3}{2}$	5	82.93(3)	D	BUC-59
				4	66.42(5)		
				3	49.94(3)		
		$8p\ ^2P$	$\frac{3}{2}$	5	38.093(30)	D	BUC-62b
				4	30.502(130)		
				3	22.912(3)		
		$9d\ ^2D$	$\frac{5}{2}$		(0.195 Mc $< A$	E	ARC-60
					< 0.45 Mc)		
Cs^{135}	$\frac{7}{2}$	$7p\ ^2P$	$\frac{3}{2}$	5	89.42(5)	D	BUC-59
				4	69.6(3)		
				3	51.2(1)^c		
Cs^{137}	$\frac{7}{2}$	$7p\ ^2P$	$\frac{3}{2}$	5	92.99(5)	D	BUC-59
				4	72.3(3)		
				3	53.3(1)^c		
Ba^{135}	$\frac{3}{2}$	$6s\ 6p\ ^3P$	1	$\frac{5}{2}$	2536.8(5)	D	BUC-61b
				$\frac{3}{2}$	1603.5(5)		
Ba^{137}	$\frac{3}{2}$	$6s\ 6p\ ^3P$	1	$\frac{5}{2}$	2824.5(5)	D	BUC-61b
				$\frac{3}{2}$	1819.6(5)		
Hg^{197}	$\frac{1}{2}$	$6s\ 6p\ ^3P$	1	$\frac{3}{2}$	23083.4(6.7)	L	HIR-60

TABLE IV (*continued*)

Isotope	Nuclear spin	Atomic term	J	F	$\Delta\nu_{F,F-1}(\text{Mc})^a$	Method^b	Reference
Hg^{197}*	$\frac{13}{2}$	6s 6p ^3P	1	$\frac{15}{2}$	18246(14)	D	HIR-61
				$\frac{13}{2}$	14234.86(9)	D	BRO-61
Hg^{199}	$\frac{1}{2}$	6s 6p ^3P	1	$\frac{3}{2}$	22126.1(7.5)	L	HIR-61
		6s 6f ^3F	4	$\frac{9}{2}$	5800(100)	E	PEB-59
Hg^{201}	$\frac{3}{2}$	6s 6p ^3P	1	$\frac{5}{2}$	13986.557(8)	D	KOH-61
				$\frac{3}{2}$	7551.613(13)		
		6s 6f ^3F	4	$\frac{11}{2}$	2860(50)	E	PEB-59
				$\frac{9}{2}$	2340(50)		
				$\frac{7}{2}$	1820(50)		

^{a} Error estimates in parentheses apply to last figure of quoted value.
^{b} D—double resonance; E—electron bombardment; L—level crossing.
^{c} Reference gives values of the coupling constants A and B which have been used to calculate $\Delta\nu$ from Eq. (4.1.2.17).

ARC-60   Y. Archambault, J. P. Descoubes, M. Prioce, A. Omont, and J. C. Pebay-Peyroula, *J. Phys., Radium* 21, 677 (1960).
BRO-61   C. Brot, *J. Phys., Radium* 22, 412 (1961).
BUC-59   H. Bucka, H. Kopfermann, and E. W. Otten, *Ann. Physik* [7] 4, 39 (1959).
BUC-61a H. Bucka, H. Kopfermann, and A. Minor, *Z. Physik* 161, 123 (1961).
BUC-61b H. Bucka, H. Kopfermann, and G. zu Putlitz, *Z. Physik* 165, 72 (1961).
BUC-62a H. Bucka, H. Kopfermann, and J. Ney, *Z. Physik* 167, 375 (1962).
BUC-62b H. Bucka and G. von Oppen, *Ann. Physik* [7] 10, 119 (1962).
BUC-62c H. Bucka, H. Kopfermann, and G. zu Putlitz, *Z. Physik* 168, 542 (1962).
DOD-60   J. N. Dodd and R. W. N. Kinnear, *Proc. Phys. Soc. (London)* 75, 51 (1960).
FOX-61   W. N. Fox and G. W. Series, *Proc. Phys. Soc. (London)* 77, 1141 (1961).
GEN-60   E. Geneux and B. Wanders-Vincenz, *Helv. Phys. Acta* 33, 185 (1960).
HIR-60   H. R. Hirsch and C. V. Stager, *J. Opt. Soc. Am.* 50, 1052 (1960).
HIR-61   H. R. Hirsch, *J. Opt. Soc. Am.* 51, 1192 (1961).
KOH-61   R. H. Kohler, *Phys. Rev.* 121, 1104 (1961).
PEB-59   J. C. Pebay-Peyroula, *J. phys., radium* 20, 721 (1959).

vapor, when light from a cadmium lamp falls on cadmium vapor, and so on. The reason for this phenomenon is that an atomic vapor absorbs most efficiently just those radiations that the same vapor, when hot, emits. Since the absorbing vapor is "cold" however (the atoms are in their ground state) it cannot absorb all of the spectral lines emitted by the lamp, but only those lines that correspond to transitions to the atomic ground state, the so-called resonance lines of the atom. In absorbing a resonance line, atoms are placed in a particular excited state of the atom. If undisturbed, they eventually decay from the same state, giving back the same resonance radiation that they absorbed. In other circumstances, where the atoms may suffer collisions or be exposed to electric or magnetic fields while in the excited state, the character of the re-emitted resonance radiation may be changed in respects such as polarization and intensity. The polarization, in particular, is very sensitive to disturbing influences, and many of the classical experiments on resonance radiation, performed during the 1920's and early 1930's, were concerned with the depolarizing effects of weak magnetic fields and of foreign gases present in the absorption cell.

After a lapse of 20 years came the radio-frequency resonance experiment of Brossel and Bitter,[5] which stimulated a renewed interest in the properties of resonance radiation. These experimenters, following a suggestion by Brossel and Kastler,[70] found that a radio-frequency field, when tuned to a certain frequency, was also capable of depolarizing resonance radiation. This frequency was the Larmor frequency of the excited atom in the weak magnetic field used in the experiment, and so it was clear that the depolarization was caused by radio-frequency transitions among the magnetic sublevels of the excited resonance level. The new "double resonance" technique, as it was called by its inventors, was subsequently used to measure the Zeeman effect and hyperfine structure of all the excited atoms that had been studied in the earlier days of resonance radiation.

Following upon these double resonance experiments, other radio-optical methods of measuring hyperfine structure were developed, including those which involve optical pumping, depolarization of collision light, and the illumination of atomic beams with resonance light. Recent studies[71] of interference effects in resonance radiation have led to further measurements of hyperfine structure by the "level crossing" technique. Representative experiments in each of these categories will be described below, following a brief discussion first of why resonance radiation is polarized, and what optical pumping consists of. Review articles by Kastler,[72] Bitter,[73] Brossel,[74] and Series[22] give further details on radio-optical techniques; monographs by Mitchell and Zemansky[75] and by Pringsheim[76] are valuable guides to the older

[70] J. Brossel and A. Kastler, *Compt. rend.* **229**, 1213 (1949).

[71] P. A. Franken, *Phys. Rev.* **121**, 508 (1960); M. E. Rose and R. L. Carovillano, *ibid.* **122**, 1185 (1961).

[72] A. Kastler, *J. Opt. Soc. Am.* **47**, 460 (1957).

[73] F. Bitter, *Appl. Opt.* **1**, 1 (1962).

[74] J. Brossel, *in* "Quantum Electronics" (C. H. Townes, ed.), p. 81. Columbia Univ. Press, New York, 1960.

[75] A. G. Mitchell and N. W. Zemansky, "Resonance Radiation and Excited Atoms." Cambridge Univ. Press, London and New York, 1934.

[76] P. Pringsheim, "Fluorescence and Phosphorescence." Wiley (Interscience), New York, 1949.

work on resonance radiation. Series, in his article, lists all measurements of hyperfine structure in excited atoms prior to 1959. Table IV brings this list up to mid-1963 and includes a few of the earlier measurements as well. Table V lists optical pumping measurements of hyperfine structure in ground state atoms, and is complete to the same date.

TABLE V. Atomic Hyperfine Structure Intervals Measured by
Optical Pumping Methods

Isotope	Nuclear spin	Atomic term	J	F	$\Delta\nu_{F,F-1}(\text{Mc})^a$	Reference
H	$\frac{1}{2}$	^2S	$\frac{1}{2}$	1	1420.4057491(60)	PIP-62
D	1	^2S	$\frac{1}{2}$	$\frac{3}{2}$	327.384349(5)	AND-60
T	$\frac{1}{2}$	^2S	$\frac{1}{2}$	1	1516.7014768(60)	PIP-62
N^{14}	1	^4S	$\frac{3}{2}$	$\frac{5}{2}$	26.127326(18)	LAM-63
				$\frac{3}{2}$	15.676392(12)	
N^{15}	$\frac{1}{2}$	^4S	$\frac{3}{2}$	2	29.290914(10)	LAM-63
Na^{23}	$\frac{3}{2}$	^2S	$\frac{1}{2}$	2	1771.6262(1)	ARD-58
P^{31}	$\frac{1}{2}$	^4S	$\frac{3}{2}$	2	$110.111382(16)^b$	LAM-62
K^{39}	$\frac{3}{2}$	^2S	$\frac{1}{2}$	2	461.719690(30)	BLO-60
K^{41}	$\frac{3}{2}$	^2S	$\frac{1}{2}$	2	254.013870(35)	BLO-60
Rb^{87}	$\frac{3}{2}$	^2S	$\frac{1}{2}$	2	6834.682608(7)	BEN-58
Cs^{133}	$\frac{7}{2}$	^2S	$\frac{1}{2}$	4	9192.631770(10)	ARD-61

^{a} Error estimates in parentheses apply to last figure of quoted value.
^{b} Reference gives value of the coupling constant A which has been used to calculate $\Delta\nu$ from Eq. (4.1.2.17).

AND-60 L. W. Anderson, F. M. Pipkin, and J. C. Baird, Jr., *Phys. Rev.* **120**, 1279 (1960).
ARD-58 M. Arditi and T. R. Carver, *Phys. Rev.* **109**, 1012 (L) (1958).
ARD-61 M. Arditi and T. R. Carver, *Phys. Rev.* **124**, 800 (1961).
BEN-58 P. L. Bender, E. C. Beaty, and A. R. Chi, *Phys. Rev. Letters* **1**, 311 (1958).
BLO-60 A. L. Bloom and J. B. Carr, *Phys. Rev.* **119**, 1946 (1960).
LAM-62 R. H. Lambert and F. M. Pipkin, *Phys. Rev.* **128**, 198 (1962).
LAM-63 R. H. Lambert and F. M. Pipkin, *Phys. Rev.* **129**, 1233 (1963).
PIP-62 F. M. Pipkin and R. H. Lambert, *Phys. Rev.* **127**, 787 (1962).

4.1.2.5.4.1. *Polarization of Resonance Radiation.* In general, any anisotropic excitation process may be expected to populate certain of the magnetic sublevels of an excited atomic level more heavily than others, and thereby lead to a net polarization of the spontaneous decay radiation. In excitation by electron bombardment, it is the unidirectional nature of the electron beam that does the job. The same is true for excitation by a unidirectional beam of resonance light; furthermore, here the anisotropy of the excitation process may be increased still further by artificially polarizing the incident light.

In detail, the means by which resonance radiation becomes polarized may be understood with the help of Fig. 13(a). This shows the magnetic sublevels of two atomic levels: at bottom a ground level of total angular momentum $F = \frac{1}{2}$, and at top an excited level of total angular momentum $F = 3/2$. Lines drawn between the sublevels represent the unresolved Zeeman components of the optical resonance line, and numbers give the relative transition probabilities of these components, calculated from the formulas of Section 4.1.2.2.4.2. The sublevels of the excited state all have the same radiative lifetime, and so their relative populations under resonance excitation will be determined by their relative excitation rates.

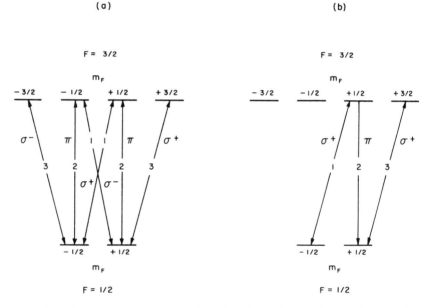

FIG. 13.   Zeeman components of an $F = \frac{1}{2} \rightarrow F = 3/2$ transition in (a) unpolarized excitation and (b) circularly polarized excitation.

(Collision effects are neglected.) For purposes of illustration one may assume that the ground sublevels are equally populated, so that the excitation rates are given by products of transition probabilities and the intensities of the various polarization components in the incident light beam. Light of any polarization may be represented as a superposition of three polarization components, parallel (π), right-hand circular (σ^+), and left-hand circular (σ^-), all referred to the quantization axis of the experiment. (If, as usual, a magnetic field is present, the quantization axis is the direction of the field; otherwise it may be taken either parallel or perpendicular to the direction of the incident light beam.) A beam of *unpolarized* natural light, incident at right angles to the quantization axis, is equivalent to a superposition of π, σ^+, and σ^- light in the intensity proportions 2:1:1. Applying to these proportions the upward transition probabilities in Fig. 13(a), one finds relative populations of 3:5:5:3 in the four excited sublevels. The polarization of the re-emitted resonance radiation, defined according to (4.1.2.16), may be found by applying the relative transition probabilities a second time, and is, for this case, approximately 18 %. It is clear that a greater polarization, up to 100 %, could be induced by artificially π-polarizing the excitation light.

4.1.2.5.4.2. *Optical Pumping.* The classical studies of resonance radiation concentrated, naturally enough, on the excited atomic level, the level that is primarily involved in the reradiation process. The ground level was treated as an inert reservoir of unexcited atoms; the distribution of population among its sublevels was assumed to be uniform and unvarying with time. This is true enough when the beam of incident light is either unpolarized or linearly polarized, but it may be very far from true when the incident light is circularly polarized. Fig. 13(b) shows what happens when the resonance transition of Fig.13(a) is excited with right-hand circularly polarized (σ^+) light. Starting with an equal number of atoms in the two sublevels of the ground level, the absorption and re-emission process will deposit more atoms back into the $m_F = +\frac{1}{2}$ sublevel than into the $m_F = -\frac{1}{2}$ sublevel. A second absorption and re-emission process will increase the population disparity further, and so on. In time, and in the absence of competing processes, all of the atoms that were originally in the $m_F = -\frac{1}{2}$ sublevel will be "optically pumped" into the $m_F = +\frac{1}{2}$ sublevel; the atoms will become completely oriented.

Practically, of course, the sublevel into which atoms are pumped will be somewhat leaky, making complete orientation unattainable. The leakage occurs during collisions of oriented atoms with other gas particles or with the walls of the containing vessel; the fluctuating electromagnetic fields experienced by an atom during such a collision can cause transitions between the sublevels of the ground state, and this obviously will tend to undo the optical pumping. (When happening to atoms in the excited state, the same kinds of collisions act to depolarize the resonance radiation.)

The degree of orientation caused by optical pumping may be measured by several methods, among them the classical method of analyzing the polarization of the resonance radiation. From Fig. 13(b) it may be seen that, provided collision depolarization effects are small, this radiation initially will be a definite mixture of σ- and π-polarized light, but that as the atoms become oriented the relative intensity of the π-polarized light will decrease, and approach zero at 100 % orientation. Another very simple method, which works even at gas pressures so high that the resonance radiation is completely depolarized, is to monitor the intensity of the pumping light transmitted through the atomic vapor. Devised by Dehmelt,[77] this scheme is particularly effective when the angular momentum of the ground level is equal to or greater than that of the excited level, for in such cases the pumping process transfers atoms to a sublevel from which they cannot absorb the circularly polarized pumping light. The reason is simply that there is no excited sublevel to which absorption transitions can occur, subject to the selection rule $\Delta m = \pm 1$ for σ^+ radiation. Accordingly, a completely oriented vapor becomes completely transparent to the pumping light, and a disorientation of the atoms produces a dimming of the transmitted light. A third detection method, also suggested by Dehmelt,[78] makes use of intensity fluctuations in a secondary "cross" beam of resonance light; this method is discussed separately in Section 4.1.2.5.4.4.

With better understanding of the phenomenon, it became clear that the essence of optical orientation lay in the absorption of the resonance light and not in its subsequent re-emission. The beam of resonance light, intense and nearly completely circularly polarized, emptied certain sublevels of the ground level much faster than they could be refilled by optical decay, regardless of the population distribution in the excited level. Primarily, the phenomenon of optical pumping was due to differences in absorption transition rates. Since absorption transition rates depend on the *intensity* of the incident light, as well as on its polarization, it was logical to inquire whether, in certain cases, optical pumping could not be done with light that was perhaps unpolarized, but that had an unnatural distribution of intensity over the profile of the optical absorption line. For example, by filtering out of the incoming light beam just one hyperfine component of the resonance line, it should be possible to pump atoms of the absorbing vapor into the corresponding hyperfine structure level of the ground level. As a second example, one could excite an atomic vapor with the light of another atom whose resonance line happened to coincide, but not quite perfectly, with the resonance line of the vapor atoms. Both of these methods have been applied, with success, to radio spectroscopic experiments which are described below.

4.1.2.5.4.3. *The Quadrupole Moment of Sodium*-23. Many atoms, sodium for one, have no electric quadrupole hyperfine structure in their ground levels, not because their nuclei lack quadrupole moments but

[77] H. G. Dehmelt, *Phys. Rev.* **105**, 1487 (1957).
[78] H. G. Dehmelt, *Phys. Rev.* **105**, 1924 (1957).

because the ground levels happen to have angular momenta $J = 0$ or $\frac{1}{2}$. To measure the nuclear quadrupole moments of such atoms it is necessary to deal with excited levels of higher angular momenta; optical spectra, for instance, yield rough values of quadrupole moments when measured very carefully. Following Brossel and Bitter's exploratory experiment on mercury, Sagalyn[79] realized that the double resonance technique offered an excellent way to measure quadrupole hyperfine structure in excited atoms and he proceeded to do such an experiment on the $3^2P_{3/2}$ level of sodium. His experimental apparatus was essentially identical with that of Brossel and Bitter, which is described in Section 4.1.2.6.3 and illustrated by Fig. 17.

The nuclear spin of common Na^{23} is $3/2$, and the $3^2P_{3/2}$ excited state has four hyperfine structure levels, with $F = 0$, 1, 2, and 3. Each of these closely spaced levels is populated by absorption of the 5890 Å sodium line (the shorter wavelength member of the familiar yellow resonance doublet) but the sublevels with small magnetic quantum numbers are populated preferentially by π-polarized resonance light. Radio-frequency transitions of the $\Delta m_F = \pm 1$ type, either among the sublevels of a single hyperfine structure level ($\Delta F = 0$) or between the sublevels of two different hyperfine structure levels ($\Delta F = \pm 1$), tend to smooth out this population distribution, and hence depolarize the re-emitted 5890 Å line. At the low magnetic field strengths that Sagalyn used, the sublevels of a single hyperfine structure level were not separated from each other (the natural level width is about 11 Mc), and only the desired $\Delta F = \pm 1$ transitions gave discrete radio lines. Sagalyn found two of these, each giving depolarizations of 0.1 % at frequencies of 37 and 61 Mc, and identified them with the transitions $F = 2 \leftrightarrow 3$ and $F = 1 \leftrightarrow 2$. Comparing these frequencies with the theoretical hyperfine structure intervals [see (4.1.2.17)], he derived values of the coupling constants A and B and, from B, a value of the nuclear quadrupole moment.

Nearly simultaneously with Sagalyn's work on sodium, Perl, Rabi, and Senitzky[80] developed a different technique for measuring hyperfine structure in excited atoms, and their first experiment was also a measurement, somewhat more precise than Sagalyn's, of the sodium quadrupole moment. This was an atomic beam method, conventional in all respects but one: the atomic beam was illuminated with resonance light as it passed through the radio-frequency exciter, in the C field region. This light tended to disorient the beam atoms, since there was a good chance that the sublevels in which the beam atoms found themselves after optical excitation and decay would be different from sublevels that they

[79] P. L. Sagalyn, *Phys. Rev.* **94**, 885 (1954).

[80] M. L. Perl, I. I. Rabi, and B. Senitzky, *Phys. Rev.* **98**, 611 (1955).

had occupied coming out of the A magnet. Radio-frequency resonance disoriented the beam atoms further by equalizing the populations of excited sublevels, and this extra disorientation could be detected with a conventional B magnet and surface ionization detector. In this beam double resonance method, the essential anisotropy of the excitation process is provided by the controlled motion of the beam atoms, so that unpolarized and even isotropic illumination may be used. The primary advantage of the beam method over the double resonance method of Brossel and Bitter, an advantage that may overweigh its greater complexity, is that there are no collisions to disorient atoms in the excited state, and hence to interfere with the radio-frequency resonance process.

4.1.2.5.4.4. *Superprecise Measurements of Alkali Hyperfine Structure.* Optical pumping offers an alternative method of measuring hyperfine structure in ground state atoms, a method that is at once simpler than the atomic beam method and more sensitive than the microwave absorption method. Just as in double resonance experiments on excited atoms, one applies a radio-frequency field to the optically pumped vapor, and looks for changes in the polarization or intensity of the resonance radiation. Early experiments showed that the method worked, and demonstrated some interesting multiple quantum effects, but yielded no new or more precise measurements of hyperfine structure. The method seemed applicable only to alkali atoms, and perhaps a few others that had figured in the classical work on resonance radiation, and this was a field that atomic beam spectroscopists had already tilled pretty thoroughly.

Optical pumping remained an interesting phenomenon, but one of little use to radio spectroscopy, until experiments by Brossel, Margerie, and Kastler[81] and by Dehmelt[77] got rid of the notion that collisions between oriented atoms and other gas particles are necessarily bad, something to be avoided scrupulously. Such collisions did, of course, tend to depolarize the resonance radiation, and thereby make it harder to detect radio-frequency resonance by the classical polarization method. Nevertheless, Brossel, Margerie, and Kastler, working with sodium, found that foreign gases at a pressure of a few tenths of a millimeter Hg actually increased the *change* in polarization due to radio-frequency transitions by an order of magnitude or more. The reason, they soon realized, was that the foreign gas was acting as a buffer; by slowing down the diffusion of oriented atoms to the wall of the absorption cell, it was giving the optical pumping process more time to act, and thereby leading to a higher degree of orientation. Evidently the ground ^2S state of sodium was relatively impervious to the disorienting effects of collisions with foreign gas particles, at least as compared to the excited ^2P state. Just *how* impervious was shown by Dehmelt, who, working with buffer gas pressures up to 40 cm Hg, measured relaxation times as long as 1/5 second for optically pumped sodium. At such high pressures the resonance radiation was completely depolarized, but this did not interfere with Dehmelt's detection method, which was to monitor the intensity of the pumping light transmitted by the sodium vapor–buffer gas mixture.

Dehmelt's was not a radio spectroscopic experiment, but its implications for radio spectroscopy were clear. A relaxation time of 1/5 second would produce a radio line width of less than 2 cps, a remarkably small figure, if other sources of line broadening were absent. Line broadening due to magnetic field inhomogeneities and radio-frequency power saturation were reducible to within hailing distance of 2 cps, and this left the Doppler effect, small as it is in radio spectroscopy, the major broadening influence. But, according to Wittke and Dicke's microwave absorption experiment (Section 4.1.2.5.3.), Doppler broadening could be reduced by adding buffer gas, the very same technique that also gave the long relaxation time. At a single stroke, therefore, by simply adding an inert buffer gas to the optical pumping vessel, it appeared that one could eliminate both collision broadening and Doppler broadening as sources of radio line width. There was only one serious limitation on the use of buffer gases: their pressure narrowing effect on radio lines is peculiar to atoms in S states. Generally, atoms with orbital angular momentum (e.g., P and D states) stand a much greater chance of being disoriented by collisions and, for such atoms, buffer gases are worthless; they only broaden the radio lines.

A typical apparatus for radio spectroscopic studies of optically oriented atoms is diagramed in Fig. 14. This apparatus was used in exploratory experiments on sodium and potassium by Bell and Bloom,[82] who also developed a phenomenological theory of optical orientation and radio-frequency resonance in alkali vapor–buffer gas mixtures. To compare the two detection schemes proposed by Dehmelt there are two light beams—a "z beam" parallel to the direction of a weak magnetic field and a "crossbeam" perpendicular to the field. The absorption cell is filled with argon at 30 mm Hg together with a little alkali metal, and is surrounded by an oven which maintains the alkali vapor pressure at about 2×10^{-6} mm Hg.

The z beam orients the atoms, and thereby induces in the vapor a macroscopic magnetization which precesses at the Larmor frequency about the z axis, with constant projection M_z. The intensity of the light

[82] W. E. Bell and A. L. Bloom, *Phys. Rev.* **107**, 1559 (1957).

reaching the z beam photocell bears a direct relation to the magnitude of M_z, and the disorienting effect of radio-frequency resonance causes a change in the dc current of the photocell. To display the radio line on an oscilloscope, the dc magnetic field is modulated at a low audio frequency. The crossbeam provides an alternate means of detecting the radio-frequency signal; being perpendicular to the magnetic field,

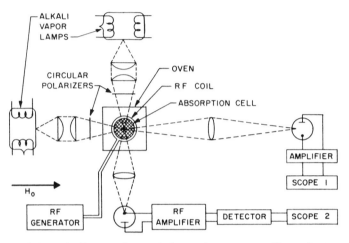

FIG. 14. Schematic diagram of an optical pumping apparatus, illustrating two different methods of detecting radio-frequency resonance.

it has no net orienting effect itself on the alkali vapor. The intensity of the light reaching the crossbeam photocell is related to the transverse component of magnetization, M_x, in the same way that the light reaching the z beam photocell is related to M_z. At the radio-frequency resonance condition, M_x can take on nonzero values because of the phase coherence induced by the radio-frequency field. Whereas M_z is constant, however, M_x varies sinusoidally at the Larmor frequency. Thus the crossbeam, on passing through the absorption cell, becomes amplitude-modulated at the Larmor frequency. Striking the photocell detector, the crossbeam generates a radio-frequency signal, which is then amplified and fed to a second detector. The dc output of this detector measures the strength of the radio-frequency resonance signal, just as does the dc output of the z beam photocell, and the low frequency modulation of the magnetic field allows the signal to be displayed on a second oscilloscope.

    An advantage of the crossbeam detection method is that the photocell detector output is amplified in a radio-frequency amplifier, which is less subject to electrical noise and drift than the dc or audio amplifier that must be used in the z beam detection method. Notice also that the crossbeam signal is at the Larmor frequency, which is just the correct frequency to induce weak field Zeeman transitions among the magnetic sublevels of the oriented atoms. If the output of the radio-frequency signal amplifier is fed back properly to the coil which is wound around the absorption cell, the radio-frequency generator in Fig. 14 may be turned off, for the apparatus has become a self-oscillator. The frequency of self-oscillation is determined solely by the magnetic field strength. Optical pumping devices designed on this principle make simple and extremely sensitive magnetometers,[83,84] and they have been used effectively in explorations of planetary and interplanetary magnetic fields.

Bell and Bloom observed radio lines as narrow as 1 kc; this was a great improvement over earlier optical orientation experiments, but it fell short of what the buffer gas technique was capable of. Magnetic field inhomogeneities were blamed for the excess width. The low-frequency Zeeman transitions which Bell and Bloom observed had a field sensitivity of about 2 kc per milligauss, and so very small field inhomogeneities had an appreciable broadening influence. The obvious solution to this field broadening problem, if one wants to make hyperfine structure measurements of the highest precision, is to work with the field-insensitive $\Delta m_F = 0$ transitions, instead of the $\Delta m_F = \pm 1$ Zeeman transitions. However, it is just these $\Delta m_F = 0$ transitions that the optical orientation method is not equipped to detect, since they have no disorienting effect on the atomic vapor. The optical orientation apparatus makes a very good magnetometer, but a somewhat poorer radio spectrometer.

Undeterred by such arguments, Arditi and Carver[85] measured the $\Delta F = 1$, $m_F = 0 \leftrightarrow m_F = 0$ transition in optically oriented sodium vapor, using an apparatus very similar to that of Fig. 14. The line was 400 cps wide (due to experimental causes other than field broadening), and the hyperfine structure separation could be measured to a precision of a few parts in 10^8. A likely explanation for the success of this experiment was provided by some independent and nearly simultaneous work of Bell and Bloom,[86] who showed that the same $\Delta m_F = 0$ transition could be observed with unpolarized light, i.e., with no orientation of the sodium vapor. Apparently, a different optical pumping process was operating, and Bell and Bloom suggested that this was a pumping due to intensity differences. In the front part of the cell, Nature provides more atoms in the $F = 2$ hyperfine structure level than in the $F = 1$ hyperfine structure level, because of the greater number of $F = 2$ sublevels, and so there will be a greater absorption of the $F = 2$ com-

[83] A. L. Bloom, *Appl. Optics* 1, 61 (1962).
[84] F. D. Colgrove and P. A. Franken, *Phys. Rev.* 119, 680 (1960).
[85] M. Arditi and T. R. Carver, *Phys. Rev.* 109, 1012(L) (1958).
[86] W. E. Bell and A. L. Bloom, *Phys. Rev.* 109, 219(L) (1958).

ponent of the incident resonance light. Progressing through the cell, the light takes on an altered intensity division between the two hyperfine components, and, toward the rear end of the cell, is capable of pumping an appreciable excess of atoms into the $F = 2$ level. Radio-frequency transitions between the two hyperfine structure levels transfer atoms back to the $F = 1$ level, and increase the overall opacity of the cell to the pumping light. This is what was happening, presumably, in Arditi and Carver's experiment as well.

At this point, with a method available for detecting field-independent transitions, the optical pumping apparatus began to show very desirable qualities as an atomic frequency standard. Efforts were made to reduce the radio-frequency line widths as far as possible, and to investigate sources of instability and frequency shifts, in particular the relatively large frequency shifts caused by the high-pressure buffer gas. This work culminated in the rubidium optical pumping frequency standard, which is described in Section 4.1.2.7. Line widths as small as 20 cps have been observed for the field-independent transition of rubidium, in helium and neon buffer gases, which has a center frequency of 6.8 Gc. Smaller widths, down to a few cycles per second, have been observed for the low-frequency Zeeman ($\Delta F = 0$) transitions in rubidium and cesium.

4.1.2.5.4.5. *Hydrogen, Deuterium, and Tritium.* Simple and extremely precise, the optical pumping buffer gas technique of observing radio spectra nevertheless had one serious deficiency: it worked only for S state atoms which had intense optical resonance lines (oscillator strength ~1). Practically, this included only the alkali atoms sodium, potassium, rubidium, and cesium. Dehmelt[87] broke this restriction by showing that optically oriented alkali atoms could *transfer* their orientation to other paramagnetic particles that had been introduced deliberately into the buffer gas. Dehmelt oriented free electrons in this way; succeeding experiments by others showed that the transfer of orientation could take place between two different alkali atoms, for example sodium and rubidium, and also between an alkali atom and an entirely different atom such as hydrogen or nitrogen. The transfer of orientation was explained in each case as due to electron spin exchange collisions, the mechanism whose role in radio line broadening had been discussed earlier by Wittke and Dicke.

The orientation transfer technique had obvious applications to radio spectroscopy; in fact, it was by observing the radio-frequency spin resonance line of oriented electrons that Dehmelt established that a collisional transfer of orientation was taking place. In its application

[87] H. G. Dehmelt, *Phys. Rev.* **109**, 381 (1958).

to atomic spectroscopy, the technique is well-illustrated by the recent experiment of Anderson, Pipkin, and Baird,[88] a remeasurement of the hyperfine structure of hydrogen and its isotopes. This experiment was done with a conventional optical orientation apparatus, similar to Fig. 14, modified only by placing two electric discharge electrodes in the wall of the absorption cell. The cell contained rubidium vapor, hydrogen gas, and a buffer gas; the approximate partial pressures were 10^{-7}, 1, and 10 mm Hg, respectively. Circularly polarized light from a rubidium lamp oriented the rubidium vapor in the usual way, and the orientation was monitored by the light transmission method. Hydrogen atoms were formed within the cell by an electric discharge between the two electrodes. These atoms became oriented by spin exchange collisions with rubidium atoms, which themselves, as a result, tended to become disoriented. The pumping light repaired this damage, and the system settled down to a steady state in which both rubidium and hydrogen atoms were oriented, and only enough pumping light was being absorbed to counteract the weak disorienting effect, on both types of atoms, of wall and buffer gas collisions. This was the situation in the absence of a radiofrequency field. When the radio-frequency generator was turned on it had a strong disorienting effect on the hydrogen atoms, provided it was tuned to the frequency of a hyperfine structure transition of the type $\Delta m_F = \pm 1$. Spin exchange collisions passed the extra disorienting effect back to the rubidium atoms and, consequently, the absorption cell became more opaque to the rubidium pumping light. This cycle was made repetitive by a low-frequency (18 cps) on-off modulation of the radio-frequency generator; the corresponding ac output of the photocell detector was measured by a lock-in detector.

In this manner, Anderson, Pipkin, and Baird measured the hyperfine structure separations of all three hydrogen isotopes to an accuracy of about 2 parts in 10^8, a considerable improvement over the earlier atomic beam and microwave absorption experiments. When this is compared with the superprecision attainable in alkali optical pumping experiments, however, it is clear that a price has been paid for the orientation transfer process. In addition to the field inhomogeneity broadening that afflicts nearly all optical orientation experiments (and which can be eliminated in alkali work by using intensity pumping), there is a further unavoidable broadening of the radio lines caused by the very collision process that makes the orientation transfer method work. In the experiment under discussion, the breadth of the deuterium radio lines was 175 cps; the lines are nearly field-independent, and it seemed likely that their width was due entirely to spin exchange collisions between deuterium atoms

---

[88] L. W. Anderson, F. M. Pipkin, and J. C. Baird, *Phys. Rev.* **120**, 1279 (1960).

(deuterium-rubidium collisions were less important because of the very low rubidium vapor density). The strongly field-dependent lines of hydrogen and tritium were two to eight times broader than this, presumably because of irreducible field inhomogeneities.

4.1.2.5.4.6. *Mercury*. Because of its very intense resonance line and its ready availability in vapor form, the mercury atom has long been a favorite test atom for new radio-optical techniques. The original double resonance method cut its teeth on mercury, and since then the methods of electron bombardment and optical pumping have been tried successfully. Two more new techniques, "double resonance by frequency change" and "level crossing," have been applied recently to the excited mercury atom, and have yielded precise measurements of the hyperfine structure of the several odd isotopes of mercury.

The new double resonance method, developed by Kohler,[89] detects radio-frequency transitions in an excited atom by a change in the re-emitted resonance radiation, as did the original method of Brossel and Bitter. Instead of a change in polarization, however, this is a change in the intensity distribution over the resonance line profile. The 2537 Å resonance line of natural mercury has a complex profile, chiefly because of the resolved hyperfine structure of the two stable odd isotopes Hg^{199} and Hg^{201}. Natural mercury also contains several even isotopes which, although lacking hyperfine structure, complicate the line profile with their isotope shifts. As it happens, the single line component due to the even isotope Hg^{198} coincides almost exactly with the center one of the three hyperfine components due to Hg^{201}; this sort of partial overlap of one optical line on the resolved hyperfine structure of another line is essential to Kohler's method.

To measure the hyperfine structure of Hg^{201}, Kohler illuminated the mercury absorption cell with a Hg^{198} lamp. This light could be absorbed and reradiated by the Hg^{198} fraction of the vapor, and also, through the center hyperfine component of its resonance line only, by the Hg^{201} fraction of the vapor. This populated the $F = 3/2$ hyperfine structure level of the 6^3P_1 resonance level of Hg^{201}, but not the $F = 1/2$ nor the $F = 5/2$ hyperfine structure levels. The intensity of the re-emitted resonance radiation was monitored by a photomultiplier detector, in front of which was placed a second absorption cell filled with Hg^{198} vapor at a fairly high pressure. This second cell acted as a narrow-band rejection filter for the Hg^{198} resonance line and also for the central hyperfine component of the Hg^{201} line; to the other two hyperfine components, at their slightly different wavelengths, it was nearly transparent. Radio-frequency transitions among the excited

[89] R. H. Kohler, *Phys. Rev.* **121**, 1104 (1961).

hyperfine structure levels of Hg^{201} tended to equalize their populations, and hence increased the intensity of the light reaching the photo-multiplier.

This method was highly successful for Hg^{201}; the signal-to-noise ratio of the radio-frequency lines was much larger than that yielded, in a similar experiment, by the older polarization method. Further hyperfine structure measurements have been made recently on the other odd isotopes of mercury. In principle, the technique can be applied to any optical resonance line that shows resolved hyperfine structure, provided a suitable light source is available. In cases where two isotopic components of a resonance line are close but do not overlap, a magnetic field may be used to broaden or split one of the isotopic components, so as to produce a partial overlap with the other.

The level crossing technique, soon after its original demonstration on the fine structure of helium (Section 4.1.2.4.4.1.), was used by Hirsch and Stager[90] to measure the hyperfine structure of Hg^{197}. Although it shares some of the properties of radio-optical resonance methods, in particular their freedom from Doppler broadening, level crossing is a purely optical method. It works by intensity changes in the optical resonance radiation of excited atoms, these changes being caused by the intersection of pairs of magnetic sublevels at particular values of an external magnetic field. (Examples of sublevel intersections may be seen in Fig. 2.) When such an intersection is brought about between a pair of excited sublevels, each of which is participating in the absorption and re-emission of resonance radiation, interference effects modify the angular distribution of the resonance radiation from the two sublevels[71]; an optical detector, fixed in position, records this change in angular distribution as an intensity change. From a measurement of the magnetic field strenth and prior knowledge of the Zeeman effect of the resonance level, one can then deduce the original hyperfine structure separation of the two sublevels which have been brought into coincidence. Conversely, if one knows the hyperfine structure interval already, the measured field strength yields the atomic g factor. The width of the level crossing "resonance," like that of a radio-frequency resonance, is determined entirely by the natural radiative width of the sublevels, and so the level crossing method has the same inherent precision as the older radio-optical methods.

4.1.2.5.5. MUONIUM. Slowing down in a gas, a positive mu meson (muon) can pick up an electron and exist, for about 2 microseconds, as a free "muonium" atom. This is somewhat more like a genuine hydrogen atom than is positronium (Section 4.1.2.4.4.2.), since the muon forms a

[90] H. R. Hirsch and C. V. Stager, *J. Opt. Soc. Am.* **50**, 1052 (1960).

respectably heavy nucleus for the atom, and one can feel more confident in classifying the magnetic interaction between muon and electron as a hyperfine structure interaction, rather than as a fine structure interaction. Apart from being about 200 times heavier, though, the muon is surprisingly like an electron in all its measurable properties, including its charge states (+ and −), its spin, its magnetic moment (corrected for the mass difference), and its interactions with other particles. There remains the possibility that the muon might be different in internal structure, and a good way to settle this point is to measure the hyperfine structure interval of muonium. Such internal structure effects, in the proton, do show up in a close analysis of the ordinary hydrogen hyperfine structure.

A measurement of the muonium hyperfine structure became conceivable after the discovery of parity nonconservation in weak interactions, and in particular after it was verified that (1) muons formed in the decay of pi mesons had their spins oriented along their directions of motion, and that (2) electrons formed in the decay of oriented muons came off with an anisotropic angular distribution. Since muonium made from oriented muons would be to some extent oriented too, all the necessary conditions for a radio-frequency resonance experiment were satisfied. Parity nonconservation would fill the function both of state selector and state analyzer, and radio-frequency transitions between the hyperfine structure levels of muonium would be detectable by changes in the angular distribution of the high-energy (up to 50 Mev) decay electrons.

The experiment has been performed successfully by Ziock et al.[91] working with a muon beam from the Columbia University synchrocyclotron. The beam passes through a high-pressure argon tank, within which is located a resonant microwave cavity. Decay electrons emitted in the beam direction are registered by external detectors and counters, and counts are made with the microwave oscillator (a 1-kw 2.5-Gc klystron) alternately on and off while slowly varying the strength of an external magnetic field. To preserve the orientation axis of the muons, the field must be parallel with the muon beam; to prevent the muonium hyperfine structure interaction from disorienting the muons, the field must be strong, of the order of several thousand gauss. It is difficult to achieve a homogeneous field under these conditions, and inhomogeneity broadening of the radio-frequency line is the main source of experimental error. Measurements are made on the strong field $(m_J, m_\mu) = (\frac{1}{2}, \frac{1}{2}) \leftrightarrow (\frac{1}{2}, -\frac{1}{2})$ line, whose frequency is [see Eq. (4.1.2.20)] approximately $\Delta\nu/2$. An accurate value of $\Delta\nu$ is found by applying the Breit–Rabi formula (4.1.2.9) to the resonance data. The best experi-

[91] K. Ziock, V. W. Hughes, R. Prepost, J. M. Bailey, and W. E. Cleland, *Phys. Rev. Letters* **8**, 103 (1962).

mental value obtained to date confirms, but is considerably less precise than, the theoretical value calculated on the basis that the muon is just a heavy electron.

4.1.2.6. Zeeman Effect. From the magnetomechanical relations, Eq. (4.1.2.2), the magnetic moment of an atom can be written as

$$\mu = -g_I\mu_0 \mathbf{I} - g_l\mu_0 \sum \mathbf{l}_i - g_s\mu_0 \sum \mathbf{s}_i \qquad (4.1.2.23)$$

where $\mathbf{I}$ is the spin angular momentum of the nucleus and $\mathbf{l}_i$ and $\mathbf{s}_i$ are the orbital and spin angular momenta of an electron. The summations are made over all the electrons of the atom. According to quantum mechanics, μ is to be regarded as an operator, and the interaction of an atom with a magnetic field $\mathbf{H}$ can be calculated by diagonalizing the perturbation matrix of the scalar product $\mu \cdot \mathbf{H}$. A general calculation of this sort would yield the Zeeman energies of the atom in terms of angular momentum quantum numbers, the three g factors, g_I, g_l, and g_s, and certain additional parameters to specify the angular momentum coupling scheme; one of these parameters, for example, would serve to locate the atom in its correct place along the road from $L - S$ coupling to $j - j$ coupling. In general, most of the theoretical Zeeman energy can be lumped into a term linear in H, which represents the direct interaction of the electronic orbital and spin magnetism with the external field. This term, when written in the form $g_J\mu_0 m_J H$, defines the atomic g factor, g_J. The theoretical expression for g_J will depend on the coupling scheme, and also may contain small corrections for relativistic effects. For atoms which do not deviate markedly from the $L - S$ coupling scheme, and for which the relativistic corrections are small, the Landé formula (4.1.2.7) is a useful approximation to the theoretical g factor. Radio-frequency Zeeman spectra occasionally are studied to find out quantum numbers and coupling schemes, for example in very heavy, complex atoms, but more typically this information is already available from optical spectra. The ground levels of many light atoms, in particular, exhibit almost pure L-S coupling, and experiments on such atoms can provide fundamental tests of the Zeeman theory itself.

The primary result of any radio-frequency measurement of the atomic Zeeman effect is a numerical value of g_J, the atomic g factor. This is gotten from an analysis of the radio spectrum, based on energy formulas like (4.1.2.9) and (4.1.2.10). To achieve precision, and also to minimize the complicating effects of hyperfine structure, it is best to work with the strongest possible magnetic field, consistent with the requirement of good homogeneity. This usually means field strength within the range 1–5 kilogauss. The accuracy of a g factor measurement is limited mostly by the difficulty of making accurate measurements of magnetic field strengths. Field inhomogeneities and diamagnetic shielding effects may be serious sources of error. Nuclear magnetic resonance techniques of measuring field strengths are limited in absolute accuracy to about 1 part in 10^5, although they perform much better in relative field measurements. It is because the ratio of two field strengths can be measured more accurately than either one alone that the most precise g factor measurements are always quoted in the form of ratios—ratios of pairs of atomic g factors or ratios of atomic and nuclear g factors.

Field-sensitive "Zeeman" lines, $\Delta m_F = \pm 1$ transitions at weak fields and $\Delta m_J = \pm 1$ transitions at strong fields, are used for g factor measurements, and hence the operating frequency is largely a matter of choice. With this extra degree of experimental freedom, the various methods of radio spectroscopy become more evenly matched in sensitivity and precision. The microwave absorption method, in particular, becomes much more sensitive when a strong magnetic field is used to shift the Zeeman lines to a high microwave frequency. The three general methods of radio spectroscopy have each been applied successfully to g factor measurements on many atoms; in this section only a few representative experiments are described. Apart from the special problems of generating and measuring strong, homogeneous magnetic fields, techniques of radio Zeeman spectroscopy are the same as those of radio hyperfine structure spectroscopy, which are described more fully in the general references of the preceding section. For a resumé of the theory of atomic magnetism, as well as a discussion of selected experiments, the more specialized review article by Hughes[92] should be consulted.

4.1.2.6.1. ATOMIC BEAM RESONANCE. In the early days, beam spectroscopists took little interest in the atomic Zeeman effect, save as a means of calibrating their C fields for determinations of hyperfine structures and nuclear moments. These calibrations depended on the implicit assumption that both the orbital and spin magnetic moments of an atomic electron were exactly one Bohr magneton in size, an assumption that there was no reason to doubt until 1947, when Nafe, Nelson, and Rabi made their historic measurement of the hydrogen hyperfine structure—and found it slightly bigger than expected. If, as this result caused Breit to suggest, the electron spin moment could possibly be larger than one Bohr magneton, then the time had come for a critical examination of the Zeeman effect, in order to pin down the real size of the spin moment, and also to check on the field calibration procedure that had been used in the past. With these thoughts in mind, Kusch and Foley[93]

[92] V. W. Hughes, in "Recent Research in Molecular Beams" (I. Estermann, ed.). Academic Press, New York, 1959.

[93] P. Kusch and H. M. Foley, Phys. Rev. **74**, 250 (1948).

TABLE VI. Atomic g Factors Measured by the Atomic Beam
Magnetic Resonance Method

Atom	Atomic term	J	$g_J{}^a$	Reference
H	^2S	$\frac{1}{2}$	2.002285(2)	KOE-52
He^4	^3S	1	2.002238(2)	DRA-58
B^{11}	^2P	$\frac{1}{2}$	0.6656(4)	LEW-60
Ne^{20}	^3P	2	1.500888(5)	LUR-60
A^{40}	^3P	2	1.500964(8)	LUR-60
Sc^{46}	^2D	$\frac{5}{2}$	1.1995(18)	PET-62
		$\frac{3}{2}$	0.7990(8)	
Mn^{56}	^6S	$\frac{5}{2}$	2.0012(1)	CHI-61b
As^{76}	^4S	$\frac{3}{2}$	1.994(3)	CHR-61
Y^{89}	^2D	$\frac{5}{2}$	1.20028(19)	PEN-59
		$\frac{3}{2}$	0.79927(11)	
Sb^{121,123}	^4S	$\frac{3}{2}$	1.9705(2)	FER-60
Ce^{140}	—	—	0.7651(1)	SMI-61
		—	0.9454(1)	
		—	1.0772(2)	
Pr^{141}	^4I	$\frac{9}{2}$	0.7311(2)	CAB-61
Pr^{142}	^4I	$\frac{9}{2}$	0.7322(3)	CAB-62
Nd^{144}	^5I	7	1.19(2)	SMI-61
		6	1.0715(20)	
		5	0.9002(2)	
		4	0.6032(1)	
Pm^{147}	^6H	$\frac{9}{2}$	1.070(7)	CAB-61
		$\frac{7}{2}$	0.831(5)	
Sm^{152}	^7F	6	1.49419(10)	PIC-61
		5	1.49533(6)	
		4	1.49625(4)	
		3	1.49707(3)	
		2	1.49779(3)	
		1	1.49840(5)	
Eu^{151,153}	^8S	$\frac{7}{2}$	1.99340	SAN-60
Gd^{158}	^9D	6	1.67(2)	SMI-61
		5	1.73(1)	
		4	1.8392(5)	
		3	2.0708(4)	
		2	2.6514(6)	
Dy^{164}	^5I	8	1.24166(7)	SMI-61

TABLE VI (continued)

Atom	Atomic term	J	$g_J{}^a$	Reference
Ho^{165}	^4I	$\frac{15}{2}$	1.19515(10)	GOO-62
Ho^{166}	^4I	$\frac{15}{2}$	1.19509(7)	CHI-61a
Er^{166}	^3H	6	1.1638(2)	SMI-61
Tm^{169}	^2F	$\frac{7}{2}$	1.14119(4)	RIT-62b
Tm^{170}	^2F	$\frac{7}{2}$	1.14122(15)	CAB-60
Lu^{175}	^2D	$\frac{5}{2}$	1.20040(16)	RIT-62a
		$\frac{3}{2}$	0.79921(8)	
$Hg^{199,201}$	6^3P	2	1.50099(10)	MCD-60
	6^3D	3	1.0867(5)	
Bi^{209}	^4S	$\frac{3}{2}$	1.6433(2)	TIT-60
$Po^{204,205,206}$	—	2	1.39609(4)	AXE-61
Pa^{233}	—	$\frac{11}{2}$	0.8141(4)	MAR-61
		$\frac{9}{2}$	0.8062(15)	
		$\frac{7}{2}$	0.7293(15)	
Pu^{239}	^7F	1	1.4975(10)	HUB-58
Am^{241}	^8S	$\frac{7}{2}$	1.9371(10)	MAR-60
Cm^{242}	—	—	1.671(3)	HUB-59
		—	1.776(2)	
		—	2.000(3)	
		—	2.561(3)	

[a] Based on a scale in which the magnetic moment of protons in a spherical sample of mineral oil is exactly $(657.446)^{-1}$ Bohr magnetons. This figure is the unweighted average result of three experimental determinations of g_p/g_l, the proton g factor relative to the orbital g factor of free electrons [J. H. Gardner, Phys. Rev. 83, 996 (1951); P. Franken and S. Liebes, Jr., ibid. 104, 1197 (1956); S. Liebes, Jr., and P. Franken, ibid. 116, 633 (1959)]. As compared to the tabulation of Kusch and Hughes [in "Handbuch der Physik—Encyclopedia of Physics" (S. Flugge, ed.), Vol. 37, Part I. Springer, Berlin, 1959], which was composed prior to the most recent measurement of g_p/g_l, this new figure scales all absolute values of atomic g factors upward by 4 parts in 10^6. The error estimates in parentheses apply to the last figure of the quoted g factor, and do not include the experimental uncertainty in g_p/g_l itself, which is approximately 1 part in 10^5.

AXE-61   S. Axensten and C. M. Olsmats, Arkiv Fysik 19, 461 (1961).
CAB-60   A. Y. Cabezas and I. Lindgren, Phys. Rev. 120, 920 (1960).
CAB-61   A. Y. Cabezas, I. Lindgren, and R. Marrus, Phys. Rev. 122, 1796 (1961).
CAB-62   A. Y. Cabezas, I. Lindgren, R. Marrus, and W. A. Nierenberg, Phys. Rev. 126, 1004 (1962).
CHI-61a   W. J. Childs and L. S. Goodman, Phys. Rev. 122, 591 (1961).
CHI-61b   W. J. Childs, L. S. Goodman, and L. J. Kieffer, Phys. Rev. 122, 891 (1961).
CHR-61   R. L. Christensen, D. R. Hamilton, H. G. Bennewitz, J. B. Reynolds, and H. H. Stroke, Phys. Rev. 122, 1302 (1961).

DRA-58   C. W. Drake, V. W. Hughes, A. Lurio, and J. A. White, *Phys. Rev.* **112**, 1627 (1958).
FER-60   P. C. B. Fernando, G. D. Rochester, I. J. Spalding, and K. F. Smith, *Phil. Mag.* [8] **5**, 1291 (1960).
GOO-62   L. S. Goodman, H. Kopfermann, and K. Schlüpmann, *Naturwissenschaften* **49**, 101 (1962).
HUB-58   J. C. Hubbs, R. Marrus, W. A. Nierenberg, and J. L. Worcester, *Phys. Rev.* **109**, 390 (1958).
HUB-59   J. C. Hubbs, R. Marrus, and J. O. Winocur, *Phys. Rev.* **114**, 586 (1959).
KOE-52   S. H. Koenig, A. G. Prodell, and P. Kusch, *Phys. Rev.* **88**, 191 (1952).
LEW-60   H. Lew and R. S. Title, *Can. J. Phys.* **38**, 868 (1960).
LUR-60   A. Lurio, G. Weinreich, C. W. Drake, V. W. Hughes, and J. A. White, *Phys. Rev.* **120**, 153 (1960).
MAR-60   R. Marrus, W. A. Nierenberg, and J. Winocur, *Phys. Rev.* **120**, 1429 (1960).
MAR-61   R. Marrus, W. A. Nierenberg, and J. Winocur, *Nuclear Phys.* **23**, 90 (1961).
MCD-60   M. N. McDermott and W. L. Lichten, *Phys. Rev.* **119**, 134 (1960).
PEN-59   S. Penselin, *Z. Physik* **154**, 231 (1959).
PET-62   F. R. Petersen and H. A. Shugart, *Phys. Rev.* **128**, 1740 (1962).
PIC-61   F. M. J. Pichanick and G. K. Woodgate, *Proc. Roy. Soc.* **A263**, 89 (1961).
RIT-62a G. J. Ritter, *Phys. Rev.* **126**, 240 (1962).
RIT-62b G. J. Ritter, *Phys. Rev.* **128**, 2238 (1962).
SAN-60   P. G. H. Sandars and G. K. Woodgate, *Proc. Roy. Soc.* **A257**, 269 (1960).
SMI-61   K. F. Smith and I. J. Spalding, *Proc. Roy. Soc.* **A265**, 133 (1961).
TIT-60   R. S. Title and K. F. Smith, *Phil. Mag.* [8] 5, 1281 (1960).

proceeded to investigate, by the atomic beam method, the radio Zeeman spectra of sodium, gallium, and indium to an accuracy of about 1 part in 10^4. Their goal was to measure several atomic g factors and, from these, to derive a value for the electron spin g factor, g_s. The experiment gave clear evidence that g_s was in fact larger than 2, its value according to the Dirac theory, and by about the right amount (1 part in 10^3) to account for the hydrogen hyperfine structure.

Soon after this important experiment, the existence of the "spin moment anomaly" of the electron was rationalized, and its value calculated, by the theoretical methods of quantum electrodynamics. To test the theoretical value it was necessary to measure g_s to a precision of at least 1 part in 10^6. Only recently, in a precession experiment on free electrons,[94] has such a measurement been made successfully. For several years prior to this the best numerical values of g_s were those to be found from radio spectroscopic experiments on simple atoms, especially the hydrogen atom. Hydrogen in its ground level is well-suited to such measurements because its coupling scheme is known very precisely (essentially pure L-S coupling) and because relativistic corrections to the Landé g factor can be evaluated exactly.

Interest in the atomic Zeeman effect for its own sake continued, once aroused by the Kusch–Foley experiment, and succeeding atomic

[94] D. T. Wilkinson and H. R. Crane, *Phys. Rev.* **130**, 852 (1963).

beam experiments have yielded many precise measurements of atomic
g factors. Kusch and Hughes, in their encyclopedia article,[53] tabulate
these measurements up to 1959, and Table VI continues from there
with more recent (to mid-1963) results. These experiments demonstrate
several approaches to the problem of calibrating the C field, which was
the only new problem encountered in Zeeman spectroscopy with atomic
beams. For work of the highest precision, the field must be calibrated in
an auxiliary radio-frequency resonance experiment, and the two most
reliable ways of doing this are exemplified by the two experiments
described below.

4.1.2.6.1.1. *Hydrogen.* For their measurement of the hydrogen
g factor, Koenig, Prodell, and Kusch[95] made an atomic beam apparatus
with the C field electromagnet outside the vacuum can. In this exposed
position the magnet could be adjusted and shimmed for the best possible
field homogeneity over the portion of the radio-frequency hairpin,
inside the can, through which the hydrogen beam passed. Suspended
just below the hairpin (a resonant UHF cavity) was a nuclear resonance
magnetometer probe, which contained a small vial of mineral oil. The
magnetic field strength was calibrated in terms of the nuclear magnetic
resonance frequency of protons in the oil molecules; a movable mount
allowed the hairpin to be raised and the magnetometer probe to be
positioned accurately on the center line of the beam, prior to making a
field calibration. Apart from this movable hairpin-magnetometer
structure, and the external location of the C magnet, the beam apparatus
was conventional in design, and indeed the same apparatus was also
used for a precise weak field measurement of the hydrogen hyperfine
structure.[57]

The C magnet was capable of producing a homogeneous field of 1500
gauss, which is a moderately strong field ($x \simeq 3$) for hydrogen. Under
these conditions two field-dependent transitions, which in the notation
$(F, m_F) \leftrightarrow (F', m_F')$ are $(1, 0) \leftrightarrow (1, -1)$ and $(1, 1) \leftrightarrow (0, 0)$, were
observable. The former was chosen for the g factor measurement,
because its frequency is less dependent on the hyperfine structure
separation and because it occurs, conveniently, at a lower frequency.
The experiment was performed by measuring, alternately and in the
same region of magnetic field, the center frequency of the atomic hydrogen line, ν, and the center frequency of the proton resonance line, ν_p.
The Breit–Rabi formula (4.1.2.9), with H expressed in terms of ν_p by
the proton resonance equation

$$h\nu_p = g_p\mu_0 H, \qquad (4.1.2.24)$$

[95] S. H. Koenig, A. G. Prodell, and P. Kusch, *Phys. Rev.* **88**, 191 (1952).

then allowed the ratio $g_J(H; {}^2S_{1/2})/g_p$ to be calculated from the measured frequencies. The fundamental constants h and μ_0 cancel out of this calculation; except for a modest dependence on the experimental value of the hyperfine structure frequency, $\Delta\nu$, the numerical value of the g factor ratio is determined entirely by the measured frequencies ν and ν_p. The major source of uncertainty in the g factor ratio was inhomogeneity of the C field, which careful shimming could reduce but could never quite eliminate. In addition to its broadening and distorting effects on the two resonance lines, this residual field inhomogeneity could cause systematic errors because of the different volumes of magnetic field that were sampled by the atomic resonance and the nuclear resonance processes. The possibility of this "field sampling error" arises, no matter how carefully two radio-frequency resonance systems are interchanged in a magnetic field, whenever the two systems differ either in the physical size or shape of the resonance sample, or differ in the spatial distribution of radio-frequency field intensity. After the two systems have been made as nearly alike as possible in these respects, field sampling errors can be reduced further only by averaging the numerical results of a series of repeated experiments, during the course of which the spatial pattern of residual field inhomogeneity is changed several times. Koenig, Prodell, and Kusch did this, and arrived finally at a value for $g_J(H)/g_p$ which was accurate to 1 part in 10^6. From this they derived a value for the more fundamental electronic ratio g_s/g_l by subtracting the relativistic correction (which is the only difference between g_J and g_s in hydrogen) and then combining the result with an earlier cyclotron resonance measurement of the ratio g_l/g_p. The latter, a very difficult measurement, was accurate to 1 part in 10^5, and this limited the accuracy of the derived ratio g_s/g_l to the same degree. Within this experimental error, the value of g_s/g_l was found to agree with the more precise theoretical calculation.

4.1.2.6.1.2. *Helium*. The hydrogen experiment loses much of its force in the final interpretation, at the point where a relatively crude calibration of the proton g factor in terms of the electron orbital g factor must be brought in. A second experimental method, better in that it steers clear of g_p and at the same time reduces field sampling errors, consists of measuring an atomic g factor in terms of a second atomic g factor. As far as the precise interpretation of results is concerned, however, this trades one problem for another; only for hydrogen (and its isotopes) can the relativistic g factor corrections be evaluated exactly, since only for hydrogen are exact wave functions known. For this reason, measured ratios of atomic g factors usually are better looked upon as tests for atomic wave functions rather than as tests of the finer details of atomic Zeeman theory. An important exception to this rule is the ratio $g_J(\text{He}; {}^3S_1)/g_J(\text{H}; {}^2S_{1/2})$, measured by Drake et al.[96] Accurate wave functions for helium are available, and the experimental result, good to 1 part in 10^6, could be used to test the theory of relativistic g factor corrections to the same precision. (The g factor ratio is not sensitive to the value of g_s/g_l because both atoms are in S states, with spin-only magnetism.)

The experiment employed interchangeable beams of hydrogen atoms and metastable helium atoms, produced by the same electric discharge effusion source. The beam was alternated between hydrogen and metastable helium by simply changing the inlet gas to the discharge tube. A Pirani gauge detected the hydrogen beam; an electron ejection target detected the metastable helium beam. Because the cross sections and paths of the two beams were identical, and the same radio-frequency exciter could be used for both beams, field sampling errors were negligible. Freed from the necessity of matching their radio-frequency exciter to a magnetometer probe, the experimenters chose to design their apparatus on the Ramsey principle, with two separated hairpins. In turn, this relaxed the homogeneity requirement of the C field electromagnet, and allowed it to be placed in its normal position, inside the vacuum can.

4.1.2.6.2. MICROWAVE ABSORPTION (PARAMAGNETIC RESONANCE). A precision electromagnet added to a microwave absorption apparatus converts the latter into what is commonly called an electron paramagnetic resonance (or EPR) spectrometer. A special name is justified, for the absorption apparatus cum electromagnet is a much more flexible and sensitive radio spectroscopic device than the absorption apparatus alone. It is more flexible because of the magnetic scanning capability imparted by the electromagnet; it is more sensitive because the magnetic field, via the Zeeman effect, shifts the absorption spectrum to higher frequencies, where the microwave quanta are more energetic, the natural population differences between atomic sublevels are larger, and the microwave apparatus itself becomes more sensitive. For frequencies up to 10 or 20 Gc, these three factors combine to make the sensitivity of the absorption method vary approximately as the cube of the frequency. Higher frequencies yield diminishing returns, as the microwave apparatus becomes less sensitive and inconveniently small in size, and the necessary magnetic field strengths become so high that good homogeneity cannot be maintained, due to saturation of the electromagnet iron. The requirements of high sensitivity and moderate field strengths (and low cost) are met best by spectrometers that operate at frequencies within the X band, the radar band that covers 8.2–12.4 Gc. All of the several

[96] C. W. Drake, V. W. Hughes, A. Lurio, and J. A. White, Phys. Rev. 112, 1627 (1958).

measurements of atomic g factors by paramagnetic resonance spectroscopy have been made within this frequency band. A complete current (mid-1963) list of these measurements is given by Table VII.

TABLE VII. Atomic g Factors Measured by the Paramagnetic
Resonance Method

Atom	Atomic term	J	$g_J{}^a$	Reference
H	^2S	$\frac{1}{2}$	2.002287(1)	BER-54
D	^2S	$\frac{1}{2}$	2.002284(3)	GEI-57
N^{14}	^4S	$\frac{3}{2}$	2.002122(4)	HEA-54
O^{16}	^3P	2	1.500922(1)	RAD-59
		1	1.500988(1)	
F^{19}	^2P	$\frac{3}{2}$	1.333862(1)	RAD-61
Na^{23}	^2S	$\frac{1}{2}$	2.00229(5)	CON-61
P^{31}	^4S	$\frac{3}{2}$	2.0019(4)	DEH-55
$Cl^{35,37}$	^2P	$\frac{3}{2}$	1.333923(2)^b	HAR-60, BEL-61
K^{39}	^2S	$\frac{1}{2}$	2.00232(5)	CON-61
$Br^{79,81}$	^2P	$\frac{3}{2}$	1.333917(4)	HAR-60
$Rb^{85,87}$	^2S	$\frac{1}{2}$	2.00234(5)	WIL-61
I^{127}	^2P	$\frac{3}{2}$	1.333994(3)	BOW-57
Cs^{133}	^2S	$\frac{1}{2}$	2.00252(5)	WIL-61

^{a} Based on $\mu_p(\text{oil}) = (657.466)^{-1}\mu_0$; see footnote to Table VI. Error estimates in parentheses apply to last figure of quoted value, and do not include the uncertainty in μ_p .
^{b} Unweighted average of two results from cited references.

BEL-61 V. Beltran-Lopez and H. G. Robinson, *Phys. Rev.* **123**, 161 (1961).
BER-54 R. Beringer and M. A. Heald, *Phys. Rev.* **95**, 1474 (1954).
BOW-57 K. D. Bowers, R. A. Kamper, and C. D. Lustig, *Proc. Phys. Soc. (London)* **B70**, 1176 (L) (1957).
CON-61 D. Conrad, *Z. Physik* **162**, 160 (1961).
DEH-55 H. G. Dehmelt, *Phys. Rev.* **99**, 527 (1955).
GEI-57 J. S. Geiger, V. W. Hughes, and H. E. Radford, *Phys. Rev.* **105**, 183 (1957).
HAR-60 J. S. M. Harvey, R. A. Kamper, and K. R. Lea, *Proc. Phys. Soc. (London)* **76**, 979 (1960).
HEA-54 M. A. Heald and R. Beringer, *Phys. Rev.* **96**, 645 (1954).
RAD-59 H. E. Radford and V. W. Hughes, *Phys. Rev.* **114**, 1274 (1959).
RAD-61 H. E. Radford, V. W. Hughes, and V. Beltran-Lopez, *Phys. Rev.* **123**, 153 (1961).
WIL-61 W. Wilke, *Z. Physik* **165**, 562 (1961).

A typical paramagnetic resonance spectrometer is shown schematically by Fig. 15. The microwave circuit is a standard hybrid tee impedance bridge, one arm of which terminates on a sample-containing resonant cavity. The bridge operates at a fixed frequency, usually about 9.5 Gc, and the microwave absorption spectrum is swept through by varying the electromagnet current. A small Zeeman modulation, superposed on the main field, modulates the change in cavity impedance caused by microwave absorption, and the resulting ac detector signal is amplified and displayed either on the oscilloscope or, after lock-in detection, on a chart recorder. Hybrid tee spectrometers are popular for studies of the paramagnetic resonance spectra of solids, and several commercial versions of the apparatus shown in Fig. 15 are available. For work on atomic vapors, it is only necessary to substitute an appropriate microwave cavity for the usual sample holder type that is supplied with the commercial spectrometer. An alternative microwave circuit to that of Fig. 15,

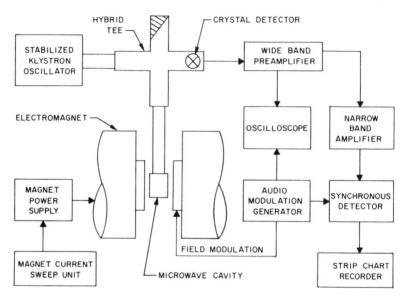

Fig. 15. Block diagram of a hybrid tee paramagnetic resonance spectrometer with crystal video detection.

about equally sensitive, is the simple transmission circuit, in which a detector monitors the microwave power transmitted through the resonant cavity. Either of these basic circuits may be made more sensitive at low microwave power levels (< 1 mw) by the use of superheterodyne detection. Further details on these and other paramagnetic resonance spectrometers may be found in the book by Ingram.[28] A paper by Feher[97] analyzes the sensitivity of the paramagnetic resonance spectrometer in its various configurations.

[97] G. Feher, *Bell System Tech. J.* **36**, 449 (1957).

4.1.2.6.2.1. *Hydrogen.* Shortly after Koenig, Prodell, and Kusch's atomic beam measurement of $g_J(H)/g_p$, Beringer and Heald[98] measured the same quantity by paramagnetic resonance; their intent was to check the value of this important ratio by a different experimental method. Beringer and Heald flowed hydrogen gas, partly dissociated by an electric discharge, through the microwave cavity of a transmission spectrometer, in the manner illustrated by Fig. 16. In its essentials, this

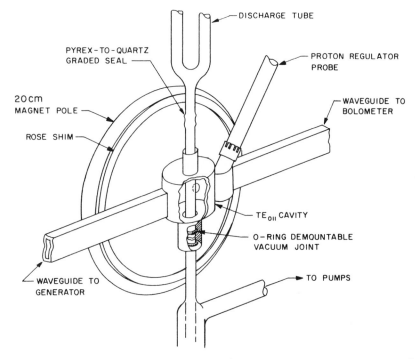

FIG. 16.   Apparatus for precise paramagnetic resonance measurements on atomic hydrogen.

experimental arrangement is very similar to that with which Wittke and Dicke later measured the hydrogen hyperfine structure. (One difference is that here the microwave cavity is much smaller, since it operates at 9 Gc rather than at 1420 Mc.) The cavity shape and dimensions are chosen to make it resonate in the circular cylindrical TE_{011} mode, a high-Q mode whose microwave field distribution is particularly well-suited to the experiment. A high Q (i.e., low absorption by the cavity walls) is necessary to make the spectrometer sensitive to the very small absorption of microwave power by the atomic vapor. The proper micro-

[98] R. Beringer and M. A. Heald, *Phys. Rev.* **95**, 1474 (1954).

wave field distribution is necessary to minimize field sampling errors, the same errors that prompted Koenig, Prodell, and Kusch to make their radio-frequency exciter and proton magnetometer probe as nearly alike as possible. Herein the paramagnetic resonance experiment had an edge over the atomic beam experiment, for the electromagnetic field distribution of the TE_{011} cavity is quite similar to that of a short solenoid, centered within the cavity and coaxial with it. Accordingly, a proton resonance probe with a properly wound radio-frequency coil would, when substituted for the atom vapor tube, sample just the correct volume of magnetic field. Sampling errors are reduced further by the cylindrical shape of the atom vapor sample, which can be matched accurately by a liquid proton resonance sample.

Beringer and Heald did their experiment by measuring alternately the microwave resonance frequency and the proton resonance frequency at the magnetic field setting that corresponded to the center of the microwave resonance line. The field was regulated continuously by a second proton resonance probe, located, as shown in Fig. 16, just outside the microwave cavity. The value of $g_J(H)/g_p$ was found by averaging the results of several measurements on each of the two field-sensitive hyperfine structure lines, using the Breit–Rabi formula to derive g_J/g_p values from the measured frequencies ν and ν_p. The microwave line width, caused chiefly by field inhomogeneity broadening, was about 200 kc, which was comparable with line widths observed in Koenig, Prodell, and Kusch's atomic beam experiment. Within the experimental uncertainties, which were in both cases 1 part in 10^6, the paramagnetic resonance and atomic beam measurements of $g_J(H)/g_p$ agreed completely.

4.1.2.6.2.2. *Other Atoms*. An apparatus like that of Fig. 16 will accept any of the permanent gases, and, following Beringer and Heald's measurement of the hydrogen g factor, similar experiments were done on nitrogen, oxygen, deuterium, fluorine, and chlorine. In the later experiments, electrodeless radio-frequency discharge tubes were substituted for the Woods-type dc discharge tube. Being simply a straight tube slipped through a radio-frequency coil or cavity resonator, the electrodeless discharge tube is handier than the Woods tube, easier to clean and, if necessary, to apply special wall coatings to. A source of discharge power that has become popular in the last few years is the commercial diathermy generator, a small magnetron unit which supplies up to 125 watts of power at 2450 Mc.

Vapors of volatile substances, as well as permanent gases, can be studied by the paramagnetic resonance method. Substances that vaporize in monatomic form, the alkali metals in particular, need simply to be sealed in an evacuated tube, placed in the microwave cavity, and heated to an appropriate temperature. Conrad[99] and Wilke[100] have, by this method, remeasured the g factors of the alkali atoms in their ground ^2S levels, in an effort to resolve small discrepancies that appeared in earlier atomic beam measurements of the g factors. Other substances, those that vaporize at moderate temperatures in diatomic or polyatomic form, require some means of dissociating the vapor once it is formed. The correct choice of method depends on the vapor. Iodine vapor, for example, is easy to dissociate optically, and the paramagnetic resonance spectrum of atomic iodine has been observed in a sealed tube of iodine vapor, illuminated by a mercury lamp.[101] Bromine vapor is dissociated more readily by an electric discharge, and the bromine atom has been studied in a flow apparatus similar to that of Fig. 16.[102] Thermal dissociation in an electric arc, also in a flow system, was the method chosen for atomic phosphorus.[103]

Optical dissociation produces little or no ionization of the vapor, and can be carried out directly within the microwave cavity of the paramagnetic resonance spectrometer. Dissociation by an electrical discharge or arc requires, however, that there be a time lag between the production and detection of atoms, long enough to allow the ionic fraction of the dissociation products to decay. The simplest way to achieve this time lag is to locate the dissociator upstream from the paramagnetic resonance cavity, in a gas flow system. This technique, represented by Fig. 16, works because free atoms are quite stable in low-pressure gases; lifetimes of $1/10$ second or so are not uncommon. Two-body recombination of atoms at the surface of the containing vessel appears to be the major decay process. Various coatings have been tried in attempts to "poison" the walls against this recombination process; one of the best wall treatments has been found to be a thorough washing of the glassware, followed by a rinse with hydrofluoric acid. A second means of reducing wall recombination of atoms is, by adding a high-pressure buffer gas, to prevent them from reaching the wall. As in its application to optical pumping experiments, this method works best for atoms in S states, whose radio spectra are not subject to collision broadening.

4.1.2.6.3. RADIO-OPTICAL RESONANCE. From its start, the double resonance method has been used to study the Zeeman effect of excited

[99] D. Conrad, Z. Physik 162, 160 (1961).

[100] W. Wilke, Z. Physik 165, 562 (1961).

[101] K. D. Bowers, R. A. Kamper, and C. D. Lustig, Proc. Phys. Soc. (London) B70, 1176(L) (1957).

[102] J. S. M. Harvey, R. A. Kamper, and K. R. Lea, Proc. Phys. Soc. (London) 76, 979 (1960).

[103] H. G. Dehmelt, Phys. Rev. 99, 527 (1955).

TABLE VIII. Atomic g Factors Measured by Radio-Optical Methods

Atom	Atomic term	J	F	g^a	Method[b]	Reference
He[3]	$1s\,3p\;^3P$	1	$\frac{3}{2}$	1.53(5)	E	DEC-61
		2	$\frac{5}{2}$	1.20(5)		
			$\frac{3}{2}$	1.25(5)		
	$1s\,4d\;^1D$	2	$\frac{5}{2}$	0.82(2)		
			$\frac{3}{2}$	1.18(4)		
He[4]	$1s\,3p\;^3P$	1, 2	—	1.500(5)	E	DEC-60
	$1s\,3d\;^1D$	2	—	1.0006(20)		
	$1s\,4d\;^1D$	2	—	1.0012(20)		
	$1s\,5d\;^1D$	2	—	1.0006(20)		
Na[23]	$3s\;^2S$	$\frac{1}{2}$	—	2.002371(6)[c]	O	DEH-58
	$3p\;^2P$	$\frac{3}{2}$	—	1.3341(3)	D	DOD-60
K[39]	$5p\;^2P$	$\frac{1}{2}$	—	0.665(3)	D	FOX-61
Ca[40]	$4s\,4p\;^3P$	1	—	1.50105(7)	D, E	OTT-62
Zn[65]	$4s\,4p\;^3P$	1	—	1.4950(4)	E	MAY-60
	$4s\,4d\;^1D$	2	—	0.9962(4)		
	$4s\,5d\;^1D$	2	—	0.9982(4)		
	$4s\,6d\;^1D$	2	—	1.0020(4)		
Cd[111]	$5s\,5p\;^3P$	1	—	$\frac{3}{2} - 154(9) \times 10^{-6}$ [d]	L	THA-62
Cd[113]	$5s\,5p\;^3P$	1	—	$\frac{3}{2} - 140(9) \times 10^{-6}$ [d]	L	THA-62
Ba[138]	$6s\,6p\;^1P$	1	—	1.025(8)	D	BUC-61
Hg[197]	$6s\,6p\;^3P$	1	—	1.4861(3.6)	D	HIR-61
Hg[199]	$6s\,6p\;^3P$	1	—	1.48634(5)	L	DOD-61a
	$6s\,6f\;^3F$	4	$\frac{9}{2}$	1.1082(5)	E	PEB-59
			$\frac{7}{2}$	1.3850(5)		
Hg[even]	$6s\,6p\;^3P$	1	—	1.48635(30)	D	DOD-61b
		2	—	1.14402(7)	E	PEB-59
	$6s\,6f\;^3F$	4	—	1.2477(4)		
	$6s\,6d\;^1D$	2	—	1.1203(3)		
Hg[201]	$6s\,6p\;^3P$	1	—	1.48606(15)	L	DOD-61a
		2	$\frac{5}{2}$	1.15(5)	E	PEB-59
	$6s\,6f\;^3F$	4	$\frac{11}{2}$	0.9051(5)		
			$\frac{9}{2}$	1.0237(10)		
			$\frac{5}{2}$	1.781(1.5)		
	$6s\,6d\;^1D$	2	$\frac{5}{2}$	0.902(5)		
			$\frac{3}{2}$	1.34(1)		

[a] Where specific values of F are listed in the preceding column, the results given below are g_F values; otherwise they are g_J values. Estimated errors in parentheses apply to the last figure of the quoted value.

[b] E—electron bombardment; O—optical pumping; D—double resonance; L—level crossing.

[c] Obtained from the value of $g_J(\text{Na})/g_s$ quoted in the reference by multiplying by $g_s = 2(1.0011596)$.

[d] Based on $\mu_p(\text{oil}) = (657.466)^{-1}\mu_0$; see footnote to Table VI.

BUC-61   H. Bucka and H. J. Schüssler, *Ann. Physik* [7] **7**, 225 (1961).
DEC-60   B. Decomps, J. C. Pebay-Peyroula, and J. Brossel, *Compt. rend.* **251**, 941 (1960).
DEC-61   B. Decomps, J. C. Pebay-Peyroula, and J. Brossel, *Compt. rend.* **252**, 537 (1961).
DEH-58   H. G. Dehmelt, *Phys. Rev.* **109**, 381 (1958).
DOD-60   J. N. Dodd and R. W. N. Kinnear, *Proc. Phys. Soc. (London)* **75**, 51 (1960).
DOD-61a   J. N. Dodd, *Proc. Phys. Soc. (London)* **77**, 669 (1961).
DOD-61b   J. N. Dodd, *Proc. Phys. Soc. (London)* **78**, 65 (1961).
FOX-61   W. N. Fox and G. W. Series, *Proc. Phys. Soc. (London)* **77**, 1141 (1961).
HIR-61   H. R. Hirsch, *J. Opt. Soc. Am.* **51**, 1192 (1961).
MAY-60   A. D. May, *Compt. rend.* **250**, 3616 (1960).
OTT-62   E. W. Otten, *Z. Physik* **170**, 336 (1962).
PEB-59   J. C. Pebay-Peyroula, *J. phys., radium* **20**, 721 (1959).
THA-62   P. Thaddeus and R. Novick, *Phys. Rev.* **126**, 1774 (1962).

atoms; the atomic g factor of mercury in its 6^3P_1 resonance level was one of the results of Brossel and Bitter's original experiment. The precision of such measurements, however, is orders of magnitude poorer than that of experiments on ground state atoms. This must be so, for the widths of radio lines in excited atoms are typically 10 to 100 Mc, due to the irreducible natural broadening, while line widths in ground state atoms are typically less than 1 Mc. Really precise g factors, then, are not to be had for excited atoms, although measurements of the Zeeman effect remain valuable for identifying the particular excited level involved in the radio-frequency resonance, and for investigating deviations from L-S coupling. In many cases, also, the Zeeman effect provides a radio spectrum where otherwise, because of small or non-existent hyperfine structure, there would be none to observe. Table VIII lists the g factors of atoms that have been measured to date (mid-1963) by radio-optical methods.

For g factor measurements on ground state atoms, radio-optical methods have been little used. Certainly the inherent precision is there, since radio line widths in optical pumping experiments range from a few kilocycles down to a few cycles per second. These widths, however, correspond to weak field conditions; in magnetic fields strong enough to allow accurate measurements of g factors, field inhomogeneity broadening dominates, just as it does in the atomic beam and paramagnetic resonance methods, and limits the attainable precision to the same degree. Although no more precise than other methods of measuring g factors, optical pumping nevertheless is a great deal more sensitive, and may succeed where other methods fail. This is especially true for measurements on atoms which, because of rarity or some other reason, are available only in small numbers. Dehmelt demonstrated the extreme sensitivity of optical pumping methods in the experiment, already mentioned in Section 4.1.2.5.4.5, in which free electrons were oriented by spin exhange collisions with optically oriented sodium vapor.[87] Working with electron densities of less than 10^9/cc, Dehmelt was able to detect the magnetic resonance transition of both electrons and sodium atoms, and he determined thereby, to a precision of 3 parts in 10^5, the g factor ratio $g_s/g_J(\mathrm{Na})$.

4.1.2.6.3.1. *Mercury.* Brossel and Bitter's[5] double resonance apparatus is shown schematically by Fig. 17. Light from a mercury arc lamp,

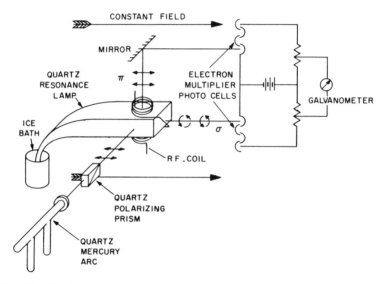

FIG. 17. Double resonance apparatus for detecting the radio spectrum of excited mercury.

π-polarized by a polarizing prism, falls on a mercury absorption cell, or "resonance lamp," which is located in the magnetic field of a pair of Helmholtz coils (not shown in the figure). Two photocells, connected in opposition in a dc bridge circuit, monitor the re-emitted resonance radiation. One photocell accepts the σ-polarized resonance radiation emitted parallel to the field direction, while the other photocell accepts the mixture of σ- and π-polarized resonance radiation emitted perpendicular to the field direction. The photocurrents of the two detectors under quiescent conditions, differ because of the preponderant π polarization of the re-emitted light, but the bridge circuit may be adjusted so that the galvanometer current is zero. This reduces greatly the undesirable effects of intensity fluctuations in the light source. When radio-frequency resonance increases the intensity of the σ radiation at the expense of the π radiation, the bridge becomes unbalanced, and the galvanometer indicates this unbalance, which is the double resonance signal, directly. Wound around the absorption cell is a radio-frequency coil which is energized by a tunable power oscillator. To depolarize the resonance radiation, the radio-frequency field must cause magnetic dipole transitions of the Δm_F (or Δm_J) $= \pm 1$ type, and so the axis of the radio-frequency coil is aligned perpendicular to the steady magnetic field. A radio-frequency field strength of several gauss is needed, but this presents no technical problem at the frequencies of double resonance experiments, which seldom exceed a few hundred megacycles. Brossel and Bitter's oscillator was capable of supplying up to 100 watts at frequencies between 50 and 150 Mc. To avoid the nuisance of accidental glow discharges within the absorption cell at high power levels, the cell must be pumped free of foreign gases to a pressure below 10^{-6} mm Hg. The mercury vapor pressure is maintained at 2×10^{-4} mm Hg by placing the tail of the absorption cell in an ice bath.

The double resonance spectrum of natural mercury, traced out be a slow sweep of the Helmholtz field strength (at a fixed radio frequency), consists of a single strong line due to the even isotopes and several weaker lines, displaced by hyperfine structure interactions, due to the odd isotopes Hg[199] and Hg[201]. Brossel and Bitter were concerned primarily with investigating the phenomenon of double resonance itself, and did not stop to make precise measurements of g factors and hyperfine structure, except to establish that the g factor of the even isotopes had a value close to $3/2$, the Landé value for a $^3P_1$ level.

Recently, Dodd, Fox, Series, and Taylor[104] have discovered a new way to detect double resonance which they call the method of "light beats." Rather than analyze changes in polarization, they monitor the total intensity of the re-emitted resonance radiation with a single photodetector. Under the influence of the radio-frequency resonance condition the light becomes modulated at the Larmor frequency, in much the same way that, in optical pumping experiments, the intensity of a "crossbeam" becomes modulated at the Larmor frequency. This new kind of double resonance signal can be amplified and detected with

[104] J. N. Dodd, W. N. Fox, G. W. Series, and J. M. Taylor, *Proc. Phys. Soc. (London)* 789 (1959). J. N. Dodd and G. W. Series, *Proc. Roy. Soc.* **A263**, 353 (1961).

a tuned radio-frequency amplifier, with all the advantages of low noise, stability, and fast response that this implies.

4.1.2.6.3.2. *Helium.* Limited by the intensities of available light sources, and more fundamentally by the selection rules for optical excitation, double resonance has remained a specialized technique, applicable only to the lower resonance levels of mercury and a few other atoms. What is needed for a systematic study of radio spectra in excited atoms is a more general method of selective excitation, one which, ideally, works on any atom and is unhampered by selection rules. This need is filled reasonably well by the electron bombardment method. First used in radio spectroscopy by Lamb and Maiman in their measurement of the helium fine structure, this method of exciting and orienting atoms by bombarding them with electrons of just the right energy has been applied successfully in recent years to measurements of the hyperfine structure and Zeeman effect of several excited atoms.

The principle of the method, the way in which atoms are both excited and oriented by the collision process, is discussed in Section 4.1.2.4.4.1. In the original fine structure experiments, the reorientation of helium atoms by microwave transitions was detected through changes in the intensity or polarization of the collision light, viewed in a given direction, and these methods remain good for the low-frequency hyperfine structure and Zeeman transitions. The newly discovered phenomenon of "light beats" provides an alternative method of detecting these transitions. Another detection method, tried successfully (on mercury) by Dehmelt,[105] works by the *absorption* of polarized light, rather than by its emission, and allows radio spectra to be observed in metastable, nonradiating states. Unrestricted by optical selection rules, collision excitation can reach these and other states that are forbidden to direct optical excitation. Another important capability of collision excitation, also pointed out by Dehmelt, is that of simultaneously *ionizing* and orienting an atom. Although showing only limited success so far, this technique is important for the foothold it gives in the difficult field of ionic radio spectroscopy.

A good example of the electron bombardment method of measuring atomic g factors is the experiment on helium performed by Decomps, Pebay-Peyroula, and Brossel.[106] The experimental apparatus, developed originally for work with mercury, is described in two comprehensive papers by Pebay-Peyroula.[107] It consists of a planar triode vacuum tube, filled with helium to a pressure of 5 μ Hg and located within a single-turn radio-frequency coil. Large Helmholtz coils produce a

[105] H. G. Dehmelt, *Phys. Rev.* **103**, 1125(L) (1956).
[106] B. Decomps, J. C. Pebay-Peyroula, and J. Brossel, *Compt. rend.* **251**, 941 (1960).
[107] J. C. Pebay-Peyroula, *J. phys., radium* **20**, 669 and 721 (1959).

reasonably homogeneous magnetic field of up to 500 gauss, oriented parallel to the direction of electron motion within the bombardment tube. The radio-frequency field is perpendicular to the Helmholtz field, as is required for the $\Delta m_J = \pm 1$ Zeeman transitions. Also perpendicular to the field, so as to receive collision light of the maximum polarization, is the optical detection system. This consists of two photomultiplier tubes arranged in a dc resistance bridge circuit whose balance condition is monitored by a long-period galvanometer. Polaroid filters send light which is polarized parallel to the field into one photo-multiplier, and light polarized perpendicular to the field into the other. The galvanometer deflection is therefore proportional to the percentage polarization, P, defined by Eq. (4.1.2.16). Unlike resonance radiation, collision light may show a multitude of atomic line radiations, and it is necessary to select out a line which originates in the particular excited level to be studied. This is done by placing band pass filters or wide-slit monochromators in the two light paths.

Decomps, Pebay-Peyroula, and Brossel measured the g factors and (from the radio line widths) the radiative lifetimes of four excited levels in helium, 3^1D, 4^1D, 5^1D, and 3^3P, none of which is a resonance level. Their method was to select one of the bright visible helium lines in the collision light, adjust the bombardment voltage for maximum polarization in this line, and then, monitoring the polarization constantly, sweep the Helmholtz field strength while keeping the radio-frequency excitation fixed. This gave the radio spectrum of the known upper level of that helium line. This procedure was repeated for the other bright helium lines and their corresponding upper levels. Each level gave a simple one-line spectrum. Lacking hyperfine structure, helium exhibits a linear Zeeman effect up to quite high field strengths, and the various $\Delta m_J = \pm 1$ transitions were almost exactly superposed under the conditions of the experiment. In a later investigation of He[3] by the same method, the radio spectra were more complex, because of hyperfine structure.

4.1.2.7. Atomic Frequency Standards. Increasing precision in radio spectroscopy, the product of Ramsey's two-field excitation method and Dehmelt's buffer gas method, has brought with it, unavoidably, problems of measurement. The usual techniques of frequency measurement fail when they are asked to locate the center of a radio line 100 cps wide, say, at a frequency of 10 Gc, for the frequency to be measured is more stable and better defined than the comparison frequencies generated by the best quartz crystal oscillator.

Faced with this breakdown of his standards of measurement, the radio spectroscopist takes the pragmatic course worn smooth by others, in similar predicaments, before him. He gives up, at least for the time being, the hope of reaching the ultimate accuracy of his experiment, and settles instead for its precision: he sets up a permanent working replica of the ultraprecise experiment in his laboratory and uses *it* thereafter as a working standard of frequency. Spectroscopists in other laboratories set up their own, somewhat different versions of the new working standard. This is, of course, scientific anarchy, and cannot be tolerated for very long. If, after a suitable evaluation period, the new frequency standard has not been supplanted by an even more precise experiment, it will be declared, by fiat, a primary standard, and moved to the central standards laboratory, there to be used to calibrate lesser instruments and to regulate comparable instruments.

In the past decade, several frequency standards of this sort, based on atomic or molecular radio lines and having inherent precisions of 1 part in 10^{10} or better, have been developed. It is likely that one of them will be chosen in 1964, at the next General Conference of Weights and Measures, as the new international standard of frequency and time, replacing the astronomical observations that have served in the past. (Since radio-frequency oscillations can be counted, a frequency standard is also a time standard.) The two strongest contenders for the title are, at the present, the cesium atomic beam standard and the hydrogen atomic beam maser. These two devices, as well as the rubidium optical pumping standard, are described briefly in this section. Further information on these and other frequency standards may be found in the published proceedings of the recent International Conference on Precision Electromagnetic Measurements.[108]

4.1.2.7.1. CESIUM BEAM STANDARD. The atomic beam frequency standard, first tested as such by Sherwood, Lyons, McCracken and Kusch[109] in 1952, owes its origin to Ramsey's method of exciting beam resonances with two widely separated radio-frequency fields. In its laboratory form, the cesium standard resembles very closely the conventional atomic beam spectrometer, illustrated schematically by Fig. 12. The only real difference is one of emphasis; the beam spectrometer is a scanning instrument, flexible enough to cover the radio spectra of many different atoms, while the beam standard is a fixed instrument, meant to operate constantly at the peak of a single radio line of a single atom. Cesium is chosen because of its low vaporization temperature and low ionization potential, which make it one of the easiest atoms to produce and detect in beam form, and also because of its large hyperfine structure, approximately 9 Gc for the $F = 3 \leftrightarrow F = 4$ transition. The greater the frequency of a standard radio line, the greater the relative

[108] *IRE Trans. on Intrumentation* **I-11**, 177–256 (1962).

[109] J. E. Sherwood, H. Lyons, R. H. McCracken, and P. Kusch, *Bull. Am. Phys. Soc.* **27** (1), 43 (1952).

precision with which it can be measured. (Thallium, with a hyperfine structure interval of 21 Gc, is the most favorable atom from this point of view, but, because of its high ionization potential, is much harder to detect.) The standard radio line of cesium is the $(F, m_F) = (3, 0) \leftrightarrow (4, 0)$ Zeeman component, which is field-independent in the weak field limit, although at the C field strength required to resolve the several Zeeman components, about 0.1 gauss, it exhibits a small quadratic Zeeman effect.

The cesium standard, like all atomic frequency standards, achieves its extremely narrow radio line width by prolonging to the utmost the interaction of atom and radio-frequency field. One way to do this is to make the interaction region long; the Ramsey excitation method permits the C field region to be made a meter or more in length without serious interference from C field inhomogeneities. The other way to lengthen the interaction time is to slow down the atoms; practically, this means velocity selection—constructing the beam apparatus in such a way that, out of the normal velocity distribution of beam atoms, only the slower ones reach the detector. Both of these methods reduce the beam intensity at the detector, and this is why detection efficiency is an important consideration in the choice of an atom for a beam frequency standard. Pushed to their practical limit, velocity selection and lengthening of the C field can narrow the standard cesium line to well below 100 cps, a relative width of 1 part in 10^8 or less. The short-term stability of the cesium standard is about 1 part in 10^{11}; the long-term stability and reproducibility, determined by comparing over a period of several years the frequencies of standards constructed in various laboratories around the world, is about 1 part in 10^{10}.

4.1.2.7.2. HYDROGEN BEAM MASER. The interaction time of a beam atom with a radio-frequency field can also be prolonged, Goldenberg, Kleppner, and Ramsey[110] have found recently, by firing the beam atoms into a bottle, from which they can escape only by finding their way back out through the entrance hole. The bottle, more precisely a teflon-lined quartz bulb, is located within a tuned radio-frequency cavity, and during the time an atom remains inside it is acted on constantly by a radio-frequency field. If the entrance hole is small, just large enough to admit the beam, this time may be a second or more, much longer than the corresponding time for the cesium beam standard.

For sensitivity in detecting the standard radio line (the field-independent component of the 1420-Mc hyperfine structure line) the hydrogen frequency standard is made into a beam maser, much like the older and more familiar ammonia maser. The apparatus is shown

[110] H. M. Goldenberg, D. Kleppner, and N. F. Ramsey, *Phys. Rev.* **123** 530 (1961); *Phys. Rev. Letters* **5**, 361 (1960).

schematically by Fig. 18. Atomic hydrogen produced in a radio-frequency discharge passes through a beam-defining aperture and then through a state selector, a symmetrical six-pole permanent magnet. The inhomogeneous field of this magnet focuses on the entrance hole of the storage bottle only those hydrogen atoms that occupy the $(F, m_F) = (1, 1)$ and $(1, 0)$ sublevels. Atoms in the lower-energy $(F, m_F) = (1, -1)$ and $(0, 0)$ sublevels are thrown out of the beam. Entering the radio-frequency cavity, then, the beam atoms have the population inversion necessary for maser action on the $(F, m_F) = (1, 0) \rightarrow (0, 0)$ line. Through stimulated emission the atoms give up energy to the radio-frequency field and, if the cavity losses are small enough, the maser breaks into spontaneous oscillation at the standard frequency. This actually occurs;

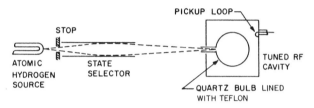

FIG. 18.   Schematic diagram of the atomic hydrogen maser.

the device oscillates as soon as the hydrogen beam is turned on, and a standard frequency signal may be taken directly out of the radio-frequency cavity via a pickup loop. This eliminates the need for an external driving oscillator and a frequency control servo system such as the cesium beam standard requires. The unparalleled spectral purity of this signal (the line width is less than 1 cps) suggests, at the present time, that a frequency standard with a short-term stability of 1 part in 10^{13} may be made from the hydrogen maser. Long-term stability and reproducibility, the two other important characteristics of a frequency standard, are as yet unknown.

4.1.2.7.3. RUBIDIUM OPTICAL PUMPING STANDARD. Buffer gases produced very narrow radio lines in optical orientation experiments, but these were field-dependent lines, unsuited to the requirements of a frequency standard. The method of optical pumping by intensity differences removed this difficulty by making field-independent transitions observable, and led to the development of the rubidium frequency standard.

The basic apparatus of the rubidium standard, as used in the original experiment of Bender, Beatty, and Chi,[111] is illustrated by Fig. 19. The optical pumping takes place in a cell which contains Rb^{87} vapor

[111] P. L. Bender, E. C. Beaty, and A. R. Chi, *Phys. Rev. Letters* **1**, 311 (1958).

and a buffer gas; the pumping light comes from a rubidium lamp, in front of which is placed a filter bulb which contains Rb^{85} vapor. Because the optical resonance lines of Rb^{85} and Rb^{87} do not quite coincide, the filter bulb absorbs preferentially one of the two hyperfine components, the $F = 2$ component, of each Rb^{87} resonance line emitted by the lamp. The remaining light, entering the absorption cell, pumps Rb^{87} atoms from the ground state $F = 1$ hyperfine structure level into the $F = 2$ hyperfine structure level and thereby makes the Rb^{87} vapor less absorptive to the pumping light. This is detected by a photomultiplier tube as a decrease in the intensity of re-emitted resonance radiation. (The constant background of Rb^{85} light would interfere with detection of pumping by the light transmission method, although this problem can be eliminated by using a pure Rb^{87} lamp as a source of pumping light.)

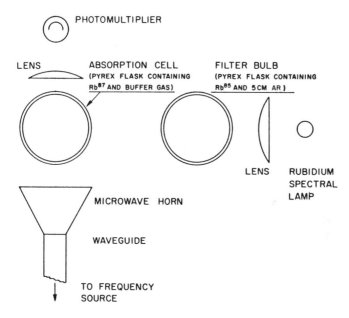

FIG. 19.   Optical pumping apparatus for detecting field-independent transitions in rubidium.

Microwaves at 6835 Mc, launched from the horn antenna, cause hyperfine structure transitions between the $F = 1$ and $F = 2$ levels, thereby repopulating the $F = 1$ level and increasing the intensity of re-emitted resonance radiation.

The field-insensitive standard transition, $(F, m_F) = (2, 0) \rightarrow (1, 0)$, can be reduced in width to 20 cps, and the corresponding short-term stability of the device, operated as a frequency standard, is about 1 part in 10^{11}. Comparisons of two rubidium standards over a period of 1 year indicate that the long-term stability is roughly 1 part in 10^{10}. An unfortunate characteristic of the rubidium standard, and indeed of any optical pumping standard that relies on buffer gases, is the appreciable dependence of the standard frequency on buffer gas pressure. This raises questions concerning reproducibility and long-term stability which have not been completely answered yet, but which will probably make the rubidium standard more useful as a secondary, rather than primary, standard of frequency and time.

4.2. Lifetime of Excited States*

4.2.1. Introduction

Atoms, as well as other quantum-mechanical systems, can exist in well-defined energy states. These states are characterized by a set of discrete quantum numbers. Transitions from one such state to another can occur under the influence of an external perturbation (induced transitions), or spontaneously if the initial state has a higher energy.

The probability of radiative transitions and hence the lifetime of the states involved with respect to such transitions can be calculated using a semiclassical approach[1] or, with the same result, from the interaction between the atom and a quantized radiation field.[2] While the principles involved in the theory of radiative transitions are understood, actual calculations of lifetimes have been made only for the simplest cases because of the mathematical difficulty of treating a many-body system.

Although Dirac's article "The Quantum Theory of the Emission and Absorption of Radiation"[2] was one of the milestones in the development of quantum field theory, the measurement of lifetimes or transition probabilities has never been of much importance as a practical proof of the validity of the theory. However a knowledge of absolute and relative lifetimes is of great interest to astrophysicists who need them to calculate the abundance of elements in stellar atmospheres from the measured strength of their emission or absorption lines. In recent years additional interest has been stimulated by the advent of lasers, for whose design a knowledge of the lifetimes of the states involved is essential.[3]

---

[1] L. I. Schiff, "Quantum Mechanics." McGraw-Hill, New York, 1955.

[2] P. A. M. Dirac, *Proc. Roy. Soc.* **A114**, 243 (1927).

[3] For a review of the field from the point of view of laser applications see W. R. Bennett, Jr., P. J. Kindlmann, and G. N. Mercer, *Appl. Optics* Suppl. **2**, 34 (1964).

---

* Chapter 4.2 is by K. Ziock.

4.2.2. Definitions

Lifetime: The lifetime τ_i of an excited atomic state[4] u_i is defined as the decay time of this state due to all possible radiative transitions to lower-energy states u_k . Hence:

$$N(t) = N(0) \cdot e^{-t/\tau_i} \qquad (4.2.1)$$

where $N(0)$ = number of atoms initially in the state u_i and $N(t)$ = number of atoms in the state u_i at time t.

The lifetime of a state is closely related to the following quantities:

(1) matrix elements for the transitions involved;

(2) Einstein probability coefficients;

(3) oscillator strengths of the transitions;

(4) line strengths of the transitions;

(5) natural linewidth of the emitted or absorbed radiation.

In the following we shall define these quantities and briefly discuss their relationship to each other. For a more exhaustive treatment of the subject the reader is referred to one of the standard works.[5-8]

4.2.2.1. Matrix Element: $\langle u_i \mid Q \mid u_k \rangle$. All the other quantities can be calculated if the matrix elements of the transitions involved are known. The matrix elements are related to the probability A_{ik} of a spontaneous radiative transition from a state u_i to a state u_k by

$$A_{ik} = \frac{64\pi^4 \nu_{ik}^3}{3hc^3 g_i} \sum_{m,n} \langle i_m \mid Q \mid k_n \rangle^2 \qquad \text{sec}^{-1}, \qquad (4.2.2)$$

where Q is an operator, $g_i = 2J_i + 1$ is the statistical weight of the initial state, h = Planck's constant, c = velocity of light, and the sum is taken over the $2J + 1$ substates of both levels.

Since the radiation emitted in atomic transitions is usually electric dipole radiation, Q is usually the operator of the electric dipole moment. However, if the electric dipole matrix element vanishes, the transition can sometimes still take place via higher moments such as the magnetic dipole or electric quadrupole moment.

---

[4] Whenever the subscripts i and k are used here, i refers to the state of higher energy regardless of the kind of transition.

[5] A. Unsöld, "Physik der Sternatmosphären." Springer, Berlin, 1955.

[6] J. C. Slater, "Quantum Theory of Atomic Structure." McGraw-Hill, New York, 1960.

[7] W. Heitler, "The Quantum Theory of Radiation." Oxford Univ. Press, London and New York, 1957.

[8] E. U. Condon and G. J. Shortley, "The Theory of Atomic Spectra," 2nd ed. Cambridge Univ. Press, London and New York, 1957.

4.2.2.2. Einstein Probability Coefficients A_{ik}, B_{ik}, B_{ki}. The Einstein coefficient A_{ik} is the time-independent probability for a spontaneous radiative transition from an excited state u_i to a state u_k of lower energy.

In the presence of an external radiation field of energy $\varphi(\nu_{ik})$ per unit volume and per unit frequency at the frequency ν_{ik} it is possible that an atom in an excited state u_i is stimulated to emit a photon of the energy $h\nu_{ik}$. The atom is afterwards in the energetically lower state u_k, just as in the case of spontaneous emission. The probability of this induced emission is given by[9] $\varphi(\nu_{ik}) B_{ik}$ and the total probability of a transition from u_i to u_k in the presence of a radiation field is thus:

$$\Gamma = A_{ik} + \varphi(\nu_{ik})B_{ik} \qquad \text{sec}^{-1}. \tag{4.2.3}$$

An external radiation field also makes possible transitions from the energetically lower state u_k to the higher state u_i through the absorption of a photon of energy $h\nu_{ik}$. The probability of this process is given by:

$$B_{ki}\varphi(\nu_{ik}).$$

The following relations exist between the Einstein probability coefficients:

$$g_i B_{ik} = g_k B_{ki}, \tag{4.2.4}$$

where $g_i = 2J_i + 1, g_k = 2J_k + 1$ are the statistical weights of the states and J_i, J_k are the quantum numbers of their total angular momenta. Also

$$A_{ik} = \frac{8\pi h\nu_{ik}^3}{c^3}, \qquad B_{ik} = \frac{8\pi h\nu_{ik}^3 g_k}{c^3 g_i} B_{ki}. \tag{4.2.5}$$

From the definitions of the transition probabilities it follows that

$$P_{ik} = N_i A_{ik} h\nu_{ik}, \tag{4.2.6}$$

where P_{ik} is the power emitted spontaneously by N_i atoms in the higher state, due to the transition $u_i \rightarrow u_k$.

The power absorbed by N_k atoms in the lower state is given by

$$P_{ki} = N_k B_{ki} h\nu_{ki}\varphi(\nu_{ik}), \tag{4.2.7}$$

where $\varphi(\nu_{ik})$ is the energy density of the external radiation field as defined above. We assume without loss of generality that this radiation is a plane wave, in which case we can rewrite (4.2.7) in the form

$$P_{ki} = N_k B_{ki} h\nu_{ik} c^{-1} \, \partial I/\partial \nu, \tag{4.2.8}$$

[9] Provided that the energy density $\varphi(\nu_{ik})$ is independent of frequency in the vicinity of ν_{ik}.

where $\partial I/\partial \nu$ is the incident energy per unit area per unit frequency which we assume again to be constant over the width of the absorption line $\Delta \nu_{ik}$.[9,10]

The mean life τ_i of the upper level u_i and the transition probability A_{ik} are related by

$$\frac{1}{\tau_i} = A_{ik} \qquad (4.2.9)$$

or in case there is more than one lower level u_k:

$$\frac{1}{\tau_i} = \sum_k A_{ik} . \qquad (4.2.10)$$

4.2.2.3. Oscillator Strength, f_{ki}. According to classical electron theory $N(\nu_0)$ linear harmonic oscillators (i.e., elastically bound electrons) each with a resonant frequency ν_0 absorb from an isotropic radiation field with an energy density $\varphi(\nu_0)$ the following power:

$$P(\nu_0) = \frac{\pi e^2 N(\nu_0)}{m} \varphi(\nu_0) \qquad (4.2.11)$$

where m = electron mass and e = electron charge.

The same quantity, expressed in quantum mechanical terms, is given by Eq. (4.2.7). Equating the two expressions we have

$$N(\nu_0) = \frac{B_{ki} h \nu_{ik} m N_k}{\pi e^2} = f_{ki} N_k . \qquad (4.2.12)$$

In other words, $N(\nu_0)$ classical oscillators are equivalent to $f_{ki} N_k$ quantum-mechanical oscillators. The dimensionless quantity f_{ki} is called the oscillator strength or f-value of the transition $u_k \rightarrow u_i$.

f_{ki} is frequently expressed in terms of the probability of the spontaneous transition $u_i \rightarrow u_k$ through the use of Eq. (4.2.4):

$$f_{ki} = A_{ik} \cdot \frac{g_i}{g_k} \frac{mc^3}{8\pi^2 e^2 \nu_{ik}^2} . \qquad (4.2.13)$$

An important theorem, known as the Kuhn–Thomas sum rule, can be derived for the oscillator strength.[11-13] This rule states that

$$N = \sum_n f_{mn} , \qquad (4.2.14)$$

[10] For the definition of $\Delta \nu_{ik}$ see Eq. (4.2.16).
[11] W. Kuhn, *Z. Physik* **33**, 408 (1925).
[12] W. Thomas, *Naturwissenschaften* **13**, 627 (1925).
[13] For a derivation of this sum rule using quantum-mechanical methods see Unsöld.[5]

where N is the total number of electrons in the atom. The sum is taken over all final states n for a given initial state m. For transitions to states n with an energy $E_n > E_m$, f_{mn} is taken positive, and for those with $E_n < E_m$, it is taken negative. Equation (4.2.14) can be used to estimate the f value of the resonance transition from the ground state to the first excited state of atoms which have a one-electron spectrum, such as the alkali atoms. In this case (4.2.14) yields with good approximation

$$f \approx 1.$$

4.2.2.4. Line Strength, S_{ik}. The line strength is less often used to state experimental results but it is sometimes preferred in theoretical papers because of its symmetry between initial and final level. It is defined as:

$$S_{ik} = S_{ki} = \sum_{m,n} \langle i_m \mid Q \mid k_n \rangle^2. \qquad (4.2.15)$$

4.2.2.5. Natural Linewidth, Δv. The natural width of a line is by definition the frequency difference between the two points of half intensity on either side of the line center, when the emitting or absorbing atom is at rest and unperturbed by collisions. According to Weisskopf and Wigner[14] this linewidth is related to the lifetimes τ_i and τ_k of the initial and final state by

$$\Delta \nu_{ik} = \frac{1}{2\pi \left(\dfrac{1}{\tau_i} + \dfrac{1}{\tau_k} \right)}. \qquad (4.2.16)$$

4.2.3. Methods of Measurement

In principle all the above quantities can be calculated, but, since the calculations require knowledge of the eigenfunctions of the states involved, reliable calculations have been made only for the simplest atoms. We, therefore, have to rely mostly on experimental data for our knowledge of the lifetimes of excited atomic states. Unfortunately the experimental methods are not capable of high accuracy and an absolute measurement with an error of less than 10 % is considered excellent. As will be shown in one example, stated uncertainties in the older absolute measurements are not always in agreement with the actual accuracy of the experiment and caution should be exercised in the use of these values.

4.2.3.1. Lifetime Measurements. Some direct measurements of lifetimes have been made in the past few years. Ziock[15,16] measured the lifetime

---

[14] V. F. Weisskopf and E. P. Wigner, *Z. Physik* **63**, 54 (1930).

[15] K. Ziock, *Z. Physik* **147**, 99 (1957).

[16] O. Osberghaus and K. Ziock, *Z. Naturforsch.* **11a**, 762 (1956).

of the $^5f_5$ state, and the probability of the $^5f_5 \rightarrow {}^5d_4$, 3720 Å transition in iron, using the following method.

The light from a hollow iron cathode [(1) Fig. 1] is chopped in a Kerr cell (2) at a frequency of 1 Mc/sec. The modulated light traverses a beam of iron atoms (3). A quartz spectrograph (4) separates the resonance scattered light of the 3720-Å line and focuses it onto a photomultiplier (5). The output of the photomultiplier is sampled with a 1 Mc/sec pulse from a pulse generator (6), which is triggered after a variable delay (7) from the rf generator (8) that drives the Kerr cell. The apparatus is calibrated by inserting a mirror in the position

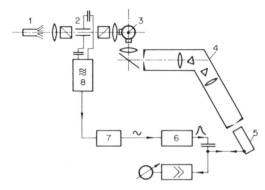

FIG. 1. Apparatus used to measure the lifetime of excited states.

of the iron beam (3) and measuring the photomultiplier current at different delays of the sampling pulse. The result of this measurement is shown in curve 1 of Fig. 2. The measurement is then repeated with the iron beam in place and curve 2 results, it shows a phase shift due to the finite lifetime of the $^5f_5$ state. An analysis of these curves with an analog computer yields a lifetime of 5.9×10^{-8} ($\pm$ 30 %) sec. This result confirms a measurement made by Kopfermann and Wessel,[17] which disagreed with an earlier measurement by King[18] by a factor of three. Curve 3, Fig. 2, shows the phase shift that would have resulted if King's value had been correct.

This method was improved by Ottinger[19] who refined the sampling technique and remeasured the 3720-Å iron line obtaining $A_{fd} = 1.37 \times 10^7$/sec $\pm$ 10 %. He also used the same arrangement to measure the $5^2S_{1/2} \rightarrow 4^2P_{3/2}$ transition in Gallium for which the obtained $f_{SP} = 0.087 \pm 25$ %. W. Demtröder[20] replaced the Kerr cell with a

[17] H. Kopfermann, and G. Wessel, *Z. Physik* **130**, 100 (1951).
[18] R. B. King, *Astrophys. J.* **95**, 78 (1941).
[19] C. Ottinger and K. Ziock, *Z. Naturforsch.* **16a**, 720 (1961).
[20] W. Demtröder, *Z. Physik* **166**, 42 (1962).

quartz-driven light modulator using standing sound waves in an alcohol–water mixture. In this way he could extend the range of this method further into the ultraviolet. He determined f values in the Ga, Al, Tl, Mg, and Na spectra and was able to increase the absolute accuracy of oscillator strength measurements to an unprecedented value of 1 %.

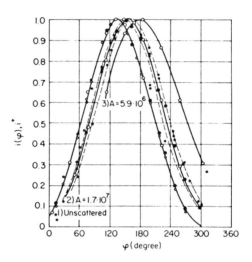

FIG. 2.   Photocurrent as a function of the phase angle between light modulation and sampling pulse. Solid dots = measured points. Open circles = calculated points.

Heron, McWhirter, and Rhoderick[21] applied the delayed coincidence technique, so extensively used in the field of nuclear physics, to the measurement of lifetimes of optical levels in atoms. They used electrons from a pulsed electron gun to excite He atoms and measured the time delay between the pulse used to pulse the electron gun and the subsequently emitted light quanta from several different levels using the delayed coincidence technique of Bell, Graham, and Petch.[22] They also found an increase in lifetime with pressure, for He pressures above 3×10^{-3} mm Hg, which they ascribe to resonance trapping of the emitted radiation. Since their counting rates became too small at pressures below 3×10^{-3} mm of Hg, they used several higher pressures and extrapolated to zero pressure. The influence of electrons which cascaded down from higher states and therefore excited the level under investigation with a delay given by the lifetimes of the higher levels was estimated to be smaller than 5%. A detailed investigation of the

[21] S. Heron, R. W. P. McWhirter, and E. H. Rhoderick, *Proc. Roy. Soc.* **A234**, 565 (1956).
[22] R. E. Bell, R. L. Graham, and H. E. Petch, *Can. J. Phys.* **30**, 35 (1952).

radiative lifetimes of excited neon levels, of interest to the operation of neon lasers, was undertaken by Bennett and Kindlmann.[23] The authors employed a delayed coincidence method similar in principal to the one used by Heron *et al.*,[21] but increased the efficiency by using a multichannel data collection method.

The increased efficiency made it possible to excite the atoms with pulsed electrons of just above threshold energy, thereby eliminating radiative cascades as a source of error. The authors used a vernier chronotron circuit developed by Kindlmann and Sunderland.[24] The basic circuit is shown in Fig. 3. A start pulse is derived from the pulse generator that drives the electron gun. The pulse is recirculated in a loop with a circulation period $T + \Delta T$. The excited gas is viewed through a grating spectrometer by a photomultiplier tube, and a photo-multiplier output pulse, indicating the de-excitation of the level under observation, is fed into the stop input of the chronotron. The stop pulse is also recirculated, but with a recirculation period that is slightly shorter, T. Because of the shorter recirculation time in the stop loop, the stop pulse

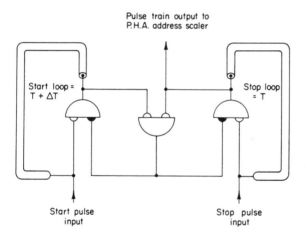

Pulse train output to
P.H.A. address scaler

Start loop =
T + ΔT

Stop loop
= T

Start pulse
input

Stop pulse
input

FIG. 3.   Vernier chronotron of Kindlmann and Sunderland.

eventually overtakes the start pulse and after $(T \text{ stop} - T \text{ start})/\Delta T$ transits the start and stop pulses pass through their respective amplifiers simultaneously, and thereby activate the coincidence circuit. The coincidence circuit triggers a gate circuit (not shown) which prohibits further circulation of the pulses and readies the system for the next timing cycle. The total number of pulses generated by a recirculat-

[23] W. R. Bennett, Jr. and P. J. Kindlmann, *Phys. Rev.* (1966) **149**, 38 (1966).
[24] P. J. Kindlmann, and J. Sunderland, *Rev. Sci. Instr.* **37**, 446 (1966).

ing amplifier is a digital measurement of the elapsed time between start and stop pulses in units of ΔT. The pulse train is fed directly into the address scaler of a multichannel analyzer. Using this technique Bennett and Kindlmann measured the following lifetimes (in nsec) for levels in the $2p^53p$ configuration of neon

$2p_1(14.4 \pm 0.3)$; $2p_2(18.8 \pm 0.3)$; $2p_3(17.6 \pm 0.2)$; $2p_4(19.1 \pm 0.3)$;

$2p_5(19.9 \pm 0.4)$; $2p_6(19.7 \pm 0.2)$; $2p_7(19.9 \pm 0.4)$; $2p_8(19.8 \pm 0.2)$;

$2p_9(19.4 \pm 0.6)$; and $2p_{10}(24.8 \pm 0.4)$.

The authors investigated the influence of radiative cascades and of excitation transfer in two-body collisions on the measured lifetime and corrected their results for these effects.

4.2.3.2. Absorption Measurements. According to Eq. (4.2.7) it is possible to obtain the probability of a transition from an absorption measurement if the number of absorbing atoms is known. In this way King and Stockbarger[25] obtained the absolute f values of a number of lines in the Cu, Cd, and Fe spectrum. They evaporated their samples in a quartz cell, held at a very uniform and precisely known temperature, and calculated the number of atoms in the lower state from vapor pressure values given in the literature and the Boltzmann distribution. This procedure, as discussed below, seems to be open to error possibilities and an absorption method used by Kopfermann and Wessel[17] to measure f values in the Fe and Ba spectrum is preferable. The latter authors measured the density of the absorbing atoms during their experiment and eliminated in this way the main source of ambiguities in other absorption measurements. They used an atomic beam as absorber and measured its density immediately before and after the absorption measurement by condensing it on a sensitive magnetically compensated balance.[26] As an additional precaution they measured the line shape of the incoming resonance line with a Fabry–Perot interferometer, to assure that it was constant throughout the experiment.

4.2.3.3. Emission Measurements. Many relative determinations of oscillator strength have been made by measuring line intensities in arcs.[27–30] The intensity of an emission line is, according to Eq. (4.2.6),

$$P_{ik} = N_i A_{ik} h\nu_{ik} .$$

[25] R. B. King and D. C. Stockbarger, *Astrophys. J.* **91**, 488 (1940).
[26] W. Paul and G. Wessel, *Z. Physik* **124**, 691 (1948).
[27] D. Van Lingen, *Physica* **3**, 977 (1936).
[28] J. A. H. Kersten and L. S. Ornstein, *Physica* **8**, 1124 (1941).
[29] J. W. Schuttevaer, J. J. de Bont, and T. Van den Broek, *Physica* **10**, 544 (1943).
[30] J. W. Schouten and J. A. Smit, *Physica* **10**, 661 (1943).

N_i can be obtained from the Boltzmann equation

$$\frac{N_i}{N} = \frac{g_i \, e^{-E_i/kT}}{\sum_n g_n \, e^{-E_n/kT}} = \frac{g_i \, e^{-E_i/kT}}{S}, \tag{4.2.17}$$

where N is the total number of atoms, E_i, E_n the energy of states u_i and u_n, S the sum of states, and the T the temperature. Hence,

$$P_{ik} = \frac{N}{S} g_i \, e^{-E_i/kT} \cdot A_{ik} h \nu_{ik}. \tag{4.2.18}$$

This equation can be used to obtain the ratio of two transition probabilities from a measurement of their relative intensities if the temperature is known:

$$\frac{A_{ik}}{A_{nm}} = \frac{P_{ik} g_n \nu_{nm}}{P_{nm} g_i \nu_{ik}} e^{-(E_n - E_i)/kT}. \tag{4.2.19}$$

The relative oscillator strengths of many lines in different spectra have been determined in this fashion.[27-31] The arc temperature was obtained by adding a small amount of Cu, using the intensities of two Cu lines of known relative transition probability. W. F. Meggers used this method for a large-scale determination of relative line intensities; this effort has now resulted in the publication of 39,000 relative line intensities of seventy-five elements in an NBS Monograph.[31] Eberhagen[32,33] and Corliss[34] extended this method to the absolute measurement of transition probabilities by carefully studying all the arc parameters and calculating the particle density in the arc from the Saha equation.[35]

4.2.3.4. Other Methods. Second-order perturbation theory gives for the shift of an energy level E_i under the influence of an external perturbation:

$$\Delta E = \sum_{k(k \neq i)} \frac{H_{ik}^2}{E_i - E_k}, \tag{4.2.20}$$

where H_{ik} are the matrix elements of the perturbation. Paul[36] showed that, since in the case of the Stark effect H_{ik} is the electric dipole moment

[31] W. F. Meggers, C. H. Corliss, and B. F. Scribner, *Natl. Bur. Standards (U.S.) Monograph* **32** (1961).
[32] A. Eberhagen, *Z. Physik* **143**, 392 (1955).
[33] A. Eberhagen, *Z. Physik* **143**, 312 (1955).
[34] C. H. Corliss, *J. Research NBS* **66a**, 169 (1962).
[35] M. N. Saha, *Z. Physik* **6**, 40 (1921).
[36] W. Paul, *Z. Physik* **124**, 121 (1947-1948).

which also occurs in the expression for the transition probability (4.2.1), it is possible to obtain the transition probability from a measurement of the Stark effect. Paul used the measured data of Kopfermann and Paul[37] and carried out the necessary calculations in the case of the $3^2P_{1/2,3/2} \rightarrow 3^2D_{3/2}$ and $3^2P_{1/2,3/2} \rightarrow 4^2S_{1/2}$ transitions in sodium. He obtained $f = 0.9$ and 0.15 in satisfactory agreement with a direct calculation by Prokofjew.[38]

The *natural linewidth* does not seem to have been used systematically for the determination of transition probabilities so far. Since spectral lines are very narrow it is very difficult to measure their width the conventional means of spectroscopy. Furthermore, Doppler broadening and collision broadening can amount to many times the natural width. However, with the methods of modern rf spectroscopy it is possible to measure the width of certain lines and Pichanick et al.[39] report a lifetime of 10^{-7} sec for the 2^3P state of helium from a measurement of the linewidth of microwave transitions between its fine structure components.

4.2.4. Comparison of the Different Experimental Methods

The absorption method is certainly reliable for relative measurements and it allows one to measure the ratios of several transition probabilities in a very simple apparatus. It is, however, applicable only to those lines that can be excited from the ground state. The precautions to be taken are the use of an optically thin layer of absorbing gas or vapor, and control of the line shapes with a spectrometer of high resolution.

For absolute measurements, especially of those substances which require high temperatures for evaporation, the uncertainty in the knowledge of the vapor pressure becomes an important obstacle. It is certainly not sufficient to rely on vapor pressure curves given in the literature, since small impurities and surface contaminations, etc., can change the actual pressure by a significant amount.

The method of Kopfermann and Wessel[17] should be more reliable for absolute measurements. It could give erroneous results, though, due to incomplete condensation of the vapor on the balance and oxidation of the condensed film. (The authors showed both effects to be negligible in the case of their measurements on iron.) Another source of error could be the evaporation of polymers, which is known to occur for several elements. The measurement of the decay time presumably gives the most reliable absolute values since they do not directly depend on the density of the absorber (the only requirement being that the

[37] H. Kopfermann and W. Paul, Z. Physik **120**, 545 (1943).

[38] W. K. Prokofjew, Z. Physik **58**, 255 (1929).

[39] F. M. J. Pichanick, R. D. Swift, and V. W. Hughes, Bull. Am. Phys. Soc. [2] **9**, 90 (1964).

pressure is low enough to avoid collision de-excitation and resonance trapping). The method of Ziock[15,16] and Demtröder[20] is applicable only to resonance transitions. The delayed coincidence method used by Heron et al.[21] and Bennett and Kindlemann[23] might run into difficulties with cascading electrons in the case of more complicated spectra; it is, however, applicable to nonresonance transitions.

The intensity measurements in arc spectra have the advantage of giving the relative transition probabilities of a great number of lines, without restriction to resonance lines, in a single photographic measurement. There is, however, the danger of self-absorption in the cooler zones of the arc and of error in the calculated temperature distribution. The absolute method used by Eberhagen[32] would be convenient for determination in a single measurement of the absolute transition probabilities of most of the lines of a certain atom, but the desired result is connected with the measured parameters only in a very indirect fashion. It is therefore certainly desirable to obtain some checkpoints with a more direct method.

4.2.5. Metastable States

The methods mentioned so far were designed to measure the probabilities of allowed transitions, which are of interest for instance for the determination of the abundance of elements in stellar atmospheres, other transitions which are of great fundamental interest are those which involve metastable states. In this class the $2S \rightarrow 1S$ transitions in hydrogenlike atoms or ions are of special interest. Salpeter[40] pointed out that these transitions, if they occur by single quantum emission, would indicate an admixture of P state. This could, in the absence of an external electric field, occur only if either the electron or the proton had an intrinsic electric dipole moment. Shapiro and Breit[41] have calculated the probability for these transitions to occur via double quantum emission and obtained $A_{21} = (8.226 \pm 0.001) \times Z^6/\text{sec}$. A measurement that agrees with the calculated lifetime would therefore exclude even minute admixtures of P state wave functions. A measurement by Fite et al.[42] yielded an upper limit of $420/\text{sec}$ for hydrogen, which gives an upper limit for the electronic dipole moment of $5 \times 10^{-3}\ e\hbar/mc.$[43]

[40] E. E. Salpeter, Phys. Rev. 112, 1642 (1958).

[41] J. Shapiro and G. Breit, Phys. Rev. 113, 179 (1959); 115, 1779E (1959).

[42] W. L. Fite, R. T. Brackmann, D. G. Hummer, and R. F. Stebbings, Bull. Am. Phys. Soc. [2] 4, 263 (1959).

[43] A more sensitive method to determine the presence or absence of an electric dipole moment is the direct measurement of the first-order Stark effect it would cause. In this way E. Lipworth and P. G. H. Sandars, Bull. Am. Phys. Soc. [2] 9, 91 (1964), have set an upper limit of $7.8 \times 10^{-9}\ e\hbar/mc$ for the dipole moment of the cesium atom.

4.3. Polarized Ion Sources*†

Beams of polarized nuclear particles are used as probes of spin dependence in nuclear forces. A spin-orbit force was used profitably in explaining nuclear shell structure,[1] and it was shortly later found to be applicable as well to the nucleon–nucleus elastic scattering problem. This was first seen in a double scattering experiment by Heusinkveld and Freier[2] in which protons were scattered by He⁴. As first suggested by Schwinger[3] and expanded by others,[4] any spin-orbit terms in the nuclear force serve to cause the elastic scattering to act as a polarizer of the incident unpolarized beams (or analyzer of an incident polarized beam). Higher-energy experiments on p-nucleus and p-p scattering soon followed which showed polarization effects[5] capable of being analyzed in terms of a spin-orbit interaction analogous to a Thomas-type term.[6] Although these earlier experiments as well as many later ones were carried out with unpolarized initial beams which were polarized by an elastic scattering, it is evident that the use of a polarized source can overcome the following disadvantages of this method: low intensity; polarization variation with beam energy; beam quality degeneration due to energy and momentum spread in the first scatterer; additional background produced in the first scatterer; and usually a fairly low value of polarization caused by the necessity of accepting a finite solid angle for scattered particles with consequent variation of polarization.

4.3.1. Definitions and Nomenclature

The spin properties of a beam of particles can be described by combinations of the expectation values of the spin operators σ_i. In the case of spin-$\frac{1}{2}$, there are only three independent combinations. These may be chosen to be σ_x, σ_y, σ_z. For this case, therefore, the spin state

[1] M. Mayer, *Phys. Rev.* **75**, 1969 (1949); Haxel, Jensen, and Suess, *Phys. Rev.* **75**, 1766 (1949).

[2] M. Heusinkveld and G. Freier, *Phys. Rev.* **85**, 80 (1952).

[3] J. Schwinger, *Phys. Rev.* **69**, 681 (1946).

[4] L. Wolfenstein, *Phys. Rev.* **75**, 1664 (1949); C. L. Critchfield and D. C. Dodder, *Phys. Rev.* **76**, 602 (1949).

[5] C. L. Oxley, W. J. Cartwright, J. Rouvine, E. Basker, D. Klein, J. Ring, and W. Skillman, *Phys. Rev.* **91**, 419 (1954); *Phys. Rev.* **93**, 806 (1954); O. Chamberlain, E. Segre, R. Tripp, C. Wiegand, and J. Ypsilantis, *Phys. Rev.* **93**, 1430 (1954); H. G. De Carvalho, E. Heiberg, J. Marshall, and L. Marshall, *Phys. Rev.* **95**, 1694 (1954).

[6] E. Fermi, *Nuovo Cimento* **11**, 407 (1954).

* Chapter 4.3 is by **C. W. Drake, Jr.**
† For polarization of electrons see Volume 5B, Chapter 2.5.

of the beam may be completely characterized by a vector polarization P having components $P_i = \langle \sigma_i \rangle = (2/\hbar)\langle S_i \rangle$.

In the case of spin-1, bilinear combinations of the spin operators can also be found, necessitating in addition to the vector polarization components, $P_i = \langle \sigma_i \rangle = (1/\hbar)\langle S_i \rangle$, the use of the tensor components P_{ij} which are usually defined as $P_{ij} = \frac{3}{2}[\sigma_i\sigma_j + \sigma_j\sigma_i] - 2\delta_{ij}$.

The spin state of a beam of particles may be expressed as a wave function

$$\psi = \sum_n^{2s+1} a_n u_n$$

where the u_n are the eigenfunctions of σ_z. The usual normalization condition is $\sum |a_n|^2 = 1$. If only one a_n is nonzero the beam is completely polarized. In most physical cases, however, the beam is not completely polarized and all a_n are nonzero; in addition the beam consists of a mixture of groups of particles. Each group of weight F_i is characterized by a wave function

$$\psi_i = \sum_n a_n{}^i u_n . \tag{4.3.1}$$

Any expectation values must consist of averages over the values i, that is:

$$\overline{\langle O \rangle} = \sum_{i=1}^N F_i \langle O \rangle_i = \sum_{1=i}^N F_i \langle \psi_i| \, O \, |\psi_i \rangle. \tag{4.3.2}$$

This is most conviently expressed by means of the density matrix formulation where the density matrix is defined by

$$\langle i| \, \rho \, |j \rangle = \sum_{n=1}^N F_n a_j{}^{n*} a_i{}^n. \tag{4.3.3}$$

The observables are then expressed as

$$\overline{\langle O \rangle} = T_r(O\rho). \tag{4.3.4}$$

The density matrix formulation may be considered a method of initially averaging over nonobservable quantities instead of carrying these quantities through the calculation to be averaged over in the final result.

In the case of spin-$\frac{1}{2}$ the density matrix for a beam of noninteracting particles may be written in terms of the vector polarization since

$$\rho(\tfrac{1}{2}) = \tfrac{1}{2}(1 + \mathbf{P} \cdot \boldsymbol{\delta}) = \tfrac{1}{2}\begin{pmatrix} 1 + P_3 & P_1 - iP_2 \\ P_1 + iP_2 & 1 - P_3 \end{pmatrix}. \tag{4.3.5}$$

For the case of spin-1 the equivalent expression is

$$
\rho(1) = \begin{bmatrix}
\tfrac{1}{3} + \tfrac{1}{2} P_3 + \tfrac{1}{6} P_{33} \\[2mm]
\dfrac{1}{2\sqrt{2}} (P_1 + iP_2) + \dfrac{1}{3\sqrt{2}} (P_{12} + iP_{23}) \\[2mm]
\tfrac{1}{6}(P_{11} - P_{22}) + \dfrac{i}{3} P_{12}
\end{bmatrix}
$$

$$
\dfrac{1}{2\sqrt{2}} (P_1 - iP_2) + \dfrac{1}{3\sqrt{2}} (P_{13} - iP_{23})
$$

$$
\tfrac{1}{3} - \tfrac{1}{3} P_{33}
$$

$$
\dfrac{1}{2\sqrt{2}} (P_1 + iP_2) - \dfrac{1}{3\sqrt{2}} (P_{13} + iP_{23})
$$

$$
\begin{bmatrix}
\tfrac{1}{6}(P_{11} - P_{22}) - \dfrac{iP_{12}}{3} \\[2mm]
\dfrac{1}{2\sqrt{2}} (P_1 - iP_2) - \dfrac{1}{3\sqrt{2}} (P_{13} - iP_{23}) \\[2mm]
\tfrac{1}{3} - \tfrac{1}{2} P_3 + \tfrac{1}{6} P_{33}
\end{bmatrix}
\quad (4.3.6)
$$

The density matrix can always be diagonalized which corresponds to writing it in terms of the set of wave functions ψ_i in Eq. (4.3.1). This diagonalization is equivalent to a rotation in a real or abstract space which brings the quantization axis along an axis of symmetry. For example, in the angular momentum basis $| J, J_z \rangle$ if the symmetry axis is brought along the z axis the system is invariant under rotations about this axis and the density matrix is diagonal. These diagonal elements then give the population of the system with respect to the various J_z states. Therefore,

$$
\rho(1) = \begin{pmatrix} N_1 & 0 & 0 \\ 0 & N_0 & 0 \\ 0 & 0 & N_{-1} \end{pmatrix} \quad (4.3.7)
$$

where the N_k are the number of states having $J_z = k$. It is convenient to normalize $Tr\rho = \sum N_k = 1$. It can be seen from a direct calculation of $Tr(\rho O)$, where the O's are the operators whose expectation values are the polarization parameters P_i, P_{ij}, or more simply from an examination of Eqs. (4.3.6) and (4.3.7), that the spin dependence of a spin-1 system may be described by the two parameters $P_3 = N_1 - N_{-1}$ and $P_{33} = 1 - 3N_0 = 3(N_1 + N_{-1}) - 2$ since $P_1 = P_2 = P_{12} = P_{13} = P_{23} = 0$

and $P_{11} = P_{22} = -\frac{1}{2} P_{33}$. It is often convenient to express the polarization in terms of the expectation values of the irreducible spherical tensor operators T_{LM} (see, for example, Refs. 7–10 for definitions) possessing certain commutation rules. These parameters, called elements of the statistical tensor ρ_{LM}, transform under rotation as the spherical harmonics Y_{LM}^* or

$$\rho'_{LM} = \sum_{M'} \rho_{LM'} D_{MM'}^L(R) \tag{4.3.8}$$

where R is the rotation of the coordinate system of the ρ'_{LM} to the ρ_{LM}. The ρ_{LM}'s may also be written as

$$\rho_{LM}(l_1 l_2) = \sum (-)^{l_2-m_2}(l_1 m_1 l_2 - m_2 \mid LM)\langle l_1 m_1 \mid \rho \mid l_2 m_2 \rangle \tag{4.3.9}$$

where the $(l_1 m_1 l_2 m_2 \mid LM)$ are vector coupling coefficients and the $\langle \mid \rho \mid \rangle$ are density matrix elements. This rotation property of the ρ_{LM} is most useful in the consideration of nuclear scattering or reactions. The convention used is that of Goldfarb,[7–9] who follows that of Coster and Jauch.[10] Explicit expressions for the case of spin-$\frac{1}{2}$ and spin-1 follow:

$$\rho_{00}(\tfrac{1}{2}) = \frac{1}{\sqrt{2}}; \qquad \rho_{10}(\tfrac{1}{2}) = \frac{P_3}{\sqrt{2}}; \qquad \rho_{1\pm1}(\tfrac{1}{2}) = \mp \tfrac{1}{2}(P_1 \mp iP_2) \tag{4.3.10}$$

$$\rho_{00}(1) = \frac{1}{\sqrt{3}}; \qquad \rho_{10}(1) = \frac{P_3}{\sqrt{2}}; \qquad \rho_{1\pm1}(1) = \mp \tfrac{1}{2}(P_1 \mp iP_2) \tag{4.3.11}$$

$$\rho_{20}(1) = \frac{1}{\sqrt{6}} P_{33}; \; \rho_{2\pm1}(1) = \mp \tfrac{1}{3}(P_{13} \mp iP_{23}); \; \rho_{2\pm2}(1) = \tfrac{1}{6}(P_{11} - P_{22}) \mp \frac{i}{3} P_{13}.$$

4.3.2. Specific Applications

4.3.2.1. Nucleon-Nucleon Scattering. The use of polarized beams is particularly well-suited for the study of the nucleon-nucleon inter-actions. The experimental results may be parameterized using several different schemes.[4] It can be shown that the nucleon–nucleon scattering matrix in spin space may be represented by five complex quantities and an arbitrary phase or by nine real quantities if the usual conditions on invariance under space rotations and reflections and time reversal are

[7] S. Devons and L. J. B. Goldfarb, Angular correlations, in "Handbuch der Physik," Vol. XLII. Springer, Berlin, 1957.

[8] L. J. B. Goldfarb, Nuclear Phys. 7, 622 (1958).

[9] L. J. B. Goldfarb, in Angular correlations and polarization, "Nuclear Reactions," Endt and Demeur, eds., Vol. I. North-Holland, Amsterdam, 1959.

[10] F. Coster and J. M. Jauch, Helv. Phys. Acta 26, 3 (1953).

preserved. However, because the experimental quantities do not enter linearly, the complete determination of the nine quantities at a given energy requires more than nine experiments. If, however, a phase shift analysis is made, with appropriate assumptions as to smoothness of variation of the observables with angle and as to behavior at high l values, the scattering matrix may be determined in principle below the threshold for inelastic events by five measurements at all angles (seven if charge symmetry is violated for the n-p case). In practice ambiguities arise. There are, however, twenty-eight possible independent experiments at a given angle if all polarizations were to be measured.[11] In principle, with polarized beam-polarized target-single scattering, or polarized beam-unpolarized target-double scattering, fourteen determinations can be made which fixes the scattering matrix. The analysis of Bethe and Schumacher[12] is particularly useful in such considerations. If the invariance requirements are relaxed, further considerations must be made.[13]

4.3.2.2. Nucleon-Nucleus Scattering. Nucleon–nucleus studies using polarized protons have provided additional data for tests of models. In particular, much work has been done in fitting such data with optical potentials at intermediate energies.[14–16] These fits of polarization data provide a sensitive test of the magnitude and form of the usual assumed spin-orbit part of the average nuclear potential. Tests of possible spin-spin interaction can be made; in particular, a measurement of the final polarization of an initially polarized proton elastically scattered from a nucleus of $I \neq 0$ provides a sensitive test of such a term. Large-angle scattering with polarized protons·from series of nuclei shows strong surface structure effects, as should be the case for a surface form of the spin-orbit term.[14]

Polarization data are also used to resolve ambiguities in the phase shift analysis of nucleon–nucleus differential cross section data as well as with the nucleon–nucleon data. Indeed such was the motivation of the first polarization measurement[2] in which (p, α) scattering using polarized protons was observed.

4.3.2.3. More Complex Scattering and Reactions. The use of polarized deuterons in direct interactions such as (d, p) stripping provides further

[11] R. J. N. Phillips, *Helv. Physica Acta Suppl. VI* **429** (1961).

[12] C. R. Schumacher and H. A. Bethe, *Phys. Rev.* **121**, 1534 (1961).

[13] E. H. Thorndike, *Phys. Rev.* **138**, B586 (1965).

[14] L. Rosen, J. E. Brolley, and L. Stewart, *Phys. Rev.* **121**, 1423 (1961).

[15] L. Rosen, "Proceedings of the 2nd International Symposium on Polarization Phenomena of Nucleons," P. Huber and H. Schopper, eds., pp. 253–279, Birkhäuser, Basel, 1966.

[16] J. Perey, "Proceedings of the 2nd International Symposium on Polarization Phenomena of Nucleons," P. Huber and H. Schopper; eds., pp. 191–202. Birkhäuser, Basel, 1966.

information on the spin dependence of the nuclear reaction mechanism, since the vector polarization of the incident deuteron provides the same information as would be provided by a measure of the outgoing proton polarization. Deuteron tensor polarization can provide information in intermediate state reactions.

These complex systems require a more extended treatment of the polarization effects than that of the nucleon-nucleon case. Such formulations have been made both for very general and more specific cases.[8,18,19,*]

Polarized projectiles may also be used in providing spectroscopic information such as the spins and parities of nuclear levels that would otherwise be ambiguous. Such applications must be considered in detail for individual cases.

Measurements of parity nonconserving terms, or upper limit determination, in strong interactions have been made using polarized beams of neutrons,[20] protons,[21] and deuterons.[22] Determinations of the degree of time reversal invariance have also been made with polarized particles.[23]

The examination of interference effects of neighboring compound levels in the intermediate region of nuclear excitation will probably be a useful application of polarized ion beams, although so far these effects

[17] E. E. Gross, R. H. Bassel, L. N. Blumberg, A. van der Woude, and A. Zucker, "Proceedings of the 2nd International Symposium on Polarization Phenomena of Nucleons," P. Huber and H. Schopper, eds., pp. 336–338. Birkhäuser, Basel, 1966.

[18] A. Galonsky, H. B. Willard, and T. A. Welton, *Phys. Rev. Letters* **2**, 349 (1959).

[19] T. A. Welton, *in* Theory of polarization in reactions and scattering, "Fast Neutron Physics," Marian and Fowler, eds., Part II, pp. 1317–1377, Wiley (Interscience), New York, 1963.

[20] R. Haas, L. B. Leupuner, and R. K. Adair, *Phys. Rev.* **116**, 1221 (1959); Yu. G. Agov, P. A. Krupchitsky, and Yu. A. Oratovsky, *Phys. Letters* **12**, 25 (1964) and Abstract of Dubna Conference (1964); K. Abrahams, W. Ratynski, F. Stecher-Rasmussen, and E. Warming, "Proceedings of the 2nd International Symposium on Polarization Phenomena of Nucleons," P. Huber and H. Schopper, eds., pp. 377–379. Birkhäuser, Basel, 1966. M. Forte and O. Saavedra, "Proceedings of the 2nd International Symposium on Polarization Phenomena of Nucleons," P. Huber and H. Schopper, eds., pp. 386–390. Birkhäuser, Basel, 1966.

[21] See Reference 13 for a discussion of parity noninvariance limits in p-p scattering. L. Rosen and J. E. Brolley, *Phys. Rev. Letters* **2**, 98 (1959).

[22] C. W. Drake, D. C. Bonar, R. D. Headrick, and V. W. Hughes, "Proceedings of the 2nd International Symposium on Polarization Phenomena of Nucleons," P. Huber and H. Schopper, eds., pp. 362–364. Birkhäuser, Basel, 1966. Also *Phys. Rev.* (to be published).

[23] L. Rosen and J. E. Brolley, *Phys. Rev. Letters* **2**, 98 (1959); J. Kajfosz and J. Kopecky, "Proceedings of the 2nd International Symposium on Polarization Phenomena of Nucleons," P. Huber and H. Schopper, eds., pp. 383–384. Birkhäuser, Basel, 1966.

* See also Volume 5B, Chapter 2.4.

have only been studied with polarized neutrons.[24] A similar statement can be made for the region of applicability of the statistical model.[25]

4.3.2.4. High-Energy Scattering and Reactions. Experiments using polarized ion sources for high-energy studies (for nucleon-nucleon inelastic events) have as yet (December, 1965) not been carried out, although some work has been done using polarized targets.[26]

Information to be found using polarized beams would be similar to that found at lower energies and would include the determination of the nucleon-nucleon scattering matrix for inelastic scattering. The examination of symmetries (P and C invariance) are greatly facilitated when an initial spin is known as at lower energies. A polarized beam of high-energy electrons together with a measure of the initial or final nucleon polarization would provide additional information on nuclear form factors.[27] The theoretical formulation of the spin dependence of these high-energy processes has not been extensive but will presumably be supplied as the experimental information becomes more plentiful.

4.3.3. Production of Polarized Beams

4.3.3.1. Production by Scattering. The possibility of producing an energetic beam of polarized nucleons was first suggested by Schwinger.[28] He proposed using the polarization produced in elastic scattering of neutrons by He^4. This polarization arises from the interference term between resonance and potential scattering. The first experimental uses of polarized beams was made by using protons[2] rather than neutrons but the principle remained the same. If the process is to be invariant under time reversal the vector polarization $\mathbf{p}$ in the direction $\mathbf{n}(= \mathbf{k}_1 \times \mathbf{k}_2/|\mathbf{k}_1 \times \mathbf{k}_2|)$ produced when an unpolarized beam is scattered from nuclei through an angle θ must be equal to the asymmetry measured at the angle θ and $-\theta$ when the same beam having a polarization $\mathbf{p}$ is scattered from the same nuclei at the same energy. Therefore the magnitude, but not the sign, of p can be measured in

[24] O. Aspelund and J. Higbie, "Proceedings of the 2nd International Symposium on Polarization Phenomena of Nucleons," P. Huber and H. Schopper, eds., pp. 470–473. Birkhäuser, Basel, 1966.

[25] H. A. Widenmüller, "Proceedings of the 2nd International Symposium on Polarization Phenomena of Nucleons," P. Huber and H. Schopper, eds., pp. 219–229. Birkhäuser, Basel, 1966.

[26] O. Chamberlain, C. D. Jeffries, C. H. Shultz, G. Shapiro, and L. van Rossum, *Phys. Rev. Letters* **7**, 293 (1963); S. Suwa, A. Yakosawa, N. E. Booth, R. J. Esterling, and R. E. Hill, *Phys. Rev. Letters* **15**, 560 (1965); P. J. Duke, D. P. Jones, M. A. R. Kemp, P. G. Murphy, J. D. Prentice, J. J. Thresher, H. H. Atkinson, C. R. Cox, and K. S. Heard, *Phys. Rev. Letters* **15**, 468 (1965).

[27] A. I. Akhiezer, L. N. Rozentsveig, and I. M. Shmushkevich, *Zh. Eksperim Theo. Fiz.* **33**, 765 (1957); *Trans. JETP* **6**, 588 (1958).

[28] J. Schwinger, *Phys. Rev.* **69**, 681 (1946).

principle by a double scattering of an unpolarized beam. The asymmetry is defined as $[N(\theta) - N(-\theta)]/[N(\theta) + N(-\theta)]$ where $N(\theta)$ is the number of particles detected at the angle θ and is measured in the plane normal to $\mathbf{n}$; i.e., the momenta of incident particle, first scattered particle, and second scattered particle all lie in the same plane. The sign of the polarization must be determined by other methods or deduced from theoretical considerations. The usual convention (so-called Basel convention) is that the positive direction of the polarization axis is taken as $\mathbf{k}_1 \times \mathbf{k}_2$ where $\mathbf{k}_1$ is the incident and $\mathbf{k}_2$ the scattered wave vector. In practice the two scatterings do not take place at the same energy because of energy loss in the first scattering, but $\mid p \mid$ may be determined by three double scatterings.[29] Initial experiments were first carried out on spin-zero targets (He^4, C^{12}) for simplicity of interpretation. Once the polarization measurements have been made by a double scattering, a single scattering can be used for the production of a polarized beam at the measured energy to examine polarization effects on an unknown nucleus or can be used as a polarization-sensitive detector to examine the polarization state of an outgoing particle. Instead of producing polarized protons by scattering from He^4 it has been found advantageous to reverse the process and to use the recoil proton from alpha particles incident on protons.[14] This method has the advantage of obtaining a nearly 100% polarized beam at a convenient scattering angle because of scattering kinetics. As compared to the production of a polarized beam by means of a polarized ion source the scattering method suffers from several disadvantages. The polarization as a function of scattering angle usually is approximately proportional to the derivative of the differential cross section, so that a compromise must be made in polarization magnitude and intensity. From consideration of counting statistics alone, the quantity (polarization)$^2 \times$ (intensity) should be maximized but the experimental asymmetries usually make it advantageous to keep the polarization larger than this criterion would suggest; therefore the differential cross section is usually small at the angle accepted. The polarization varies with angle so that the acceptance solid angle must be kept small if the polarization is to be well defined. The scattering target must be thin for energy definition. These considerations lead to a loss factor of from 10^{-5} to 10^{-8} in the production of a polarized beam. As a favorable example of this method the scattering of 35 to 45 MeV protons from Ca^{40} is used to produce a polarized ion beam at the ORNL variable energy cyclotron.[30] This process produces a beam of 35% polarized

[29] M. J. Scott, *Phys. Rev.* **110**, 1398 (1958).

[30] A. van der Woude, L. N. Blumberg, E. E. Gross, and N. Zucker, "Proceedings of the 2nd International Symposium on Polarization Phenomena of Nucleons," P. Huber and H. Schopper, eds., pp. 140–142, Birkhäuser, Basel, 1966.

protons with an energy spread of 0.5 MeV. The intensity is 25 μamp per amp of primary beam. In addition, the polarizing scattering also produces other radiations which add to the background in the examination of the second scattering. These disadvantages led to the development of polarized particle sources using polarized atomic beams.

4.3.3.2. Production from Polarized Atomic Beams. The polarized sources presently in use may be described functionally in three sections. A schematic diagram is shown in Fig. 1. The first section is the hydrogen

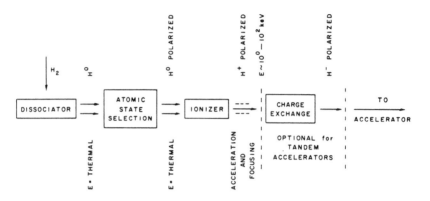

FIG. 1.   Schematic diagram of an atomic beam polarized ion source.

dissociator which produces a beam of atomic hydrogen (or deuterium) usually at thermal velocity and having a modified Maxwellian velocity distribution. The atoms then pass into the vacuum chamber through slits or holes, either simple or multiple, forming an atomic beam. The next section then spatially separates the atomic beam according to the magnetic moments of its various states by the use of an inhomogeneous magnetic field. These separated beams then have a nonzero atomic polarization. The third section ionizes the polarized atomic beam to produce a polarized ion beam which can then be extracted and with suitable ion optics injected into an accelerator. Each of these sections will now be examined in more detail.

4.3.3.2.1. MOLECULAR DISSOCIATION. Ac discharges have been used to dissociate the molecular hydrogen into hydrogen atoms. The discharges can be run from 60 cps to microwave frequencies but most sources use frequencies of from 20 to 150 Mc/sec for convenience and ease of operation. These dissociators require rf powers of from about 100 to 1000 watts depending on the discharge volume and gas pressure. Atomic densities of about 60 to 90 % are obtained using clean Pyrex discharge bulbs. In some cases the bulbs have been treated with a tetrafluorethylene[31] (Teflon) or G.E.-Silicone F-89 (Dri-Film) to enhance the atomic production. Two pressure conditions have been commonly used. The usual one is that in which the mean free path λ_k between atomic collisions in the discharge bulb is on the order of or greater than the dimensions of the discharge bulb exit. In this case the atoms diffuse into a high-vacuum region. The atomic beam thus formed has a velocity distribution proportional to $vN(v)$ where $N(v)$ is the usual Maxwell–Boltzmann distribution in the source. The most probable velocity in the beam is $1.22\,\alpha$ where α is the most probable velocity of $N(v)$; α is equal to $\sqrt{2kT/m}$ where k, T, and m are Boltzmann's constant, the absolute temperature, and the mass of the atom, respectively. The most probable source velocity is about 2×10^5 cm/sec for hydrogen with a discharge bulb whose walls are cooled to room temperature. These conditions for molecular flow limit the maximum pressure in the discharge bulb to from 0.1 to 1 mm depending on the exit dimensions.

The exit hole may have the dimensions along the length of the hole l much less than the opening diameter d. In this case the gas diffuses in a $\cos\theta$ distribution, thus forming a 60° half angle between 50 % intensity points. If l is greater than d, the distribution becomes peaked forward and the total gas flow may be reduced by a factor κ without loss of intensity in the forward direction as long as $(\lambda_k > l > d)$. The κ factor may be calculated for various shapes of openings.[32] Extended source exits have been used consisting of bundles of glass capillary canals on the order of 0.14 mm diam $\times$ 2 mm long and of up to 1200 tubes.[33,31] These arrays produce beams having half angles of 6 to 8°.

Higher source pressures (on the order of $\frac{1}{2}$ atm) can be used with shaped nozzles and diaphragms to produce supersonic flow, a jet source, in which the velocity distribution is narrowed and peaked toward the higher velocity.[34,35] This Laval nozzle however requires much greater gas flow, and it has proved difficult to maintain high molecular dissociation in the gas jet.[37,*]

4.3.3.2.2. STATE SELECTION BY THE USE OF MAGNETIC FIELD GRADIENTS. The beam of hydrogen or deuterium next passes into a region

[31] E. R. Collins, H. F. Glavish, and S. Whinery, *Nuclear Instr. Meth.* **25**, 67 (1963).

[32] N. F. Ramsey, "Molecular Beams." Oxford Univ. Press (Clarendon), London and New York, 1956.

[33] G. H. Stafford, J. M. Dickson, D. C. Salter, and M. K. Craddock, *Nuclear Instr. Meth.* **15**, 146 (1962).

[34] A. Kantrovitz and J. Grey, *Rev. Sci. Instr.* **22**, 328 (1951); G. B. Kistiakowsky and W. P. Slichter, *Rev. Sci. Instr.* **22**, 333 (1951).

[35] R. L. Keller, L. Dick, and M. Fidecaro, *Helv. Phys. Acta Suppl.* **6**, 48 (1961); R. L. Keller, L. Dick, and M. Fidecaro, Rept. CERN 60-2 (1960) (unpublished).

* For more details on some aspects of the techniques discussed here and on the following pages see also Volume 3, Part 6.

of high magnetic field gradient which produces forces on the particles in the atomic beam depending on the magnitude and configuration of magnetic field $\mathbf{B}$ and its gradient ∇B. The energies of the magnetic substates of the ground state of a hydrogen isotope are given by the diagonalization of a matrix whose elements are $(\psi_i \mid \mathcal{H} \mid \psi_j)$ where the ψ_i's are the ground state wave functions and the Hamiltonian $\mathcal{H} = a\mathbf{I} \cdot \mathbf{J} + g_J\mu_0 \mathbf{J} \cdot \mathbf{H}_0 + g_I\mu_0 \mathbf{I} \cdot \mathbf{H}_0$. $\mathbf{I}$ and $\mathbf{J}$ are the nuclear and electronic angular momentum operators, g_I and g_J are the nuclear and electronic g factors, a is the hyperfine interaction constant, μ_0 is the Bohr magneton, and H_0 is the applied external magnetic field. The resulting energy expression $W_{Fm}(H)$ is known as the Breit-Rabi equation for the case of $J = \frac{1}{2}$ and is sufficient for the analysis of the state separation. The force on an atom in the state F, m is given by

$$\mathbf{F} = -\nabla W_{Fm} = -\frac{\partial W}{\partial H} \nabla H_0, \qquad (4.3.12)$$

where F, m are the low-field quantum numbers used to designate the state, $\mathbf{F} = \mathbf{I} + \mathbf{J}$ is the total angular momentum, and $m = F_z$. F is a good quantum number only at zero external magnetic field. The quantum numbers of the decoupled (the high field) representation, m_J and m_I, could be used equally well. For hydrogen $F = 0$ and 1, for deuterium $F = \frac{1}{2}$ and $\frac{3}{2}$, and m has the values $F, F - 1, \ldots, -F$. Thus there are four states of hydrogen and six states of deuterium. These states will be designated H $-$ 1 to H $-$ 4 and D $-$ 1 to D $-$ 6, respectively, as indicated in Figs. 2 and 3. The effective magnetic moment μ_e of an atom in one of these states is defined in terms of a system having a magnetic moment independent of H_0. Since

$$W = -\mathbf{\mu} \cdot \mathbf{J} = -\mu_e H_0, \qquad (4.3.13)$$

where μ_e is the component of $\mathbf{\mu}$ along H_0, we can write for Eq. (4.3.12)

$$\mathbf{F} = -\frac{\partial W}{\partial H} \nabla H_0 = \mu_e \nabla H_0 \qquad (4.3.14)$$

and use this as the definition for the effective magnetic moment μ_e of an atom when H_0 and ∇H are both in the same direction. The variation of μ_e with H_0 is shown in Figs. 4 and 5 for hydrogen and deuterium. A beam of H or D which passes through a region of high field (x much greater than 1) will then experience a force which acts in the direction of $-\nabla H_0$ for the states H $-$ 1, H $-$ 2, D $-$ 1, D $-$ 2, and D $-$ 3 and in the $+\nabla H_0$ direction of the other states.

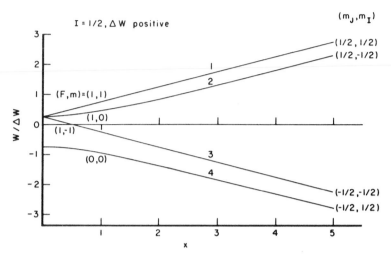

FIG. 2. Energy level diagram for hydrogen in a magnetic field H, obtained from the Breit–Rabi equation:

$$W_{F=I\pm1/2,m} = -\Delta W/[2(2I+1)] + \mu_0 g_I H_m \pm (\Delta W/2)[1 + 4mx/(2I+1) + x^2]^{1/2};$$

$F = I \pm \frac{1}{2}$; $\Delta W = W_{I+1/2}(H = 0) - W_{I-1/2}(H = 0)$; $x = (g_J - g_I)\mu_0 H/\Delta W$; g_J and g_I are the electronic and nuclear g values in units in which $g_J \simeq 2$; $\mu_0 =$ Bohr magneton. For hydrogen $J = \frac{1}{2}, I = \frac{1}{2}, \Delta W/h = \Delta\nu = 1420.4$ Mc/sec, $g_J = 2.002, g_I = -0.0030$. The levels are designated by both their weak-field quantum numbers (F, m) and their strong-field quantum numbers (m_J, m_I).

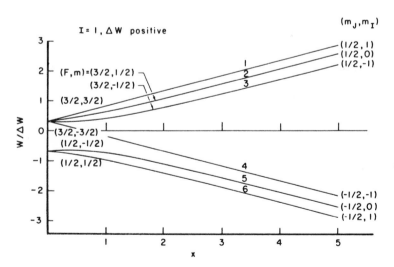

FIG. 3. Energy level diagram for deuterium in a magnetic field H. Symbols are as given in Fig. 2 except $J = \frac{1}{2}$, $I = 1$, $\Delta\nu = 327.38$ Mc/sec, $g_J = 2.002$, and $g_I = -0.00047$.

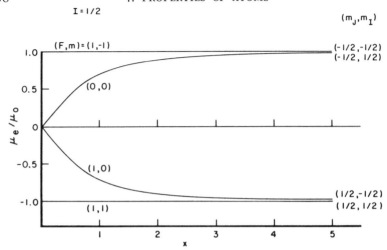

FIG. 4.   The magnetic moments of the magnetic sublevels of the hfs states of hydrogen as a function of magnetic field. Symbols are defined as in Fig. 2.

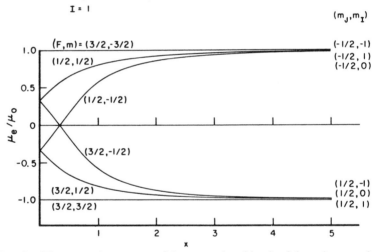

FIG. 5.   The magnetic moments of the magnetic sublevels of deuterium as a function of magnetic field. Symbols are defined as in Fig. 2.

Several types of inhomogeneous magnetic fields have been used to produce state-separated beams. The type of magnet that has proved most useful for producing intense polarized atomic beams has been the four- or six-pole type. A magnet of $2n$ poles which have hyperbolic cylindrical pole pieces produces a field in the central region whose scalar potentials are given by

$$V(r, \theta) = Cr^n \cos n\theta, \tag{4.3.15}$$

$$\therefore \mathbf{H} = -\nabla V = \hat{r}Cnr^{n-1} \cos n\theta + \hat{\theta}Cnr^{n-1} \sin n\theta, \tag{4.3.16}$$

where $C = H_0/nr^{n-1}$ for $\mathbf{H} = \hat{r}H_0$ at $r = r_0$, $\theta = 0$, and

$$\nabla | H | = \nabla[(H_r)^2 + (H_\theta)^2]^{1/2} = \hat{r}(n-1)H_0 r^{n-2}/r_0^{n-1}. \qquad (4.3.17)$$

Therefore the force on an atom having a magnetic moment is purely radial and proportional to r^{n-2}, attractive for states with a negative moment and repulsive for states with a positive moment. With the four- and six-pole geometries, the magnetic force on the atom has magnitude constant or proportional to r, respectively. The solution to the resulting equations of motion produce trajectories for atoms directed along the axis of the magnet (x axis) whose diplacement (y) from this axis in a plane is given by

$$y = \pm \frac{M_0 H_0}{r_0 m v^2} x^2 + \theta_0 x + y_0, \quad 4 \text{ pole}, \qquad (4.3.18a)$$

$$y = y_0 \begin{Bmatrix} \cos(x/\lambda) \\ \cosh(x/\lambda) \end{Bmatrix} + \theta_0 \lambda \begin{Bmatrix} \sin(x/\lambda) \\ \sinh(x/\lambda) \end{Bmatrix}, \quad 6 \text{ pole}, \qquad (4.3.18b)$$

where θ_0 and y_0 are the displacement and direction with respect to the x axis at the magnet entrance of an atom with velocity $v \approx v_x$, and $\lambda = vr_0 (m/2u_0 H_0)^{1/2}$ where m is the mass of the atom. The circular or hyperbolic functions are chosen as μ_e is negative or positive, respectively. By the use of these expressions atomic trajectories can be calculated and it is found that a focusing action is obtained; that is, the acceptance solid angle of the magnet which directs atoms from a point source on the axis of the magnet into a region of a plane following the magnet is greater than the solid angle subtended by that region at the source. This factor is usually on the order of 5. The magnet may be considered a thick lens, positive for $\mu_e < 0$, negative for $\mu_e > 0$, and treated accordingly. In particular the six-pole magnet approaches an ideal lens having no circular aberration, comma, astigmatism, or curvature of field; however

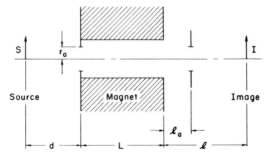

FIG. 6. Schematic diagram of the focusing magnet, four- or six-pole, in terms of optical parameters.

the lens is velocity-dependent, i.e., chromatic aberration is present. Due to this velocity dependence an image of the source cannot be produced at the ionizer for all velocities as would be most desirable; therefore the system must be designed so that the finite ionizer aperture will accept the maximum number of focused atoms ($\mu_e < 0$) while rejecting most of the defocused atoms ($\mu_e > 0$). Several useful optical expressions for the case of the six-pole magnet are listed below (see Fig. 6)[36]

Positive Lens   *Negative Lens*

$$l = \chi \frac{d\cos(L/\chi) + \chi\sin(L/\chi)}{d\sin(L/\chi) - \chi\cos(L/\chi)} \qquad l = -\chi \frac{d\coth(L/\chi) + \chi\sinh(L/\chi)}{d\sinh(L/\chi) + \chi\coth(\chi/L)} \quad (4.3.19a)$$

$$M = -\frac{\chi}{d\sin(L/y) - \chi\cos(L/\chi)} \qquad M = \frac{\chi}{d\sinh(L/\chi) + \chi\coth(L/\chi)} \qquad (4.3.19b)$$

$$l_a = -\chi\tan L/\chi \qquad\qquad l_a = -\chi\tanh(L/\chi) \qquad\qquad (4.3.20a)$$

$$M_a = [\cos(L/\chi)]^{-1} \qquad\qquad M_a = [\coth L/\chi]^{-1} \qquad\qquad (4.3.20b)$$

where L is the magnet length; d is the distance of the source from the magnet's entrance; l is the distance of the image of the source from the exit of the magnet, positive if to the right of the magnet exit; M is the magnification of the source, positive if virtual, negative if real; l_a is the distance of the exit pupil from the magnet exit, that is, the image of the magnet entrance aperture where the defining aperture is a real stop at the magnet entrance; M_a is the magnification of the entrance aperture. By the use of these expressions trajectories of limiting rays in the entrance and exit space of a real source can be drawn allowing estimates of the efficiency of the separating magnets.

A further useful set of formulas are those for the transmittance T, i.e., the ratio of atoms accepted by the detector aperture of radius r_D at a distance l from the magnet exit to the number of atoms incident on an effective entrance aperture of radius r_a at the magnet entrance:

$$T_{\mu<1} = \left(\frac{r_D}{r_a}\right)^2 \left[\left(\frac{l}{\chi} - \frac{\chi}{d}\right)\sin\left(\frac{L}{\chi}\right) - \left(\frac{l}{d} + 1\right)\cos\left(\frac{L}{\chi}\right)\right]^{-2}, \qquad (4.3.21a)$$

$$T_{\mu>1} = \left(\frac{r_D}{r_a}\right)^2 \left[\left(\frac{l}{\chi} + \frac{\chi}{d}\right)\sinh\left(\frac{L}{\chi}\right) + \left(\frac{l}{d} + 1\right)\cosh\left(\frac{L}{\chi}\right)\right]^{-2}. \qquad (4.3.21b)$$

In these expressions χ and usually r_a are functions of the velocity. Values of $T_{\mu<0}$ greater than 1 only indicate that all accepted atoms with $\mu < 0$

---

[36] G. W. Raith, private communication (to be published).

are transmitted. $T_{\mu<0}/T_{\mu>0}$ is the separation ratio. These formulas may be used to estimate the separated atom beam intensity and polarization after averaging over the atom velocities. This may be easily approximated when $l \gg r_D$ and $r_D \sim r_a$ since in that case $T_{\mu<0}$ peaks sharply and is significant only for a small velocity interval or intervals.

If the geometry is such that the detector aperture can be made greater than the magnet aperture and positioned close to the magnet exit so that all focused atoms that have a maximum deflection less than the magnet pole radius are captured, that is, so that $T_{\mu<0} = 1$ for all atoms, the only parameters to be considered are the entrance solid angle and fraction of defocused atoms. For a point source on the magnet axis the effective entrance aperture radius is given by

$$r_a = r_0[1 + \lambda^2/d^2]^{-1/2} \qquad (4.3.22)$$

where r_0 is the magnet pole radius. Since for $d \ll \lambda$, $r_a \sim r_0 d/\lambda = (d/v)(2\mu_0 H_0/m)^{1/2}$; for the case of a point source near the magnet the entrance aperture for a given velocity depends only on the magnetic field at the pole tips or the saturation properties of the material. If the expression is integrated over the velocity distribution the result is

$$r_a/d \,|_{\mathrm{rms}} = \sqrt{2}/\alpha \times (2\mu_0 H/m)^{1/2} \qquad (4.3.23)$$

where α is the most probable velocity in the source; $\therefore \Omega = 2\pi\mu_0 H_0/kT$ for the acceptance solid angle. If the ionizer used has an efficiency inversely proportional to the atom velocity, the velocity distribution to be used for an eventual estimation of the ion output should be $I'(v) \propto 1/v \times I(v)$ where $I(v)$ is the usual atomic beam velocity distribution for a gas effusing into a vacuum. The result when normalized to I_0 is

$$I'(v) = \frac{4I_0}{\sqrt{\pi}\,\alpha^3}\, v^2 \exp(-v^2/\alpha^2).$$

Estimates based on these considerations are useful for an extended source if $d \gg r_a$ and $r_s \sim r_a$ where r_s is the source radius.

Several four- and six-pole magnets used have been described in the literature.[31,33,37–40]. A typical one is shown in Fig. 7. The lengths vary from 25 to 90 cm with pole tip radii of from 0.3 to 0.5 cm when

[37] G. Clausnitzer, *Nuclear Instr. Meth.* **23**, 309 (1963).

[38] H. Rudin, H. R. Sriebel, E. Baumgartner, L. Brown, and P. Huber, *Helv. Phys. Acta* **34**, 58 (1961).

[39] H. Friedburg and W. Paul, *Z. Phys.* **130**, 493 (1951).

[40] A. Lemonick, F. M. Pipkin, and D. R. Hamilton, *Rev. Sci. Instr.* **26**, 1112 (1955).

used for separation at high fields. The four-pole magnets must be somewhat longer because of lesser deflecting power.

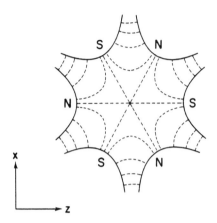

FIG. 7.   Field and potential lines for a magnetic field which varies as the square of the distance from the axis. Field lines are dashed (– – – –); potential lines are solid (—). Axis is through the geometrical center of the diagram perpendicular to the figure. The force on the atom acts radially.

If a single high-field magnet is used the states D-1 to D-3, H-1, and H-2 can be separated from the states D-4 to D-6, H-4, and H-5 to about 25 or 50 to 1 for practical magnet dimensions. When the polarized atoms are ionized the resulting nuclear polarization can be determined as a function of the magnetic field in which the ionization takes place. This may be done by writing down the density matrix for the atoms in the basis m_I, m_J assuming that at high field the assemblage consists of a known fraction F of each of the uncoupled eigenstates $| m_I, m_J \rangle$. The wavefunctions $| n \rangle$ of the assemblage at any magnetic field H arrived at adiabatically from the field of the known high-field populations are

$$| n \rangle = \sum_{m_J m_I} a^n_{m_J m_I}(H) | m_J m_I \rangle,$$

where the $a^n(H)$ can be calculated from the secular equation arising from the previously discussed Hamiltonian of the hydrogen (or deuterium) atom in the magnetic field.

The density matrix elements are, from Eq. (4.3.3),

$$\langle m_J m_I | \rho | m_J' m_I' \rangle = \sum_n F_n a^{n*}_{m_J' m_I'} a^n_{m_J m_I} . \tag{4.3.24}$$

Since we are interested only in observables depending on nuclear spins the density matrix may be summed over the electron parameters and we arrive at the density matrix of interest:

$$\langle m_I \mid \rho \mid m_I' \rangle = \sum_{m_J'} \langle m_J m_I \mid \rho \mid m_J' m_I' \rangle \, \delta m_J m_J'. \qquad (4.3.25)$$

This density matrix is diagonal since it is written with respect to the states $\mid m_I \rangle$ which are the eigenstates of the system when the magnetic field direction defines the coordinate system (the z axis). The above expression is correct for the description of the beam of ionized nuclei if the effect of the ionization process on the nuclear spins can be neglected. This will be discussed later. Observables characterizing the beam can now be calculated from the density matrix from Eq. (4.3.4), $\langle O \rangle = Tr(\rho O)$ where O is the operator corresponding to the various polarization parameters such as P_i or P_{ij}.

The discussion above, although applied to atoms of hydrogen having a magnetic moment on the order of the Bohr magneton, may equally well be applied to the He^3 atom which has no electronic moment since it is in a $^1S_0$ state. The nuclear magnetic moment can be used for state separation without impractically long magnets, however, if the gas is cooled to a few degrees absolute. This source requires no further state separation for nearly 100 % nuclear vector polarization.[41]

The P_i's or P_{ij}'s as calculated by these methods are now functions of the F_n's [Es. (4.3.24)] which depend on the magnetic state separation and of the $a_n(m_J\, m_I)$'s which depend on the value of the magnetic field in the ionization region. If the field is very low ($x \ll 1$), the $a_n(m_J\, m_I)$ values approach the appropriate Clebsch–Gordan coefficient for an $I = \frac{1}{2}, J = \frac{1}{2}$ system (hydrogen) or an $I = 1, J = \frac{1}{2}$ system (deuterium). If we assume that $F_1 = F_2 = \frac{1}{2}$ and $F_3 = F_4 = 0$ for hydrogen or $F_1 = F_2 = F_3 = \frac{1}{3}$ and $F_4 = F_5 = F_6 = 0$ for deuterium as would be the case for perfect state separation with a four- or six-pole magnet, we find that the polarization parameters approach the following value: $P_3 = 0.50$ for hydrogen; and $P_3 = 0.33$, $P_{33} = -0.33$, $P_{11} = P_{22} = 0.167$ for deuterium as the magnetic field approaches zero. Values of P_3 and P_{33} for the various states of deuterium as a function of magnetic field are shown in Figs. 8 and 9. The polarization axis is defined by the magnetic field in the ionization region which must not go to zero. If however the ionization takes place in a high field ($x \gg 1$) under the same conditions on the F_n's the polarization parameters are all 0. The necessity for high-field ionization in some cases, as for example when a neutral polarized beam is injected into a cyclotron and ionized in the center

[41] D. Axen, M. K. Craddock, K. L. Erdman, W. Klinger, and J. B. Warren, "Proceedings of the 2nd International Symposium on Polarization Phenomena of Nucleons," P. Huber and H. Schopper, eds., pp. 94–96, Birkhäuser, Basel, 1966.

region, and possible polarization improvement require further state selection.

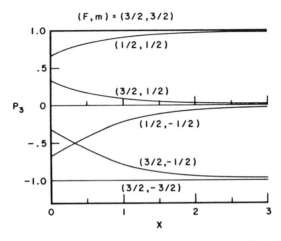

FIG. 8. Plot of the first rank (vector) polarization component P_3 which results from ionization of deuterium substates (F, m) in a magnetic field as a function of a magnetic field directed along the 3 axis. The components P_1 and P_2 are zero. x is defined as in Fig. 2.

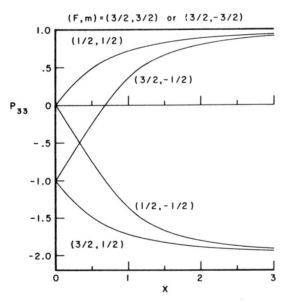

FIG. 9. Plot of the second rank (tensor) polarization component P_{33} which results from ionization of deuterium substates (F, m) in a magnetic field as a function of the magnetic field along the 3 axis. x is defined as in Fig. 2. The quantities P_{12}, P_{13}, P_{23}, and $P_{11} - P_{22}$ are zero.

One method is to use additional inhomogeneous magnetic fields in which the magnitude (and therefore the gradient) is less, so that states having the same m_J but different m_I have different effective moments. If the fields and gradients decrease with distance along the magnet it can be shown that a state separation is possible.[35] This condition requires long magnets, since the deflecting power becomes weaker as the fields decrease. The decrease in field is accomplished by making the magnet so that r_m increases along the beam path.

4.3.3.2.3. STATE SELECTION BY RADIO-FREQUENCY TRANSITIONS. Another useful method is to make radio-frequency transitions between the atomic states after atomic polarization. One method which may be used to select a single state such as H-2 or D-4 is to use the conventional two-wire magnetic fields such as is common in atomic beam spectroscopy.[42] This magnet configuration provides a uniform gradient proportional to the magnetic field and perpendicular to the beam direction, thus deflecting atoms of $\mu < 1$ and $\mu > 1$ to opposite sides. If, however, a $\Delta m_J = \pm 1$ rf transition is made following the magnet and a second magnet having the same deflecting power as the first follows the rf region, those atoms which have reversed their effective moments will be refocused to produce an image of the source slit. If the deflections take place in a high-field region, $u_e \simeq m_J u_0$ where u_0 is the Bohr magneton, the condition is easily met. A stop can be placed so that only one state such as H-3 or D-4 is refocused producing 100 % polarization for either low- or high-field ionization. Since H-3 and D-4 are pure states, that is $| n \rangle = | m_J m_I \rangle$ for all values of magnetic fields, the density matrix has only one nonzero element. Other states or groups of states can also be chosen by making different rf transitions; this produces polarization modulation. A scheme which has been found useful is shown in Fig. 10.[43] Since only those states which make an rf transition are ionized, the intensity but not the polarization depends on the rf transition probability. The great disadvantage of this type of source is the lack of intensity focusing. The acceptance solid angle with the magnet on is equal to the geometric solid angle subtended by the detector slit at the source. This solid angle is small because of the slit geometry required by the one-dimensional deflecting character of the two-wire field. This system corresponds optically to a double prism rather than to a lens.

Transitions can be made between states such as from H-2 to H-4 following a four- or six-pole focusing magnet. The state populations are

[42] C. W. Drake, D. C. Bonar, R. D. Headrick, and V. W. Hughes, *Rev. Sci. Instr.* **32**, 995 (1961); V. W. Hughes, C. W. Drake, D. C. Bonar, J. S. Greenberg, and G. F. Pieper, *Helv. Phys. Acta Suppl.* **6**, 89, 435 (1961).

[43] R. D. Headrick, PhD dissertation, Yale University, 1965.

thus modified. If initially $F_1 = F_2 = \frac{1}{2}$ and $F_3 = F_4 = 0$, after the transition the populations are $F_1 = \frac{1}{2}, F_2 = \frac{1}{2}(1 - T), F_3 = 0, F_4 = \frac{1}{2}T$, where T is the transition probability. The resulting vector polarization is $P_3 = T$ if ionized at a high field. The intensity does not depend on T. With a normal atom beam spectroscopy type rf transition the velocity spread of the atom beam limits the maximum value of T to about 0.7.

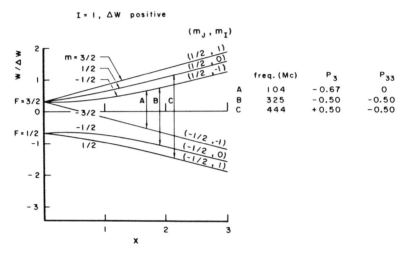

FIG. 10. Shown schematically on the Breit–Rabi diagram for deuterium are three transitions with their frequencies and resulting polarizations as used in the polarized ion source of Ref. 22. They are shown at different x coordinates only for clarity. The actual value used was $x = 0.64$ (75 G). The values of P_3 and P_{33} are for equal ionization of the two refocused states in a 4-G field.

It is practical however to obtain transition probabilities up to about 0.95 following the suggestion of Abragam and Winter,[44] by using the adiabatic fast passage method.[45] This method may be understood by considering the transition process in terms of the motion of an isolated spin in a magnetic field. If a transformation is made to a coordinate system rotating around the z axis defined by the magnetic field, the value of H_z' becomes $H' + \omega/\gamma'$ where H' is the steady magnetic field in the laboratory frame, ω is the rotation frequency, and γ' is the gyromagnetic ratio of a fictitious spin K. If a rotating rf magnetic field of angular frequency $-\omega$ is applied perpendicular to H' and H_{rf} defines the x axis of the rotating system, in the rotating system, the spin precesses about the resultant field $\mathbf{H}_e' = \hat{\imath}H_{rf}' + \hat{k}(H' - \omega/\gamma')$. If this spin experiences an initial field $H_e' > \omega/\gamma'$ which decreases smoothly with time through

[44] A. Abragam and J. M. Winter, *Phys. Rev. Letters* 1, 374 (1958).
[45] F. Bloch, *Phys. Rev.* 70, 460 (1946).

the resonant value $H'_{e0} = \omega/\gamma'$ and decreases to a value H_e' much less than ω/γ', the spin will precess about the resultant where initially $\mathbf{H}_e \simeq \hat{k}H'$ and finally $\mathbf{H}_e \simeq -\hat{k}\omega/\gamma'$ if ω/γ' is much greater than H_{rf}. The adiabatic condition is that $\Omega \ll \omega$ where Ω is the rate of rotation of the resultant field H_e'. The net result is a reversal of K. The fictitious quantities γ', H', and H'_{rf} can be written in terms of the real system through the relations

$$\hbar\gamma'H_0' = \Delta W; \qquad \hbar\gamma'H'_{rf} = \langle\, p \mid \mathscr{H} \mid q \rangle,$$

where ΔW is the field-dependent energy separation between the states p and q in the real system between which transitions are to be made and $\mathscr{H}$ is the perturbation which induces the transition. For the two-level system $K = \frac{1}{2}$. The conditions for a complete transition in terms of quantities of the real system are:

$$\frac{d}{dt}(\nabla W) \ll \frac{1}{\hbar^2}(\langle\, p \mid \mathscr{H} \mid q \rangle)^2, \qquad (4.3.26)$$

$$\Delta W_{\text{initial}} - \Delta W_{\text{final}} \gg \langle\, p \mid \mathscr{H} \mid q \rangle. \qquad (4.3.27)$$

These conditions are met by passing the atoms through a field having a gradient so that over the rf transition region the field variation from entrance to exit fulfills condition (4.3.27); (4.3.26) can be met by adjusting the length of the rf region considering the velocity and spread in velocity of the atoms. When the transitions are to be made in hydrogen (or deuterium) in a low magnetic field the fictitious system corresponds to the real system for $K = F = 1$ (or $\frac{3}{2}$) and a complete reversal of K corresponds to 100% transition probability for the transitions $m_F \leftrightarrow -m_F$. For m_J selected hydrogen atoms $F_1 = F_2 = \frac{1}{2}; F_3 = F_4 = 0$ goes to $F_1 = 0, F_2 = F_3 = \frac{1}{2}, F_4 = 0$; producing $P_3 = 1$ for high-field ionization. The corresponding deuterium transition changes for $F_1 = F_2 = F_3 = \frac{1}{3}; F_4 = F_5 = F_6 = 0$ to $F_1 = 0; F_2 = F_3 = F_4 = \frac{1}{3}$, $F_5 = F_6 = 0$, which gives $P_3 = -0.67$ and $P_{33} = P_{11} = P_{22} = 0$ for the polarization parameters when ionized at high fields. If however the low-field transition is preceded or followed by a transition in a magnetic field such that the levels are separated, the polarization is enhanced as is shown, for example, in Table I. Some of these transitions become difficult to make, that is, the power required increases as the magnetic field increases, but at intermediate fields, $x \simeq 1$, the individual transitions may be made.

In some applications it may be advantageous to follow the focusing magnet and transition region by a second magnet and transition region.[46]

[46] D. Von Ehrenstein, D. C. Hess, and G. Clausnitzer, *Bull. Am. Phys. Soc. II* **10**, 55 (1965).

In this manner it is possible to obtain complete polarization variation of protons $\Delta P_3 = 1 \leftrightarrow -1$, or deuterons $\Delta P_3 = 1 \leftrightarrow -1, \Delta P_{33} = 1 \leftrightarrow -2$ with a low-field ionization region.

TABLE I.   Deuteron Polarization Parameters[a]

Transition	a	b	c	l	$a + l$	$b + l$	$c + l$	No.
P_3	0.33	0.67	0.33	−0.67	−0.33	−0.67	−0.33	0
P_{33}	1.0	0	−1.0	0	−1.0	0	1.0	0
$P_{11} = P_{22}$	−0.5	0	0.5	0	0.5	0	−0.5	0

[a] Polarization obtained in a deuteron beam ionized at high field after a magnetic state separation followed by an rf transition or transitions in series by the adiabatic fast passage method (transition probabilities are assumed to be one). The transitions are: $a = D$-2 → D-6; $b = D$-3 → D-6; $c = D$-3 → D-5; $l = $ low-field transition $m_J \leftrightarrow -m_J$, D-1 → D-4.

4.3.3.2.4. IONIZATION. All existing proton or deuteron polarizers ionize the polarized atoms by electron bombardment. The objectives in the ionization process are maximum polarized beam intensity and minimum ionization of background. The latter can be minimized only by reducing the background gas pressure of those gases containing hydrogen (or deuterium) and by limiting the ionizing volume to the value necessary to ionize the beam. The background gas pressure will be discussed in the next section. The ionizer efficiency can be defined as the ratio of the number of ions produced by the ionizer to the number of atoms entering the ionizer and, for comparison, should be referred to the same gas, for example hydrogen, at the same source temperature. The expression for the efficiency is

$$\text{Eff.} = \frac{j/e\,\sigma\rho\,V}{\rho v A} = \frac{j\,\sigma l}{ev} \tag{4.3.28}$$

where j is the average electron current density over the beam ionization region, δ is the ionization cross section for electrons on hydrogen, ρ is the atom density, l is the length of the ionization region, e is the electron charge, and v is the atom velocity. V and A are the volume and area of ionization region. The relevant cross sections for ionization of both the beam atoms and the background producing contaminants are discussed by Dickson.[47] The expression must be averaged over the atom velocity and electron energy. Choosing an electron energy of from 60 to

[47] J. M. Dickson, "Progress in Nuclear Techniques and Instrumentation," F. J. M. Farley, ed., Vol. I, pp. 103–171. North-Holland, Amsterdam, 1965.

90 ev, a useful number can be obtained from the above, if an assumption of the effective source temperature of an rf hydrogen discharge of 500°K is made. The figure is 1.3×10^{-3} per amp/cm² of electron current per length (cm). From this an upper limit of about 1 % efficiency would seem attainable. Efficiencies reported have been from 5×10^{-5} [31,33,37,38]. to 3×10^{-3} for various geometric configurations. The higher-efficiency ionizers must consider space charge effects, and these effects are usually used for ion trapping and ejection.[48]

It should be emphasized that a true measure of the efficiency of an ionizer should include, in addition to the efficiency of ionization, a measure of the output ion beam quality or beam emittance.[49] A useful parameter is the Lagrange product $\gamma\alpha\sqrt{E}$ where γ is the beam radius, α is the beam divergence, and E is the beam energy where γ and α are measured at a real image. The emittance is invariant under the usual charge particle optical operations but is increased by collisions on residual gas atoms.

Depolarization effects in the ionizer can be considered to arise from time-dependent magnetic fields in the rest frame of the polarized particle perpendicular to the polarization axis. The polarized nucleus precesses about the transverse magnetic field through an angle whose maximum value (for $H_x \gg H_z$) is $\theta_p = \gamma \int_0^\tau H(t)\, dt$ where the field $H(t)$ arises from the ionizing electron. This field is on the order of $\mu_0/a_0^3 \sim 10^5$ G ($\mu_0 =$ Bohr magneton, $a_0 =$ Bohr radius). The characteristic time τ would be a collision time $2a_0/v \sim 2 \times 10^{-17}$ sec. This estimate puts an upper limit on θ_p of about 10^{-7} rad corresponding to an insignificant depolarization. That the ionizing depolarization is small is adequately supported by experimental evidence from polarized ion sources as well as by the slowing down of polarized particles, both nucleons and leptons, in matter without loss of polarization. These and other depolarization effects have been considered by Schlier.[50]

Ionizers may be divided into two main types, high and low field. In the low-field type the magnetic field is kept sufficiently low, on the order of 1 to 10 G, as to provide only a polarization axis. Electron focusing must be electrostatic. The atoms are best described in the low-field representation $|n\rangle \propto |F, m_F\rangle$. The geometries used in this region have been varied, from a simple diode structure to a linear Pierce gun.[51] The high-field type ionizes in a field ($\sim$1000 G) such that the electronic and nuclear spin may be considered decoupled $|n\rangle \propto |m_I, m_J\rangle$. The magnetic field also serves to contain the electron

[48] R. Weiss, *Rev. Sci. Instr.* **32**, 397 (1961).
[49] P. L. Judd, *Ann. Rev. Nuclear Sci.* **8**, 181 (1958).
[50] C. Schlier, CERN Report 58-3 (1958) (unpublished).
[51] D. C. Bonar, PhD. thesis, Yale University 1962 (unpublished).

beam since the electron cyclotron radius at the magnetic fields and electron energies used is small compared to the ionizer dimensions. The magnetic field must be considered also in extracting the ions, usually done along the field. Ionizers of this type with various geometries have also been used.[52,53]

In addition to depolarization effects by collision, care must be taken to prevent atomic depolarization by nonadiabatic passage through magnetic fields. The so-called Majorana transitions can be induced if an atom transverses spatially varying magnetic fields so that it experiences Fourier frequency components which are resonant with these transitions. This is likely to occur if the atom goes through a region of zero field since there the resonant Fourier components become large at zero frequency. If the fields are varying sufficiently slowly and the field's magnitude is sufficiently high so that the resonant Fourier components are vanishingly small the transitions are adiabatic and the atomic polarization with respect to the field direction is maintained. This condition may be written

$$| \dot{H} \times H/| H |^2 | \ll \gamma| H$$

for the case of a magnetic moment of spin I having a gyromagnetic ratio $\gamma (= \mu/\hbar I)$ where H is the variation of H in the frame of the moment. Transitions may, however, be utilized to rotate the polarization axis in a known manner with respect to the laboratory. Because of the difference between the spin precession frequency and the cyclotron frequency of an ion in a magnetic field the spin precesses through an angle $\theta_s = [(m/m_p)(g/2) - 1]\theta_p$ relative to the final momentum direction where m_p is the proton mass, m and g are the mass and nuclear g value of the ion, and θ_p is the angle through which the momentum has rotated. This method is less useful for deuterons since g is almost 1. At high energies this expression must be modified to meet relativistic requirements.[54]

4.3.3.2.5. VACUUM REQUIREMENTS. A sufficient vacuum must exist in the source and deflecting magnet region so that the mean free path between collisions be greater than the apparatus dimensions, and the

[52] D. A. G. Broad, A. P. Branford, and J. M. Dickson, "Proceedings of the 2nd International Symposium on Polarization Phenomena of Nucleons," P. Huber and H. Schopper, eds., pp. 76–78, Birkhäuser, Basel, 1966.

[53] H. F. Glavish and E. R. Collins, "Proceedings of the 2rd International Symposium on Polarization Phenomena of Nucleons," P. Huber and H. Schopper, eds., pp. 85–87, Birkhäuser, Basel, 1966.

[54] R. Hagedon, CERN 62-18, Part I (unpublished); V. Bargmann, L. Michel, and V. L. Telegdi, *Phys. Rev. Letters* **2**, 435 (1959).

components of background gas containing hydrogen (or deuterium) in the ionizer region must be reduced to a value small enough so that polarization is not appreciably reduced. These requirements are best met by providing maximum possible pumping speed in the source region. This pumping speed will provide the practical limit of the polarized source intensity; however, requirements on ultimate vacuum are not important since the usual background pressure in this region is on the order of 10^{-4} Torr of hydrogen or deuterium. Differential pumping is often provided in the magnet region by dividing the chamber into two or more sections connected by orifices only large enough to pass the atomic beam. The vacuum must be designed, not only to prevent beam attenuation by scattering but also to prevent gas streaming from the high-pressure background of the source region into the detector region. The detector region is most critical with respect to the vacuum requirements. The atomic beam density corresponds to a pressure of between 5×10^{-6} and 1×10^{-8} Torr. For a proton source the partial pressure of any gas or vapor component containing hydrogen must be reduced to well below this pressure, since the ionization cross sections for production of H^+ are comparable for H atoms and the hydrogen containing background gas, and the ionizer usually has an ionization volume larger than the atomic beam volume. The background gas containing hydrogen consists of H_2 diffusing from the source or magnet region and of water vapor and hydrocarbons from walls and pumps. The latter is not important when deuterium is used. The H_2 background can be reduced to a predetermined value by proper design of the vacuum system, and the water-hydrocarbon component must be reduced by proper pump baffling, material selection, and trapping. A clean system is also required for the proper operation of the electron bombardment ionizer and ion extraction, since contaminants degrade both cathode emission and charged particle optics. For these reasons mercury diffusion pumps and/or titanium gettering of both the sputter and sublimation types have often been used in the ionizer region. Valves to isolate this region are useful to minimize exposure to the atmosphere when other parts of the apparatus must be opened.

4.3.3.2.6. ACCELERATION. If the polarized ions are to be used for nuclear physics experiments they must be injected into an accelerator, and a consideration of the different kinds of accelerators reveals different problems with each. The low-energy accelerators to be considered are electrostatic accelerators, linear accelerators, and cyclotrons.

The electrostatic or Van de Graaff of the single ended type commonly has the ion source at high potential, usually with insufficient volume and power provided to enable a polarized source to be used. Some of the older Van de Graaffs are exceptional in that the high voltage terminal is sufficient to accommodate the polarized ion source.[55] With the usual type Van de Graaff neutral polarized atoms may be drifted into the ionizer, but the intensity is greatly reduced because of the neutral beam divergence. The tandem accelerators seem more promising since the charge exchange method may be used to produce polarized H^- ions which are accelerated to the central terminal, stripped to H^+, and accelerated to ground. The great advantage is the ground (or almost ground) potential of the ion source which removes the space and power restriction. It has been shown that the H^+ polarized ion may be charge-exchanged to H^- in a solid carbon foil without polarization loss and accelerated with an overall efficiency of about 0.1 %.[56] The charge exchange is made from 10 to 50 kev. The H^- ion is in a $1s^2\,{}^1S_0$ atomic state so there is no nuclear depolarization of the H^- ion; depolarization could take place while the particle is in the intermediate neutral state. However, with a thin solid charge exchange foil the transit time is so short (on the order of 10^{-13} sec) that depolarization is not significant. If, however, a gas or vapor charge exchange medium is used a longitudinal magnetic field must be provided, sufficient to decouple the nuclear and electronic spin in the atom. This necessitates longitudinal polarization and consequent spin precessing of the beam following the charge exchange. Recent experiments have indicated that a very favorable charge exchange process $H^+ \rightarrow H^-$ takes place with Cs vapor.[57] A preliminary measurement gave a conversion efficiency of 25 % for 1 kev deuterons on Cs vapor.

There are other possibilities with tandem accelerators. One, commercially available, Van de Graaff has a high voltage terminal large enough so that a polarized source could be used, but the reliability requirements of the complex polarized source due to the lack of accessibility as well as the lack of compatibility of this system with normal use make the scheme unattractive. The polarized H^+ ions also can be focused on the terminal, charge-exchanged to neutral atoms with high efficiency at an energy on the order of 10 kev, and then drifted to the terminal. There the atoms are stripped to H^+ and accelerated to ground. This neutral beam, however, has such poor focusing qualities due to the scattering in the charge exchange process, that the neutral flux accepted by the stripping canal in the high-voltage terminal is small. The two latter methods also result in one-half the maximum energy possible using a charge exchange to the negative ions, which seems the most promising method.

[55] L. Brown, H. Rudin, and N. P. Heydenburg, *Bull. Am. Phys. Soc.* **8**, 377 (1963).
[56] W. Gruebler, W. Haeberli, and P. Schwandt, *Phys. Rev. Letters* **12**, 595 (1964).
[57] C. W. Drake and R. Krotkov, *Phys. Rev. Letters* **16**, 848 (1966); B. Donally, private communication.

Linear accelerators have their ion source in an injection terminal from 250 to 500 kev above ground. These terminals are usually sufficiently large so that the polarized source may be mounted in the terminal. Polarized neutrals can also be drifted to the injection terminals with, however, an intensity loss.[37]

Injection to a cyclotron requires that the neutral beam be drifted either through the magnet gap into the ionizer at the usual ion source position in the magnet center, or preferably through a hole in the magnet on the magnet axis, if such has been provided in the construction of the machine. Low-energy ions can also be injected through this axial hole and electrostatically deflected at the center. It has also been proposed that low-energy ions be brought to the cyclotron center through the gap by providing compensating electric fields.

High-energy machines have either a linear or electrostatic injector, so the same considerations hold with respect to injection.

Depolarization effects in the accelerator must also be considered. Electrostatic machines present no problem in this respect. Polarization is retained in the strong unidirectional magnetic field of the cyclotron, DC or FM, if the initial polarization axis is parallel to the field, except for small effects discussed below. Polarization has been shown experimentally to be retained with no apparent depolarization in linear accelerators,[33,37] although this case has not been analyzed in detail. The situation in relativistic circular accelerators has been considered in general[58] and for specific machines.[59]

4.3.3.3. Other Methods of Production. 4.3.3.3.1. CHARGE EXCHANGE OF METASTABLE ATOMS. Other methods of producing polarized ion beams have been considered. One very appealing method was that proposed by Zavoiskii[60] and by Madansky and Owen[61] in which the metastable $2s\,^2S_{1/2}$ state in the hydrogen atom is polarized. It had earlier been noted by Lamb[62] that it was possible to obtain polarized hydrogen atoms in the metastable $2s\,^2S_{1/2}$ state by selectively quenching the $m_J = -\frac{1}{2}(\beta)$ state. The $^2S_{1/2}$, $m_J = -\frac{1}{2}(\beta)$ state becomes degenerate with the $2s\,^2P_{1/2}$, $m_J = +\frac{1}{2}(e)$ state in a magnetic field of 575 G as shown in Fig. 11 (the notation is that of Lamb Ref. 62). Any perturbing electric field perpendicular to the magnetic field will produce a parity-

[58] E. D. Courant, Int. Rept. EDC-45, Brookhaven Natl. Laboratories, 1962 (unpublished); V. W. Hughes, Intl. Conference on High Energy Accelerators, Frascati, 1965.

[59] M. Foissart and R. Stora, *Nucl. Instr. Meth.* **7**, 297 (1960) (Saclay-Saturne); D. Cohen, *Rev. Sci. Instr.* **33**, 161 (1962) (Argonne-ZGS); F. Lobkowicz and E. H. Thorndike, *Rev. Sci. Instr.* **33**, 454 (1962) (Rochester cyclotron); H. Kim and W. E. Burcham, *Nucl. Instr. Meth.* **27**, 211 (1962) (Birmingham cyclotron).

[60] E. K. Zoroiskii, *Zh. Eksperim i Teor. Fiz* **32**, 731 (1957) (*Trans. JEPT* **5**, 603 (1957)).

[61] L. Madansky and G. Owen, *Phys. Rev. Letters* **2**, 209 (1959).

[62] W. E. Lamb and R. C. Retherford, *Phys. Rev.* **79**, 549 (1950).

mixed state allowing radiative decay to the ground $1s\ ^2S_{1/2}$ state. The $m_J = -\frac{1}{2}(\beta)$ component of the $2s\ ^2S_{1/2}$ state has a decay rate of about 1500 times greater than the $m_J = +\frac{1}{2}(\alpha)$ component at a magnetic field of 575 G. A perturbing electric field is provided by the motional electric field present in the rest frame of the atom when the velocity is perpendicular to the magnetic field. If the velocity is parallel to H a small crossed electric field must be provided.[63]

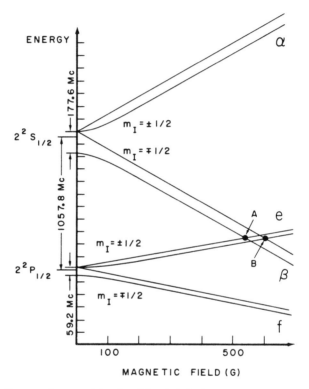

FIG. 11.   Zeeman diagram of the $J = \frac{1}{2}$ levels in hydrogen, $n = 2$, including hyperfine structure.

Madansky and Owen pointed out that an intense metastable beam could be produced by charge exchange of a fast proton beam ($\sim$10 kev) in a gas. Previously, metastable hydrogen beams had been produced by the electron bombardment of thermal velocity atomic beams. They also suggested that the preferential ionization of the polarized metastable state could be accomplished by means of photoionization at about 3650 Å. Their experiments detected a metastable beam using H_2 as a

[63] R. T. Robiscoe, *Phys. Rev.* **138**, 22A (1965).

charge exchange gas, but the consequent charge exchange ionization of the intense unpolarized fast ground state atoms on the residual gas was so great that the resulting proton polarization was too low for practical use.

Further work by Donnally et al.[64] has shown that a metastable beam with a much lower proportion of ground state atoms can be produced at a lower energy ($\sim$500 ev for hydrogen) using Cs vapor as the charge exchange gas. A nearly resonant process $H^+ + Cs \rightarrow H(2s) + Cs^+$ is used. In addition Donnally[65] has shown that the resulting metastable ions can be selectively charge exchanged to H^- in argon gas in a process peaking at 500 ev for $H(2s)$. He has indicated that the resulting negative beam can be produced from the initial H^+ beam with about a 0.5 % efficiency (recent work has indicated the efficiency may be as much as 2 %),[57] and that the negative beam arises primarily from the neutral metastable state. This method is thus well-suited for use as a polarized ion source for a tandem Van de Graaff. If high initial proton current at 500 volts (or deuterons at 1000 volts) can be provided, it is possible that a polarized negative ion source of from 0.1 to 1 μa may be obtained.[66] In addition higher polarization than that obtained by quenching the $2s\,^2S_{1/2}$ $(m_J = -\frac{1}{2})$ state may be obtained by further state selection within the hyperfine structure. Methods similar to those used on the ground state polarization may be used if the magnetic fields are not such that the atomic energy levels are in the vicinity of the crossing point of the level structure shown as A and B in Fig. 11. It should be noted however that, if transitions are made between α and β-e levels at the appropriate crossing points, only that α level connected by the rather narrow resonant transition to the β-e is *not* quenched. The other α state (hydrogen) or states (deuterium) are quenched due to the broad α-e (150 G) resonant line width. This method allows the selection of a single hyperfine state of hydrogen or deuterium, and thus maximum polarization is obtained if the $H(2s) + A \rightarrow H^- + A^+$ transfer is done in a high magnetic field. In addition, the rf transition is electric rather than magnetic dipole, thus requiring only moderate rf power. The required magnetic field and rf frequency stabilities are not unduly high. These narrow alpha–beta transitions have been observed in hydrogen and deuterium.[67]

[64] B. L. Donnally, T. Clapp, W. Sawyer, and M. Schultz, *Phys. Rev. Letters* **12**, 502 (1964).

[65] B. L. Donnally and W. Sawyer, *Phys. Rev. Letters* **15**, 439 (1965).

[66] J. L. McKibben and C. P. Lawrence, "Proceedings of the 2nd International Symposium on Polarization Phenomena of Nucleons," P. Huber and H. Schopper, eds., pp. 73–75, Birkhäuser, Basel, 1966.

[67] W. E. Lamb and R. C. Retherford, *Phys. Rev.* **81**, 222 (1951).

A schematic diagram of a charge exchange polarizer is shown in Fig. 12.

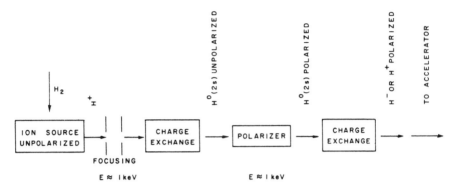

FIG. 12. Schematic diagram of the charge exchange method of producing polarized ions.

4.3.3.3.2. EFFUSION FROM OPTICALLY PUMPED SOURCE. One other possible polarized ion source is based on the use of an optically pumped sample as a polarized atom source. In a particularly favorable case, that of He³, nuclear polarization of about 40 % at a gas pressure of 1 Torr has been obtained.[68] Although these techniques were developed for use a polarized targets it seems reasonable that they could also be used as a source if so desired.

4.3.3.4. Polarized Electron Beams.* Beams of polarized electrons have been produced by methods similar to those used for ions. The more successful ones have used electron scattering from nuclei[69] and state-separated atomic beams followed by photoionization with collection of the ejected electrons.

The atomic beam method has been used successfully by a group at Yale.[70] A previous report by the late H. Friedmann[71] on the successful production of polarized electrons appears to be seriously in error, as shown both from further work by his successors[72] and from the work of Long et al.[70]

[68] F. D. Colgrove, L. D. Shearer, and J. K. Walters, *Phys. Rev.* **132**, 2561 (1963).

[69] H. Deichsel, *Z. Physik* **164**, 156 (1961); H. Deichsel and E. Reichert, *Z. Physik* **185**, 169 (1965); H. Steidl, E. Reichert, and H. Deichsel, *Phys. Letters* **17**, 31 (1965); K. Jost and J. Kessler, *Phys. Rev. Letters* **15**, 595 (1965).

[70] R. L. Long, W. Raith, and V. W. Hughes, *Phys. Rev. Letters* **15**, 1, (1965).

[71] H. Friedmann, *Sitzber. Bayer Akad. Wiss. Kl. Math-Naturw. München*, 1961, p. 13.

[72] F. Bopp, D. Maison, G. Regenfus, and H. C. Siegmann, *Z. Physik* **185**, 48 (1965).

* See also Volume 5B, Chapter 2.5, for more extensive treatment.

The atomic beam method produced a beam of polarized alkali atoms by means of spatial separation using a six-pole magnetic field and followed this by a region where the polarized atoms were ionized by photon bombardment. The alkali atom potassium was used since it has many desirable properties. These are ease of forming a beam, i.e., convenient vapor pressure at an easily maintained temperature, and ability to be ionized by light from available high-intensity lamps. The latter requires a low ionization potential and a high cross section in the near ultra-violet. It is also imperative to deal with an essentially two-state system in the high-field deflection region; therefore an atom with an electronic angular momentum, J, of $\frac{1}{2}\hbar$ is required. It is also more convenient to have a low hyperfine interaction energy, since the polarization of the electron ejected from the state-separated atoms approaches 100 % as the magnetic field in the ionization region becomes large enough so that $g_J\mu_0 H \gg W_{hfs}$ where W_{hfs} is the zero field hyperfine splitting. This should be compared to the nuclear case where for the same conditions the nuclear polarization approaches zero. The polarizer used a high-pressure mercury lamp for the photoionization. Polarized electrons were accelerated out of the ionization region to about 120 kv and scattered from a thin gold foil to measure the polarization. A polarization of the predicted value was attained (50 %) with an intensity of 1.4×10^{-12} amp. This intensity and polarization can be expected to be improved. In particular, the use of Li instead of K may be favorable since it has a much higher ionization cross section, although having a shorter wavelength ionization threshold because of its higher ionization potential. In addition, when an electron source is used, as expected, on a pulsed accelerator, the pulse intensity will be greater than the dc intensity. This is because the ionizing light sources are primarily power-limited, and because of higher electron temperature a pulsed source has a more favorable spectral distribution for photoionization than a dc source of the same average power.*

---

* See Chapter 1.5 by W. Raith, R. Christensen, and I. Ames.

5. BASIC TECHNIQUES

5.1. Ultrahigh Vacuum

Many of the experimental methods discussed in the earlier chapters of this book are predicated on the use of an adequate vacuum technique. The degree of vacuum required for a given experiment is determined largely by considerations of gas purity, particle mean free paths, and surface reaction rates. Table I lists several quantities of interest for various pressure ranges. Frequently of equal importance with the ultimate pressure is the speed with which the pressure can be changed, and the accuracy with which the constitution of the gas phase can be controlled and known. Most of the significant developments in vacuum technique since 1950 have been improvements in the means of reaching and measuring pressures in the ultrahigh-vacuum range. As a result, the achievement of ultrahigh vacuum should normally be taken as one criterion in the design of experimental apparatus for atomic and electron physics.

The chief purpose of this article is to provide a reliable guide to ultrahigh-vacuum techniques, with an effort to be selective in emphasizing the best or most useful, rather than attempting to be comprehensive and encyclopedic. It is assumed that the reader knows something about vacuum techniques in general, but wants more details on the best UHV practice and capabilities. The reader interested in a more extensive bibliography and in a more detailed treatment of the subject matter discussed here may find it in a number of books published recently. The book by Dushman[1] is a good scientific treatise on the whole field of vacuum technique. Guthrie[2] has provided a useful book on practical and operational aspects. The book by Roberts and Vanderslice[3] and the articles by Redhead, Hobson, and Kornelsen[4] and by Alpert[5]

[1] S. Dushman, "Scientific Foundations of Vacuum Technique" (J. M. Lafferty, ed.), 2nd ed. Wiley, New York, 1962.

[2] A. Guthrie, "Vacuum Technology." Wiley, New York, 1963.

[3] R. W. Roberts and T. A. Vanderslice, "Ultrahigh Vacuum and Its Applications." Prentice-Hall, Englewood Cliffs, New Jersey, 1963.

[4] P. A. Redhead, J. P. Hobson, and E. V. Kornelsen, *Advances in Electronics and Electron Phys.* **17**, 323 (1962).

[5] D. Alpert, *in* "Handbuch der Physik—Encyclopedia of Physics" (S. Flügge, ed.), Vol. 12, p. 609. Springer, Berlin, 1958.

* Chapter 5.1 is by G. E. Becker.

are concerned specifically with ultrahigh vacuum. Von Ardenne[6] has provided an encyclopedic reference work.

5.1.1. Production of Ultrahigh Vacuum

5.1.1.1. Pumps. There are a number of pumps or pump combinations which may be used to reach the ultrahigh-vacuum range. Which is the best choice in a given situation is determined primarily by the quantity and kind of gas to be pumped, the allowable species of residual gas, the time duration of vacuum conditions, and the frequency and extent of pressure cycling. Considerations of convenience and cost of operation are also important, but questions of economics must be answered by a detailed analysis of capital and operating expenses for any given application.

5.1.1.1.1. ROUGHING PUMPS. The choice of a roughing pump to reduce the pressure from atmospheric to about 10^{-2} Torr requires some discussion. The two chief alternatives are the rotary oil-sealed mechanical pump and the cryosorption pump utilizing a molecular sieve cooled by liquid nitrogen. The latter has been developed intensively in recent years, and the best designs are now quite competitive with the mechanical pump in pumping speed for air and in ultimate pressure. The cryosorption pump has a finite capacity and a poor pumping capability for certain gases such as helium. It must be kept cold as long as it is connected to the vacuum system. If these limitations are not important in a given application, the cryosorption pump is the best choice. Its chief advantage is that it does not contribute any contaminant gas to the system. It is also vibration- free, quiet, and easy to operate and maintain, if liquid nitrogen is readily available. This pump does require periodic reprocessing by bake-out. It is a natural mate for any high-vacuum pump, such as an ion-getter pump, which does not require a continuous backing pump. However, in most cases, the mechanical pump is more convenient to operate, and is a good choice, provided that some contamination from the oil pump fluid can be tolerated.

The mechanical pump is almost invariably selected for use with diffusion pumps, since it can handle the gas load from the diffusion pumps easily and cheaply over extended time periods. The possibility of contamination of the system by the pump fluid can be reduced appreciably by the use of a trap in the forepump line, and by keeping to a minimum the time during which the mechanical pump is operated without the diffusion pump being operative. Another desirable feature for a mechanical pump is a variable gas ballast,[1] which reduces the contamination of the pump fluid itself by condensable vapors. With

---

[6] M. von Ardenne, "Tabellen zur angewandten Physik," Vol. II: Physik und Technik des Vakuums, Plasmaphysik. Deut. Verlag Wiss., Berlin, 1964.

TABLE I. Properties of Nitrogen at 20°C in Various Pressure Ranges

Pressure range[a]	Pressure (Torr)	Gas density (molecules/cm³)	Mean free path (N₂ in N₂)(cm)	Monolayer time[b]	Impingement rate (molecules/cm²/sec)	$N_{surface}$[c] / N_{volume}
Rough vacuum	760	2.5×10^{19}	5.9×10^{-6}	1.7×10^{-9} sec	3.0×10^{23}	2×10^{-5}
Fine vacuum	1	3.3×10^{16}	4.5×10^{-3}	1.3×10^{-6} sec	3.9×10^{20}	1.5×10^{-2}
High vacuum	10^{-3}	3.3×10^{13}	4.5	1.3×10^{-3} sec	3.9×10^{17}	15
Very high vacuum	10^{-6}	3.3×10^{10}	4.5×10^{3}	1.3 sec	3.9×10^{14}	1.5×10^{4}
Ultrahigh vacuum	10^{-9}	3.3×10^{7}	4.5×10^{6}	22 min	3.9×10^{11}	1.5×10^{7}
	10^{-12}	3.3×10^{4}	4.5×10^{9}	360 hr	3.9×10^{8}	1.5×10^{10}
Extreme high vacuum	Below 10^{-12}	$< 3.3 \times 10^{4}$	$> 4.5 \times 10^{9}$	> 360 hr	$< 3.9 \times 10^{8}$	$> 1.5 \times 10^{10}$

[a] The names listed in this column do not have official status, but are commonly used.

[b] The monolayer time is here taken to be the time required to form one layer of adsorbed gas containing 5×10^{14} molecules/cm², assuming a sticking probability of unity.

[c] ($N_{surface}/N_{volume}$) is the ratio of the number of molecules adsorbed per cm² in a monolayer, 5×10^{14}, to the number per cm³ in the gas phase.

many mechanical pumps, an electric power failure can cause the loss of the forevacuum and even a suckback of the pump oil into the diffusion pump. Protection against this is afforded by a solenoid valve which automatically disconnects the mechanical pump from the system when the power fails.

5.1.1.1.2. ULTRAHIGH-VACUUM PUMPS. Pumps which can be used to reduce the pressure from 10^{-2} or 10^{-3} Torr to the ultrahigh-vacuum range fall into the categories of diffusion, molecular drag, chemisorption, ionization, and cryogenic adsorption pumps. The first two function by transferring the gas from the system to an exhaust point, while the last three remove the gas from the volume and retain it on or in the walls of the system.

5.1.1.1.3. DIFFUSION PUMPS. Diffusion pumps have long been the most commonly used of all high-vacuum pumps, and are still the best choice for many systems. Their chief advantages are the lack of any time-saturation characteristics and a pumping capability of the same order of magnitude for inert and active gases. The pumping speed increases as the molecular weight of the gas decreases. This is often an advantage, because residual gases are of relatively low molecular weight in many cases. Proper trapping to prevent backstreaming of the pump fluid is a crucial matter which, together with proper outgassing of system walls and contents, determines the ultimate pressure which can be reached. Systems have been constructed for ultimate pressures in the 10^{-12} Torr range with mercury diffusion pumps[7,8] and in the 10^{-11} Torr range with oil diffusion pumps.[9,10]

In many cases, base pressures in the 10^{-10} Torr range are adequate, and rather simple trapping procedures are possible. One liquid nitrogen–cooled trap is adequate with a mercury pump. The advantages of mercury as a pump fluid in comparison with oil are the following: (1) it is stable and relatively inert, and not easily damaged by sudden exposure to air; (2) all traces of mercury can be removed from a vacuum system by baking out into a liquid nitrogen–cooled trap; (3) the backing pressure is not critical, which means that the backing pump can be turned off for long periods when the gas throughput is small. This feature has been utilized in one mercury system in which the forepressure reservoir is exhausted by a cryosorption pump as required, thus eliminating the rotary oil forepump.[11] Moreover, it has been found that the

[7] A. Venema and M. Bandringa, *Philips Tech. Rev.* 20, 145 (1958).

[8] W. Kreisman, Report No. 64-8-N (Contract No. NASw-705). Geophys. Corp. of America, Bedford, Massachusetts, 1964.

[9] M. H. Hablanian and P. L. Vitkus, *Trans. Natl. Vacuum Symp.* 10, 140 (1963).

[10] I. Farkass, P. R. Gould, and G. W. Horn, *Trans. Natl. Vacuum Symp.* 9, 273 (1962).

[11] B. D. Power, N. T. M. Dennis, and L. de Csernatony, *Trans. Natl. Vacuum Symp.* 10, 147 (1963).

interaction of mercury with copper gaskets and valve seats in all-metal systems is not a serious problem. The chief disadvantage of a mercury diffusion pump is the need for continous liquid nitrogen refrigeration. The toxic nature of mercury vapor rarely causes trouble.

Oil diffusion pumps offer the possibility of reaching the UHV range by using nonrefrigerated traps. These employ a molecular sieve,[12,13] copper foil,[14] or porous glass.[15] The latter appears to be nearly as effective as a molecular sieve, without offering the hazard of dust which can come from a sieve, especially when surges of gas occur. Although such traps are adequate for pressures in the 10^{-10} Torr range, they do not entirely prevent the presence of hydrocarbon vapors in the system. Bryant et al.[16] have found that liquid nitrogen cooling of a molecular sieve trap was necessary to reduce some benzene cracking-pattern peaks characteristic of the DC705 oil which they used below the limit of detection (about 10^{-12} Torr). Moreover, when a chilled trap is brought to room temperature or higher, some contamination of the system is inevitable. Experimental results for hydrocarbon contamination depend on the exact design of the pumps, baffle, and trap and upon the exclusion of hydrocarbon sources other than the pump oil. Hablanian[17] has reviewed this subject recently. Holland et al.[18] have studied contamination as a function of the number of baffles and traps and of bakeout procedures. It seems fair to say that, with the proper selection of pump, pump fluid, baffle, and room-temperature or refrigerated trap, the hydrocarbon contamination from an oil diffusion pump will be negligibly small for many experiments. It remains true that if, because of some error in procedure, oil molecules are admitted to the high-vacuum side, they cannot be removed simply by baking. At the bakeout temperature, as well as at the operating temperatures of hot filaments, the oil is cracked, and residues are left. The necessity of cleaning by some method other than baking can be an objectionable feature of the oil pump.

Several improvements made in oil diffusion pumps in recent years are new designs of top jet caps in metal pumps,[19] methods of superheating the oil vapor in the top jets,[20] refinements in vapor jet design,

[12] M. A. Biondi, Rev. Sci. Instr. 30, 831 (1959).

[13] L. A. Harris, Rev. Sci. Instr. 31, 903 (1960).

[14] D. Alpert, Rev. Sci. Instr. 24, 1004 (1953).

[15] F. B. Haller, Rev. Sci. Instr. 35, 1356 (1964).

[16] P. J. Bryant, C. M. Gosselin, and L. H. Taylor, Report No. NASA CR-84. Office of Technical Services, Dept. of Commerce, Washington, D.C., 1964.

[17] M. H. Hablanian, Trans. Natl. Vacuum Symp. 9, 384 (1962).

[18] L. Holland, L. Laurenson, and C. Priestland, Rev. Sci. Instr. 34, 377 (1963).

[19] M. H. Hablanian and A. A. Landfors, Natl. Symp. Vacuum Technol., Trans. 7, 55 (1960).

[20] H. R. Smith, Natl. Symp. Vacuum Technol., Trans. 6, 140 (1959).

and the use of new pump oils. Hickman[21] has described one class of oils with which he obtained pressures of 10^{-10} Torr in a small glass system with a fractionating-type oil pump, without the use of any trap.

5.1.1.1.4. MOLECULAR DRAG PUMP. This mechanical pump has a series of closely spaced stator and rotor plates which move with high relative velocity. The geometry of the grooves in the plates is such that gas molecules colliding with the plates are given momentum changes which result in a preferential gas flow in one direction through the pump. A modern commercial version of this pump can reach an ultimate pressure below·10^{-9} Torr.[22] It has the advantages that no trap is required, there is no limit on the total gas load, and the pump speed for inert gases is not inferior to that for active gases. The compression ratio is much smaller than it is for a diffusion pump, and is only 250 for hydrogen. This means that the backing pressure of lighter gases such as hydrogen must be kept very low if an ultimate pressure in the UHV range is to be reached. One interesting application is the use of the pump to purify hydrogen, which is introduced on the forevacuum side and diffuses through the pump more easily than any contaminants of greater molecular weight.[23] In general, this pump finds more application in the high- than in the ultrahigh-vacuum range.

5.1.1.1.5. SPUTTER-ION-GETTER PUMPS. A gas molecule is said to be gettered by a metal film when a stable chemical compound is formed between the gas and metal atoms, so that the gas is removed from the volume. A chemically active metal may be deposited on the walls of a vacuum vessel by either sputtering or evaporation. Certain gases which form stable chemical compounds with the metal will stick to the wall and thus be pumped, or gettered, from the volume. Although titanium has been used almost exclusively in commercial pumps, there are other metals which are effective getters in the UHV range. Molybdenum, tungsten, tantalum, and zirconium have proven useful. Other metals may prove more effective for certain gases. Properties of various getters are treated in several general references.[1,24]

It has long been known that ionization, dissociation, and excitation of the gas molecules cause an increase in the pumping action, and also cause the pumping of inert gases. There has been an intensive development in recent years of pumps which combine ionization and chemical gettering in some way. One of the most successful developments

[21] K. C. D. Hickman, *Trans. Natl. Vacuum Symp.* **8**, 307 (1961).

[22] W. Becker, *Advances in Vacuum Sci. Technol., Proc. 1st Intern. Congr. Vacuum Tech., Namur, Belg., 1958* **1**, 173 (1960).

[23] E. Apgar, G. Lewin, and D. Mullaney, *Rev. Sci. Instr.* **33**, 985 (1962).

[24] W. H. Kohl, "Materials and Techniques for Electron Tubes." Reinhold, New York, 1960.

has been the sputter-ion-getter pump,[25] which offers an attractive alternative to diffusion pumps for some systems. This pump has been discussed in some detail in the book by Barrington.[26] In this pump, a discharge is initiated by application of a high voltage, preferably when the pressure is in the range from 10^{-2} to 10^{-6} Torr. An applied magnetic field forces the electrons to travel in helical paths, thus increasing the ionization probability, and making it possible to maintain the discharge down to 10^{-12} Torr. In the diode pump, positive ions strike the cathode, made of titanium, and sputter titanium on the anode and walls of the pump. Thus, the chemically active layer of titanium is continuously renewed, and the gas molecules are dissociated, excited, and ionized in the discharge. Different gases are pumped at different speeds, as shown in Table II. The pumping speed for inert gases is relatively low,

TABLE II.   Pumping Speeds of Diode Sputter-Ion Pump for Various
Gases Relative to Speed for Air[a]

Gas	Speed for gas / Speed for air
Hydrogen	2.7
Deuterium	1.9
Water vapor	1.05
Carbon dioxide	1.00
Nitrogen	1.00
Light hydrocarbons	0.9–1.6
Oxygen	0.57
Helium	0.10
Argon	0.01

[a] Courtesy of Varian Associates.

and, if appreciable quantities of inert gas are pumped, there is the difficulty that the pumped gas is frequently liberated in bursts. The inert gas atoms which are pumped are driven as ions to the cathode, where they can be liberated again as the cathode is sputtered. The best solution for this seems to be the triode pump,[27] in which a sputter cathode with an open structure is inserted between the anode and the collector electrode. Ions which strike the sputter cathode do so with maximum energy and at grazing incidence, which are optimum conditions for

[25] L. D. Hall, *Rev. Sci. Instr.* **29**, 367 (1958).
[26] A. E. Barrington, "High Vacuum Engineering." Prentice-Hall, Englewood Cliffs, New Jersey, 1963.
[27] W. M. Brubaker, *Natl. Symp. Vacuum Technol., Trans.* **6**, 302 (1959).

effective sputtering. Ions which pass through the sputter cathode reach the collector electrode at low energy and nearly normal incidence, so that sputtering is not great. The net result is a buildup of titanium on the collector electrode which buries inert gas ions and provides a chemically active surface for the gettering of other gases. By this means, the pumping speed for argon has been increased so that it is 20–30 % of the speed for nitrogen. The diode pump itself has improved characteristics for rare gases if the cathode has a slotted structure.[28] This geometry provides for sputtering at grazing incidence and also provides areas on the cathode which are weakly bombarded so that inert gases can be retained. For a system in which pumping of rare gases is a requirement, the triode design is preferable to the diode. Because the sputtered cathode in a triode is thermally isolated, it is subject more than the diode to overheating and excessive outgassing when the pump is started at pressures near 10^{-2} Torr or when pressure bursts to this range occur. There is hope that these difficulties can be overcome by provision of a power supply with a power output approximately constant at pressures in the range from 10^{-5} to 10^{-3} Torr.[29]

Since getter pumps retain the gas which is pumped, there is no need for a continuous backing pump. The backing pump can be valved off and removed from the system. Thereafter, only electrical power is required for the operation of the sputter-ion pump, which makes it attractive for systems in which a good vacuum must be maintained for long periods. If the electrical power fails, the pressure in the system rises because of outgassing from the pump and the system walls. If there is no external leak, this pressure rise is ordinarily limited to a range such that the pump can start again easily when the power is restored. The pump can be operated in any position and can be moved while it is operating, which is an advantage in some applications. The pump discharge current is a useful measure of the pressure in the pump over the 10^{-4} to 10^{-8} Torr range. In some cases, field emission currents in the pump can be large enough to give misleading pressure indications in the 10^{-8} Torr range.

The fact that the gases which are pumped are retained near the surface of the walls of the pump means that a certain fraction is re-emitted by spontaneous desorption or by sputtering. A limiting pressure is determined by the dynamic equilibrium between pumping and re-emission. Thus, the effective pumping speed is reduced in the UHV region. The

[28] R. L. Jepsen, A. B. Francis, S. L. Rutherford, and B. E. Kietzmann, *Natl. Symp. Vacuum Technol., Trans.* **7**, 45 (1960).

[29] A. R. Hamilton, Paper presented at *11th Natl. Vacuum Symp., Chicago, 1964.*

Note: Abstracts of papers presented at the Eleventh National Vacuum Symposium, Chicago, 1964, have been printed in *J. Vacuum Sci. Technol.* **1**, 72 (1964).

phenomenon of re-emission plays a large role in determining the identity of the residual gases.

Even in the absence of re-emission, the pumping speed of a typical sputter-ion pump decreases at pressures below about 10^{-8} Torr because of a change in the mode of the discharge. Rutherford[30] has shown that a suitable choice of the magnetic field and the cell diameter of the anode can produce a speed vs. pressure curve which is flat over a greater range, at the cost of a reduction in the peak speed.

It is to be expected that a variety of ions, electrons, metastable atoms, and photons may escape from an ion pump into the vacuum system under some conditions. A careful study of such effects has not yet been reported.

The use of a titanium sublimation pump is an effective way of obtaining relatively large pumping speed at lower pressures where the effective speed of a sputter-ion pump is dropping off. Sublimation from a titanium wire wrapped around a heated tungsten filament produces a clean gettering surface for active gases with speeds of the order of 2 liters/sec/cm^2 of wall area at room temperature, and 6 liters/sec/cm^2 at liquid nitrogen temperature.

The life of a sputter-ion pump is limited by the finite amount of titanium in the cathode. Before this limit is reached, the cathodes are punctured because of nonuniform sputtering. Even more likely to limit the life is the flaking of deposits of sputtered titanium and pumped gases on the anode. Approximately 1000 to 5000 hours of operation at 10^{-5} Torr can be expected before such deposits become a problem.[26]

5.1.1.1.6. ORBITRON PUMP. A recent development of some promise is a pump in which the active titanium film is produced by sublimation from a slug of titanium heated by electron bombardment, after the electrons have traveled over a long ionizing path.[31] The long path is achieved by the geometry shown in Fig. 1, without the use of a magnetic field. The electrons from the heated filament are injected into the space between two concentric cylinders, the inner being at a positive potential of some kilovolts and the outer at ground. The center electrode consists of a tungsten rod of small diameter supporting a titanium rod of relatively large diameter. All the electrons eventually reach the anode, but most miss the tungsten rod and travel long paths until they are intercepted by the titanium rod, and heat the titanium to sublimation temperature. Active gases chemically combine with the fresh titanium film, and inert gases are ionized, driven to the cathode, and buried by

[30] S. L. Rutherford, *Trans. Natl. Vacuum Symp.* **10**, 185 (1963).
[31] J. C. Maliakal, P. J. Limon, E. E. Arden, and R. G. Herb, *J. Vacuum Sci. Technol.* **1**, 54 (1964).

fresh titanium. The pump speed for argon is only a few per cent of that for air. The pump can be built in a wide range of sizes.

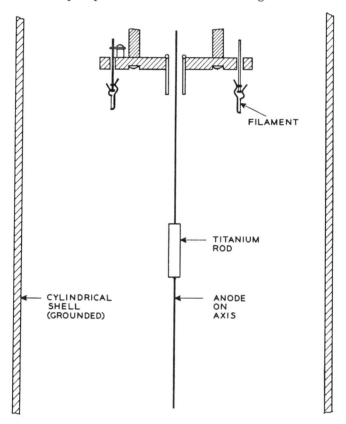

FILAMENT

TITANIUM
ROD

CYLINDRICAL
SHELL
(GROUNDED)

ANODE
ON
AXIS

FIG. 1.   Orbitron pump geometry (from Ref. 31).

5.1.1.1.7. CRYOGENIC PUMPS. It is probable that the lowest pressures thus far attained have been reached by chilling a surface in a vacuum system with liquid helium, after a pressure in the UHV range had been reached with other pumps. Systems are being developed which will utilize cryogenic pumps alone. The engineering problem is to get an area of sufficient size to a suitably low temperature. Molecular sieves provide a large effective area per unit volume. Progress has been made in bonding this sieve material to metal panels,[32] which should make it easier to chill the sieve and maintain it at a low temperature. The phenomenon of cryotrapping,[33] in which a gas which is not condensable

[32] J. R. Pitlor and J. P. Simson, *11th Natl. Vacuum Symp., Chicago, 1964*.
[33] J. Hengevoss and E. A. Trendelenburg, *Trans. Natl. Vacuum Symp.* **10**, 101 (1963).

on a surface at a given temperature is nevertheless trapped on the surface if a different gas which *is* condensable is being deposited simultaneously, can be used to advantage in reaching lower pressures. The attractions of cryopumping are the absence of contamination and the possibility of large pumping speeds even at very low pressures. A simple helium cold finger makes an inexpensive auxiliary pump on a small system. For larger systems, the relatively high cost of liquid helium or of mechanical refrigeration limits the application of cryopumping for UHV to those cases in which the advantages of the method are of particular importance.

5.1.1.2. Materials of Construction. The design of vacuum equipment requires a knowledge of the physical and chemical properties of many materials. Extensive data are given in the books by Kohl[24] and von Ardenne.[6] The book by Roberts and Vanderslice[3] contains a concise tabulation of the properties of most interest. Fabrication techniques, as well as physical properties, are described by Rosebury.[34] Modern glassworking techniques are discussed in the book by Wheeler.[35]

Requirements of low vapor pressure, relative impermeability to gases, and structural rigidity, all maintained over a temperature range from room temperature up to about 400°C, limit the materials useful for vacuum system construction to metals, glasses, and ceramics. For pressures in the ultrahigh-vacuum range, materials such as waxes, greases, brass, soft solder, and glass stopcocks are excluded. Rubber O rings are permissible only if they can be kept cold (-25°C).

5.1.1.2.1. GLASS. Much of the early work in the ultrahigh-vacuum range was done in small laboratory systems constructed mostly of glass, with metal used chiefly for electrical feedthroughs and electrodes. It is more common now to find systems made almost entirely of metal, with glass or ceramics used only for electrical insulation. One reason is that glass is not suitable for large systems of volume more than about 10 liters because of the difficulty in working glass in large sizes and the increased possibility of fracture. Another is that commercial manufacturers have made available a variety of metal-flanged demountable equipment so that one can have a versatile system without the aid of a glassblower. Nevertheless, there are advantages of a glass system which will continue to make such systems of importance for small-scale laboratory work. It is often very helpful to be able to see easily what is going on inside a system. Glass is relatively inert chemically, has a low vapor pressure, and is a good electrical insulator. In cases where it is important to have a glass area at a known electrical potential, it can be

[34] F. Rosebury, "Handbook of Electron Tube and Vacuum Techniques." Addison-Wesley, Reading, Mass., 1965.
[35] E. L. Wheeler, "Scientific Glassblowing." Wiley (Interscience), New York, 1958.

coated with a conducting layer of tin oxide which is still transparent. With readily available glass components, a glassblower can construct a small system at a cost relatively low in comparison with an all-metal system. The difference in the time required has narrowed as metal components have become more readily available.

There are several glasses which satisfy the requirement of withstanding high temperatures under vacuum. Conservative upper limits are 500°C for Corning 7740 (chemical Pyrex), 425°C for Corning 7052 or 7056, 680°C for Corning 1720, and 1000°C for Vycor.

Permeation of gases through glass is often not a negligible factor in the ultrahigh vacuum range. There are wide differences in permeation rates for different glass-gas combinations. The structure of the glass, the size of the gas molecules, and chemical interactions between gas molecules and constituents of the glass are important determining factors. The permeation rate of helium through various glasses is given in Fig. 2. Corning 7740 glass is the most commonly used glass for vacuum system construction, but the permeation of helium can be the chief source of gas at pressures near 10^{-10} Torr. Hobson[36] has constructed a small system of 1720 glass, for which the helium permeation rate is negligibly small. Techniques for working with 1720 glass are discussed by Barbour et al.[37]

Large quantities of gases are evolved when glass is heated, coming both from the surface and from within the volume of the glass. Water vapor is the chief constituent, but others, including carbon dioxide, carbon monoxide, hydrogen, nitrogen, and oxygen, are present in varying amounts. A temperature of several hundred degrees centigrade is required for a reasonably rapid outgassing. Four hours at 400°C for Corning 7740 glass under vacuum is normally an adequate treatment.

The chemical inertness of glass is another property which must be qualified in a number of cases. Two examples may be given: Allen et al.[38] have shown that the boron in Corning 7740 glass by combination with the semiconductor silicon produces a p skin or layer on the surface of the semiconductor; Hickmott[39] has studied the reactions of atomic hydrogen, produced by dissociation of molecular hydrogen at a hot tungsten filament, with the glass walls, and concluded that carbon monoxide, water, and methane were produced. An extensive review and bibliography are given in the book by Holland.[40]

[36] J. P. Hobson, *J. Vacuum Sci. Technol.* 1, 1 (1964).

[37] J. F. Barbour, H. W. Benson, F. M. Collins, and D. J. Jansen, *in* "Sixth Proceedings on the Art of Glassblowing." Am. Sci. Glassblowers' Soc., Wilmington, Delaware, 1961.

[38] F. G. Allen, T. M. Buck, and J. T. Law, *J. Appl. Phys.* 31, 979 (1960).

[39] T. W. Hickmott, *J. Appl. Phys.* 31, 128 (1960).

[40] L. Holland, "The Properties of Glass Surfaces." Wiley, New York, 1964.

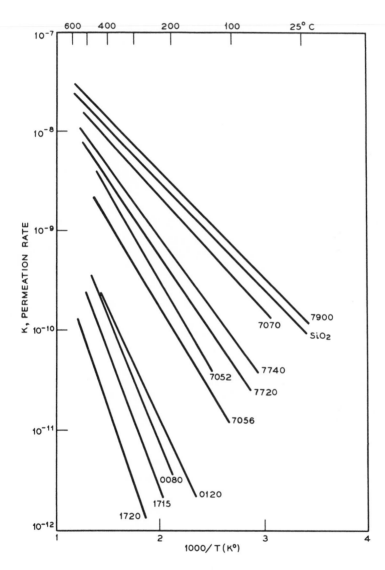

FIG. 2. Permeation rate K of helium through various glasses. Units of K are std cc per cm² per sec per mm wall thickness per 10 Torr pressure difference. Data are from V. O. Altemose, *J. Appl. Phys.* **32**, 1309 (1961).

5.1.1.2.2. CERAMICS. Ceramics are inorganic materials which are given permanent shape and hardness by firing at a high temperature. Of the many materials coming under this definition, only a few have found extensive application in ultrahigh-vacuum work. The most common applications are as insulators for electrical conductors passing through a vacuum chamber wall, or as insulating mechanical supports for electrode assemblies. Desirable characteristics are the ability to withstand higher temperatures than the borosilicate glasses, low electrical loss, chemical inertness even under oxidizing conditions, and good mechanical strength. Machining can be done to close tolerances. Steatite, which in its fired form consists essentially of closely knit crystals of $MgSiO_3$ bonded by a glass high in alkali oxides, is widely used in making electrode structures. Insulators for electrical feedthroughs are often made of ceramics with a high percentage of alumina (Al_2O_3). Sapphire is a single-crystal form of very pure Al_2O_3. It is desirable as a window in a vacuum wall because of its good transmission in the ultraviolet and infrared as well as the visible range.

5.1.1.2.3. METALS. The nonmagnetic austenitic stainless steels of the "300" series are the structural materials most commonly used for chamber walls, flanges, and valve bodies in ultrahigh-vacuum systems. Their chief advantage is good corrosion resistance, and they are satisfactory with regard to other factors such as machinability, ease of joining by welding or brazing, hardness, strength at elevated temperatures, and availability in various shapes and sizes. The permeability of stainless steel for atmospheric gases at temperatures of 600°C and above can be a serious problem, especially if thin-walled sections are used. Gold plating is an effective method of reducing the permeation. For temperatures up to 400°C, however, the permeability of stainless steels for various gases is adequately low. Data on the permeability for various combinations of gas and metal are presented in Fig. 3.

Mild steel is used extensively in vacuum system construction, but is not suitable for ultrahigh-vacuum work, because of poor corrosion properties. Corrosion products can be the source of considerable outgassing. The initial gas content of mild steel is usually greater than for stainless steel because of melting practices.

Aluminum is difficult to join to other metals, and loses strength at elevated temperatures. However, Batzer[41] has described a system made entirely of aluminum, with aluminum foil gaskets which do not require the maintenance of a hard sharp knife edge for a vacuum seal. Base pressures in the 10^{-11} Torr range were achieved.

From the many results in the literature on the outgassing of metals, one

[41] T. H. Batzer and J. F. Ryan, *Trans. Natl. Vacuum Symp.* **10**, 166 (1963).

can conclude that there are no great differences between stainless steel and aluminum in this respect. Batzer[41] has found the outgassing from aluminum alloy to be no higher than that from stainless steel. Dayton[42] has reviewed outgassing data for many materials. There are pitfalls in deducing outgassing rates from experimental observations,[43] and Farkass[44] has given reasons for doubting some of the quantitative results in the literature. Obviously, results in such work depend a great deal on the particular processing history in each case. This will usually be

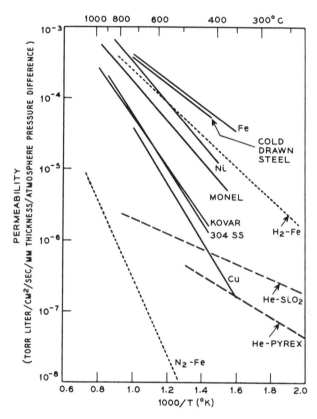

FIG. 3. Permeability of solids for gases. Solid curves are for hydrogen in various metals, from J. K. Gorman and W. R. Nardella, *Vacuum* 12, 19 (1962). Dotted curves are from F. J. Norton, *J. Appl. Phys.* 28, 34 (1957). Dashed curves for helium in silica and Pyrex are from V. O. Altemose, *J. Appl. Phys.* 32, 1309 (1961).

[42] B. B. Dayton, *Natl. Symp. Vacuum Technol., Trans.* 6, 101 (1959); *Trans. Natl. Vacuum Symp.* 8, 42 (1961).

[43] B. D. Power and F. C. Robson, *Trans. Natl. Vacuum Symp.* 8, 1175 (1961).

[44] I. Farkass, L. J. Bonis, and G. W. Horn, *Proc. 7th Ann. Conf. Vacuum Metallurgy, New York, 1963* (1964).

the determining factor in practice, rather than any inherent differences in the metals themselves.

The question of the finish on the metal surfaces has often been considered of major importance for outgassing, and much effort has been put into various methods of producing a very smooth finish on all interior surfaces of stainless steel. There is no doubt that scale from welding or forming should be removed by liquid honing or chemical methods or some combination of these, or by electrolytic polishing, but great efforts to produce an extremely smooth finish are probably not warranted.

The refractory metals tungsten and molybdenum find wide application because of their good strength at high temperatures. Tungsten is used for filaments, grids, and small electrode structures which can be fabricated from sheet. Molybdenum is more machinable and ductile, and thus can be used in a greater variety of sizes and shapes, including screws and nuts. Tantalum is very ductile, and can be obtained as drawn tubing in a greater range of sizes and lengths than tungsten or molybdenum. It must be remembered that tantalum becomes very brittle when it is heated in a hydrogen atmosphere. Rhenium has found some application as a filament material, because it is superior to tungsten in ability to operate in the presence of traces of water vapor and in retaining some degree of ductility at high temperature.

Copper should be used only in the oxygen-free high-conductivity grade (OFHC). It is commonly used as a gasket material on metal systems, and in the Housekeeper seal for metal-to-glass transitions.

Kovar is important for both glass- and ceramic-to-metal seals. It is often used for electrical feedthroughs in glass systems, although its poor electrical conductivity limits the currents which can be passed.

Platinum and gold find some applications as flexible leads inside systems in which motion is required. Platinum is a common thermocouple material, and can be sealed directly to soda lime or lead glass, which makes the only occasion for the use of such glasses in an ultrahigh-vacuum chamber wall. Gold is used as a gasket material, and as a plating on grids to reduce secondary electron emission.

Nickel and some of its alloys such as Nichrome and Monel are widely used for electron tube structures for which operating temperatures are relatively low. Nickel is easy to spot-weld and braze, and to fabricate into various shapes. Nickel itself is magnetic, but there are several alloys in the Nichrome and Monel families which have very low magnetic permeability values.

5.1.1.2.4. JOINING OF DISSIMILAR MATERIALS. The need for insulated electrical leads or windows of certain optical properties makes necessary the joining of metals, glass, and ceramics in various combinations. The joints must be vacuum tight and able to withstand temperature cycling.

The latter requirement means that the thermal expansion coefficients must be well-matched over the temperature range involved, or some provision must be made for flexibility or yield in one member to allow for unequal expansions. Most metal-to-glass seals are made by a bond between the oxide of the metal and the molten glass, under slight pressure. Glasses have been made which are rather well-matched in expansion coefficient to metals commonly used in vacuum systems. Only a few of these are widely used, however. The most common are Corning 7052 or 7056, which match Kovar, an alloy of Fe, Ni, and Co. Kovar is available in a wide range of sizes of tubing and rod. Kovar 7052 seals are reliable, rugged, and relatively easy to make. Kovar is magnetic and is not a good electrical conductor, which are disadvantages for some applications. Molybdenum does not have these disadvantages, and also matches 7052 glass quite well. The difficulty is that the oxidation of the molybdenum cannot be controlled well in air, and the trioxide is volatile at 800°C. The most practical solution is to protect the molybdenum from oxidation by forming a coating of chromium oxide on the surface.[24] The commercial process is called "chromallizing." Ordinary glass-blowing techniques may then be used. The aluminosilicate glasses such as Corning 1720 can also be sealed to molybdenum. Tungsten seals readily to a number of hard glasses, of which Corning 7720 and 3320 are the most commonly used. These glasses in turn may be sealed directly to 7740 Pyrex. The resulting electrical leads are rugged and reliable.

Tubular seals of copper to both hard and soft glasses can be made by the Housekeeper technique, in which the metal to be covered by glass is machined or rolled to a feather edge. The flexibility of the thin metal is sufficient to allow for differences in expansion between glass and metal during temperature cycling. The same technique has been applied successfully in recent years to stainless steel,[45,46] which has the advantages over copper of better corrosion resistance and easier joining to stainless steel by inert gas welding.

As a general rule, glasses form a good bond with ceramics, provided that expansion coefficients are matched. A sapphire-to-glass seal which has proved reliable in diameters up to 1 inch has been described.[47] Silicon discs can be sealed directly to 7740 Pyrex, making a window useful in the infrared range.

The most common ceramic-to-metal seals may be classified as (1) solder seals, (2) diffusion seals made under pressure, (3) sintered metal powder seals, and (4) active alloy seals. The first is suitable for small-

[45] Larson Electronic Glass, Redwood City, California.
[46] S. O. Colgate and E. C. Whitehead, *Rev. Sci. Instr.* **33**, 1122 (1962).
[47] L. S. Nelson and G. P. Spindler, *Rev. Sci. Instr.* **29**, 324 (1958).

scale laboratory work, but the last three require rather elaborate equipment and process control. The metal parts are usually designed so that there is enough flexibility to compensate for differences in expansion coefficients. In a few cases, the solder material itself is ductile enough to flow under stress. An example is AgCl, which melts at 458°C. It will wet glass and precious metals to form leak-free joints, but is decomposed by contact with base metals. Its general properties are summarized by Kohl.[24] Greenblatt[48] has described its use in sealing CaF$_2$ and sapphire to glass. The same technique can be used for other windows with desirable transmission properties, such as LiF. The vacuum properties of AgCl allow the attainment of pressures below 1×10^{-9} Torr.[49] A design for a LiF window on a metal demountable flange is shown in Fig. 4. Indium is another ductile solder with a low vapor pressure, but the allowable bakeout temperature is limited by the 155°C melting point. An example of the use of a solder glass has been given by Anderson,[50] who used a Corning Pyroceram solder glass #7572 to

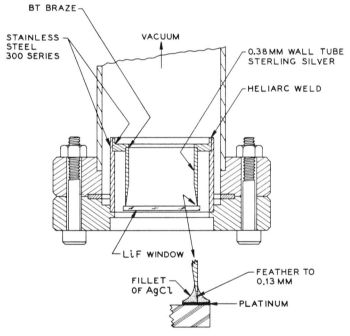

FIG. 4.   A design for sealing a window such as LiF to a silver tube on a metal demountable flange.

[48] M. H. Greenblatt, Rev. Sci. Instr. 29, 738 (1958).

[49] G. Martin, Rev. Sci. Instr. 34, 707 (1963).

[50] J. M. Anderson, Rev. Sci. Instr. 31, 898 (1960).

seal a thin mica window to a titanium flange. This seal was bakeable to 500°C.

Sapphire and quartz windows sealed to metal by a diffusion seal under high pressure[51] are available in a good range of sizes, mounted on metal flanges.[52] The sapphire seal is bakeable to 450°C, and the quartz to about 400°C. Sapphire windows sealed to Kovar rings or tubes by a titanium hydride technique and bakeable to 450°C are available commercially.[53] Some success has been reported in sealing a flat quartz window to a gold metal member by a gold diffusion bond, after the quartz was metallized by molybdenum evaporation.[54]

A good variety of ceramic-to-metal headers on standard flanges with solid electrical leads or with tubes into which any desired wire can be brazed is available commercially. Custom-built units are also readily available. Although ceramics are more rugged than glass, they should not be given unnecessary mechanical abuse. Perhaps the next most common cause of a leak at a ceramic-to-metal seal is oxidation of the metal near the bond area. This can occur as a result of repeated temperature cycling, and can be minimized by use of a nonoxidizing atmosphere or reduced temperatures. It is important to know the maximum bakeout temperature suggested by the manufacturer of a given seal. Kohl suggests that for active alloy seals it is desirable to keep the number of heat cycles to a minimum when temperatures above 300°C are used.

5.1.1.3. System Components.

5.1.1.3.1. Traps. In the design of traps for use with pumps having a working fluid, several considerations in addition to trapping effectiveness are important. These are the sensitivity of the trapping efficiency to coolant level, the conductance of the trap, and the ease of changing the trap temperature when desired. The type of trap most commonly used with a glass mercury diffusion pump is shown in Fig. 5(a). The trapping efficiency is very good, and only one trap is needed for ultimate pressures near 1×10^{-10} Torr. With the Dewar shown in the figure, there is a constant flow of cold nitrogen over the walls of the trap arising from the boil-off of liquid nitrogen. The trap temperature remains quite constant as the liquid nitrogen level falls. In a typical case, a 4-liter Dewar needs refilling only every 48 hours. Thus, the expense and effort in maintaining the liquid nitrogen trap are minor. It is easy to raise the

[51] J. A. Zollman, I. E. Martin, and J. A. Powell, *Natl. Symp. Vacuum Technol., Trans.* **6**, 278 (1959).

[52] RCA, Electronic Components and Devices, Lancaster, Pennsylvania.

[53] Ceramaseal, Inc., New Lebanon Center, New York.

[54] "Metallurgical Research and Development for Ceramic Electron Devices," Sixth Quarterly Report (Contract No. DA 36-039 SC-90903). Eitel-McCullough, Inc., San Carlos, California, 1963.

trap temperature quickly as much as desired to drive off certain trapped gases simply by lowering the Dewar. The low conductance of the trap is a disadvantage, however.

A glass trap with a relatively high conductance and a good trapping efficiency is shown in Fig. 5(b). The temperature of such a trap cannot be cycled rapidly, and some kind of automatic filling device should be used to keep the liquid nitrogen level nearly constant. The consumption of liquid nitrogen is relatively high.

For small systems using glass oil diffusion pumps, the room-temperature traps described by Alpert,[14] Biondi,[12] and Haller[15] are adequate and convenient. They are shown in Figs. 6, 7, and 8. They retain their

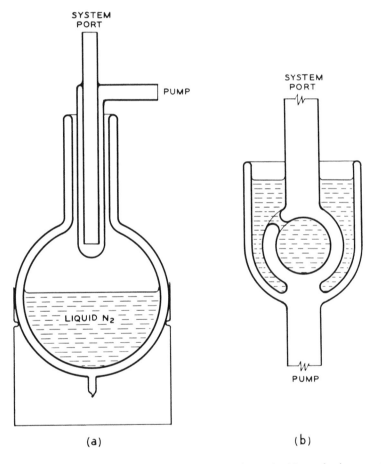

Fig. 5. Two types of glass cold traps. The trap shown in (a) can be immersed in liquid nitrogen, but the trap temperature is then less constant as the liquid nitrogen level changes.

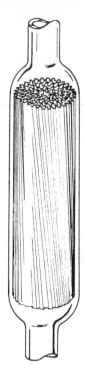

FIG. 6. Copper foil trap (from Ref. 14).

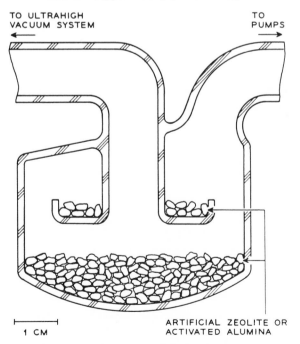

TO ULTRAHIGH
VACUUM SYSTEM
←

TO
PUMPS
→

ARTIFICIAL ZEOLITE OR
ACTIVATED ALUMINA

1 CM

FIG. 7. Molecular sieve trap (from Ref. 12).

trapping efficiency for oil molecules for a month or more, and can be reactivated by a bake-out to several hundred degrees centigrade.

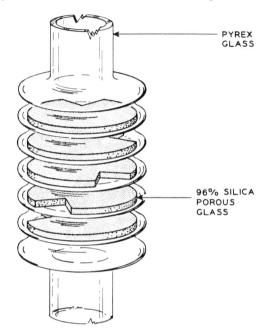

FIG. 8.   Porous glass trap (after Ref. 15).

Many different cold trap designs have been used for metal systems, some of them seriously deficient in trapping efficiency, prevention of oil creepage, and sensitivity to coolant level. A recent design which is a distinct improvement is shown in Fig. 9. There is no warm wall along which oil molecules can creep from the pump to the system. The temperature of the cold surface is not everywhere the same, but it is constant in time for periods of the order of 10 hours. The cold temperature is insensitive to changes in coolant level up or down between the levels A and B shown in Fig. 9.

With metal mercury and oil diffusion pumps, it is desirable to use a baffle directly above the pump port cooled to a temperature such that the pump fluid vapor is condensed, but not frozen, so that drops of fluid can run back to the boiler.

5.1.1.3.2. VALVES. It is often necessary to isolate one or more sections of a system, or to control the flow of gas from one section to another. The requirements that a valve be bakeable, have an adequately high conductance when open, and have a conductance not more than 10^{-14} liter/sec when closed have necessitated the design of entirely new valves for the ultrahigh-vacuum range. Of the many successful designs reported in the literature, common features are a bellows or metal diaphragm seal for the drive mechanism, and a metal-to-metal contact at the valve seat.

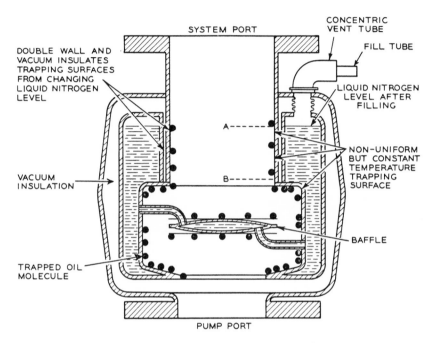

FIG. 9. Metal cold trap. Courtesy, Granville-Phillips Co.

For the control of gas flow, it is important to have smoothly variable control at very small conductances, and yet have an open conductance large enough to permit good evacuation of both sides of the valve during bakeout. These requirements are well met by the Type C valve of the Granville-Phillips Co., which is a development of the valve first discussed by Alpert,[55] and improved by Bills and Allen.[56] This valve has a conductance variable from 1 liter/sec to 10^{-14} liter/sec. The required closing torque varies from an initial value of about 34×10^7 dyne-cm (25 ft lb) to a value near 60×10^7 dyne-cm as the end of the useful life of the valve is approached. The number of closures possible depends on the manner of use, but is typically of the order of 100 or more. It is very important to keep small particles, such as glass chips from the broken tip of a gas bottle, from reaching the seat of the valve.

[55] D. Alpert, *Rev. Sci. Instr.* **22**, 536 (1951).

[56] D. G. Bills and F. G. Allen, *Rev. Sci. Instr.* **26**, 654 (1955).

The same manufacturer supplies a variable leak with precise control from 0.01 liter/sec to 10^{-13} liter/sec, with low torques of the order of 8.5×10^5 dyne-cm. Provision should be made for pumping such a valve from both sides during bakeout.

Valves of much larger conductance are needed in pumping lines. Commercial valves with openings up to 15 cm in diameter and a corresponding conductance of 650 liters/sec are available. Some type of force multiplier in the drive mechanism is used to produce the large closing force needed for a closed conductance less than 10^{-13} liter/sec. The closure at the seat is usually made by forcing a knife edge into a softer confined metal, such as copper. Some valves make use of a plating of a soft metal such as copper or gold to make the seal between a knife edge and a flat seat. Several manufacturers supply valves which can be baked in a closed as well as open position. Such models usually have provision for replacing the sealing gasket at the seat. Improvements in such features can be expected as more experience is gained with various alloys and platings which can be used at the valve seat.

It has been found that a valve in which the closure is made by forcing a smooth tungsten carbide ball against the inside sharp edge of a stainless steel ring can be baked closed at 450°C for three 8-hour periods without showing evidence of forming a solid-state bond at the seal interface.[57] The closing torque stabilized at 9.5×10^7 dyne-cm (7 ft lb) for a 1-inch valve after the first bake, with a closed conductance less than 10^{-13} liter/sec. This valve is available commercially.[58]

A number of valves have been described which employ a knife edge driven into a soft metal such as indium. Such a valve has an almost infinite life, because the seat can be reformed by melting the indium. The vapor pressure of indium is only 10^{-9} Torr at 450°C. The drawbacks are that the valve cannot be baked closed and must be operated in only one position.

Bakeable all-metal valves of very large size (2000–4000 liters/sec open conductance) have been described by Batzer[59] and Parker and Mark.[60] Thorness and Nier[61] have described several modifications of rather simple, small bakeable valves.

A different type of gas inlet "valve" which is useful for certain gases is based on diffusion through a thin wall, with the diffusion rate controlled by the temperature of the wall and the pressure of the gas on the high-pressure side. Diffusion rates fall in a range of practical usefulness for

[57] P. J. Clarke, Paper presented at *11th Natl. Vacuum Symp., Chicago, 1964.*

[58] General Electric Co., Schenectady, New York.

[59] T. H. Batzer, *Natl. Symp. Vacuum Technol., Trans.* **6**, 265 (1959).

[60] W. B. Parker and J. T. Mark, *Natl. Symp. Vacuum Technol., Trans.* **7**, 21 (1960).

[61] R. B. Thorness and A. O. Nier, *Rev. Sci. Instr.* **32**, 807 (1961).

hydrogen through nickel[62] or palladium,[63] oxygen through silver,[64] and helium through fused silica.[65] Compact bakeable units are available commercially[66] which yield a gas of high purity.

5.1.1.3.4. FLANGES AND GASKETS. Static demountable seals employing soft metal gaskets and designed to remain leak-tight over a range of several hundred degrees centigrade have been developed extensively in recent years. Such seals are now essentially just as convenient and reliable as the rubber O ring seals used earlier for high-vacuum work. There are many different designs which work well. Wheeler[67] has reviewed the requirements for reliable sealing, and has emphasized the need of confining the flow of the soft metal as it is deformed. Sealing forces of the order of 3.5×10^8 dynes/cm of seal circumference and sealing pressures of the order of 7×10^9 dynes/cm^2 are required.

Probably the most reliable metal gasket seal is the "corner-gold-wire" seal described by Hickam[68] and Grove,[69] and pictured in Fig. 10. Such flanges are available commercially.[70] The gold does not oxidize through repeated high-temperature cycling. Disadvantages are the relatively high cost which arises from close machining tolerances, and the non-symmetrical flanges. This last feature limits the interchangeability of components.

There are at least four somewhat different commercial designs now available which use flat copper gaskets and symmetrical flanges, and are interchangeable[71] with one another. They are pictured in Fig. 11. These rank highest in regard to convenience in use, and are also very reliable. Oxidation of the copper gasket after repeated high-temperature cycling can cause a leak to develop. In most cases, however, gaskets are replaced in the normal course of operations before oxidation becomes a problem.

Flat polished flange surfaces may be used with gold or aluminum O rings, or with the so-called coined copper gasket.[72] Aluminum gaskets often form a good bond to the flanges when they are baked to 400°C,

[62] E. R. Harrison and L. C. W. Hobbis, *Rev. Sci. Instr.* **26**, 305 (1955).

[63] O. M. Katz and E. A. Gulbransen, *Rev. Sci. Instr.* **31**, 615 (1960).

[64] N. R. Whetten and J. R. Young, *Rev. Sci. Instr.* **30**, 472 (1959).

[65] J. R. Young and N. R. Whetten, *Rev. Sci. Instr.* **32**, 453 (1961).

[66] K-B Glass Apparatus Co., Schenectady, *New York*, and General Electric Co., Schenectady, New York.

[67] W. R. Wheeler, *Trans. Natl. Vacuum Symp.* **10**, 159 (1963).

[68] W. M. Hickam, *Rev. Sci. Instr.* **20**, 291 (1949).

[69] D. J. Grove, *Natl. Symp. Vacuum Technol., Trans.* **5**, 9 (1958).

[70] RCA, Lancaster, Pennsylvania.

[71] C. L. Hall and L. D. Hall, Paper presented at *11th Natl. Vacuum Symp., Chicago, 1964*.

[72] J. Goertz, Jr., *Natl. Symp. Vacuum. Technol. ,Trans.* **7**, 16 (1960).

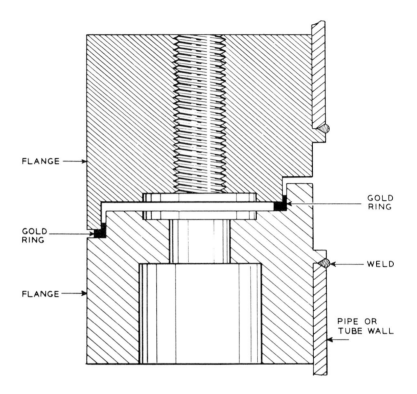

FIG. 10.   Corner-gold-wire seal. Courtesy, RCA.

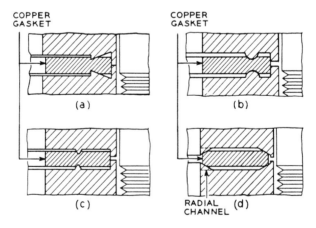

FIG. 11.   Four interchangeable copper gasket seals: (a) ConFlat, ® Varian Associates;
(b) CURVAC, Ultek Corp.; (c) G. E. Co.; (d) Andar Corp.

which is desirable for keeping the seal leak-tight, but which can cause damage to flange surfaces in disassembly. It has been found that an aluminum alloy containing 5 % silicon is resistant to attack from hot mercury vapor present in a diffusion pump.[43] (Copper gaskets have also been used successfully near a mercury pump, with mercury attack limited to the inner edge of the gaskets.[8,16]) These metal O ring gaskets are usually reliable provided that the flanges are thick enough and that there are no radial surface scratches on the flanges.

Two other nonsymmetrical flange seals which have been widely used are the step seal[73] and the conical shear seal.[74] They have been superseded by the symmetrical flange seals which are more convenient and equally reliable.

For the larger diameters, it is not practical to machine flat copper gaskets, and some kind of wire gasket must be used. This may be the corner-gold-wire or the metal O ring seal described above, or the Wheeler[67] seal shown in Fig. 12. The latter has been used in sizes up to 180 cm in diameter. The problem of maintaining the sealing surface free of scratches on a large-diameter flange has led to the use of rubber

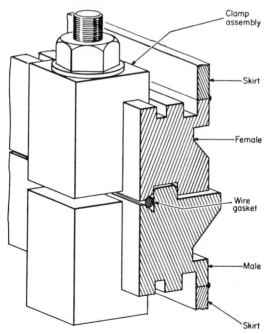

FIG. 12. Wheeler flange. Courtesy Varian Associates.

[73] W. J. Lange and D. Alpert, *Rev. Sci. Instr.* **28**, 726 (1957).
[74] R. Brymner and W. Steckelmacher, *J. Sci. Instr.* **36**, 278 (1959).

gasket seals,[75] for which the rubber is kept at a temperature of $-25°C$ by circulation of Freon in a channel near the gasket, as shown in Fig. 13. Commercial systems using such seals have been built which have attained ultimate pressures in the 10^{-11} Torr range.[76]

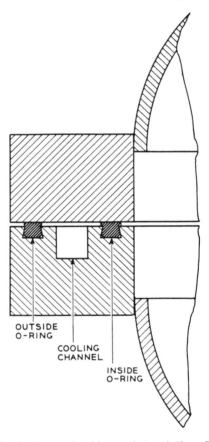

FIG. 13.   Refrigerated rubber gasket seal (from Ref. 75).

5.1.1.3.5. MOTION CONTROLS. It is frequently necessary to produce a translational or rotational displacement within the walls of a vacuum system. This may be done by means of some kind of direct mechanical linkage through the vacuum wall, or by some indirect type of coupling, such as magnetic.

A stainless steel or Monel bellows can be used for translational motion by a simple compression or extension along its own axis. Slow

---

[75] I. Farkass and E. J. Barry, *Natl. Symp. Vacuum Technol., Trans.* **7**, 35 (1960).

[76] Ilikon Corporation, Natick, Massachusetts.

rotational motion can also be achieved by using a bellows. An example of a suitable coupling to produce rotations about different axes is shown in Fig. 14. For high-speed rotation, liquid metal seals about a rotating metal shaft have been used successfully. The eutectic alloy of gallium, indium, and tin has a melting point of 10.7°C and a vapor pressure less than 10^{-8} Torr at 500°C. It readily wets a wide variety of materials. Milleron[77] has described a bakeable rotary seal using this alloy to fill a 0.013-cm gap between the rotating shaft and the vacuum wall. Differential pumping must maintain a rough vacuum on the outside of such a liquid seal. Brueschke[78] has described a seal using mercury, which allowed speeds up to several thousand revolutions per minute at a system pressure near 5×10^{-9} Torr. A liquid nitrogen trap was required for the mercury vapor.

The use of magnets to control motion through a vacuum wall has long been known, and requires no special designs for the UHV range. In glass systems, it has been found that a Kovar piece coated with glass is less subject to breakage than an iron piece enclosed in a glass tube. Permanent magnet materials are available which may be used inside the vacuum system and which retain their magnetism at temperatures as high as 400°C. High-speed rotary motion can be achieved with a rotatable magnet outside the vacuum coupled to a magnet or magnetic material inside. A variety of both mechanical and magnetic motions is now available commercially.

It has been shown that small motions such as are needed for slit width control may be obtained by means of a bimetallic element inside the vacuum, with the temperature of the element controlled by an electric heater.[79] The required materials are all compatible with ultrahigh-vacuum requirements.

5.1.1.3.6. BEARING MATERIALS AND LUBRICATION. It is a common experience that mechanisms which operate smoothly in room air often stick or jam after bakeout in an ultrahigh-vacuum system. The explanation is that increased adhesion or even cold welding of bearing surfaces has resulted from the cleaning of the surfaces by vacuum processing. One good rule is to allow only dissimilar materials to come into contact with each other. Combinations which have been used successfully are tungsten carbide on stainless steel or on molybdenum, and diamond or sapphire on hardened steel. Glass on glass or glass on metal can be used for light loads and small velocities. It is not invariably true that similar metals will adhere to each other after bakeout in vacuum.

[77] N. Milleron, *Natl. Symp. Vacuum Technol., Trans.* **4**, 38 (1957).

[78] E. E. Brueschke, *Rev. Sci. Instr.* **32**, 732 (1961).

[79] P. E. McElligott, R. W. Roberts, and J. O. Fielding, *J. Vacuum Sci. Technol.* **1**, 24 (1964).

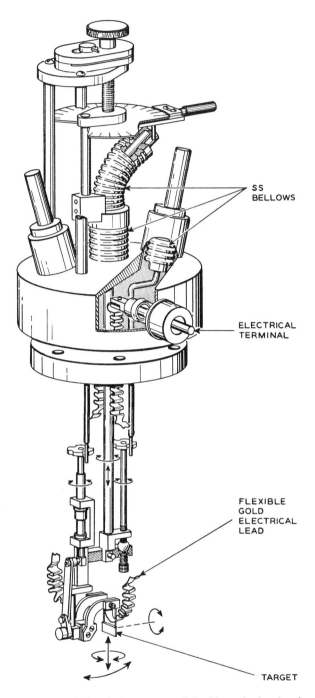

SS
BELLOWS

ELECTRICAL
TERMINAL

FLEXIBLE
GOLD
ELECTRICAL
LEAD

TARGET

FIG. 14.   Mechanical and electrical vacuum wall feedthrough showing four different motions for the sample. Courtesy, R. L. Youngs and A. U. Mac Rae.

Bryant *et al.*[16] found no increase in adhesion or cold welding when 301 stainless steel and aluminum and titanium alloys were baked at 350°C for 100 hours. They attributed this to the existence of stable metal oxide surfaces on the samples.

In most cases of low-speed motion, dry bearings can be used successfully. For cases in which some lubrication is required, a dry film of molybdenum or tungsten disulfide is permissible and effective. A number of workers have used this in ultrahigh-vacuum systems and have found no deleterious effects. Another application is its use on threads of screws which must occasionally be removed, as for the replacement of a filament. MoS_2 is available with various binders for brush or spray application. It is a wise precaution to bake out coated samples in a separate vacuum system. This eliminates any undesirable volatiles, and leaves a lubricating film.

Lubrication difficulties increase as greater speeds and longer periods of operation are required. Much effort is currently being devoted to the search for new lubrication methods suitable for vacuum use because of the applications in space exploration.

5.1.1.4. Bakeout Requirements and Procedures. It has often been stated that an ultrahigh-vacuum system should withstand bakeout to a temperature near 450°C. This particular temperature was undoubtedly selected because it is near the maximum safe temperature for some commonly used borosilicate glasses under vacuum. It is quite true that a high bakeout temperature is desirable for rapid outgassing of the walls and contents of a system. Moreover, every part of a system, including filament and electrodes, should be operated during bake-out at a temperature at least as high as any used subsequently. For small glass systems, it is ordinarily so easy to reach a temperature near 450°C that this should be done as a matter of course. A bakeout period of 4 to 6 hours at 450°C normally allows the attainment of a pressure in the low 10^{-10} Torr range within 12 hours from the start of pump-down. In the past, some workers have recommended a prescribed schedule of temperature reduction after bake-out, but a rapid cool-down is the simplest, and is quite satisfactory. There are occasions, however, when some special factor limits the temperature which may be used. An example is a small leak which has been repaired by application of a sealing compound which will not withstand temperatures above 200°C. Or, it may be desirable to incorporate some component, such as a window with particular optical properties, which will not withstand a high temperature. Such a system can be brought into the 10^{-10} Torr range even though the bakeout temperature does not exceed 200°C. The processing time will probably be several days instead of half a day. In such a case, it is particularly rewarding to maintain cleanliness of walls and components, and to prefire in a vacuum as many components as possible.

If a system has once been brought to the ultrahigh-vacuum range and is then returned to atmospheric pressure, the processing time required for subsequent attainment of ultrahigh-vacuum does depend strongly on the method used to admit air. It is definitely worthwhile to bring a system to atmospheric pressure by admission of dry nitrogen, rather than room air.

With the advent of large metal systems, there have been more reasons to examine the temperature required for bakeout. The heat power requirements go up rapidly with the maximum temperature, and oven design becomes difficult. Also, because of the large heat capacity in the metal of a typical system, it is difficult to change the temperature rapidly. Many workers report success in reaching the UHV range by using bakeout temperatures of 250°C or less.[80] Obvious aids are longer bake periods or refrigeration of large surface areas, as in a space simulation chamber, to reduce the outgassing from such surfaces. Farkass et al.[44] reports achieving pressures of 1×10^{-11} Torr in a 560-liter volume with a maximum bakeout temperature of 200°C. Subsequent evacuation to the same pressure is possible even without additional bakeout, after about 30 hours of pumping, as long as no new contaminating source is introduced. Brownell et al.[81] report that a 6-hour bakeout at 125°C is sufficient for an ultimate pressure of 5×10^{-10} Torr in a stainless steel system with a sputter-ion pump. Obviously, the results in a specific system will depend strongly on the nature of system components and the processing given them before evacuation.

It is advantageous to design the external electrical wiring and connections so that filaments and electrodes can be outgassed while the system is at bakeout temperature. Teflon insulation is satisfactory for temperatures up to 350°C, and Fiberglas sleeving is available for use up to 450°C. Some manufacturers of sputter-ion pumps now furnish high-voltage cables suitable for temperatures up to 250°C, so that the ion pump can be operated while it is still hot after a bakeout.

5.1.2. Pressure Measurement

5.1.2.1. Total Pressure Gages. This section will be limited to a discussion of gages which can be baked, and thus can be attached directly to an ultrahigh-vacuum system without intermediate traps. A more general discussion of all types of gages may be found in the book by Leck[82] or in the general references works mentioned earlier.[1,2]

[80] J. R. Young and F. P. Hession, J. Vacuum Sci. Technol. 1, 65 (1964).

[81] R. B. Brownell, W. D. McLennan, R. L. Ramey, and E. J. White, Rev. Sci. Instr. 35, 1147 (1964).

[82] J. H. Leck, "Pressure Measurement in Vacuum Systems," 2nd ed. Chapman & Hall, London, 1964.

For pressures in the ultrahigh-vacuum range, the only gages which have adequate sensitivity depend on ionization of the gas by a stream of electrons. Under circumstances in which the positive ion production is proportional to the gas density, the measured ion current is directly correlated with the pressure at a given gas temperature. Although these gages are relatively simple to operate, and are quite useful in giving a qualitative measure of pressure changes in a system, it must be remembered that it is difficult to achieve good accuracy in pressure measurement. The operation of the gage usually changes the pressure which is to be measured, often by large amounts. Moreover, it may be of little use to know the total pressure accurately if one does not know which gases are present. A partial pressure gage can be used to identify the gases, but, again, the gage itself may be the source of some or all of the observed gases, especially at very low pressures.

5.1.2.1.1. HOT-FILAMENT IONIZATION GAGES. The triode ion gages in use for the 35 years before 1950 were not capable of indicating a pressure below 10^{-8} Torr. The electrode geometry which was used is shown in Fig. 15(a). Electrons emitted from the hot filament at the center of the structure were drawn towards the grid by an accelerating potential of about 150 volts and were eventually collected at the grid. Many of the electrons passed through the open grid structure once or more before collection, and some produced positive ions in the space between

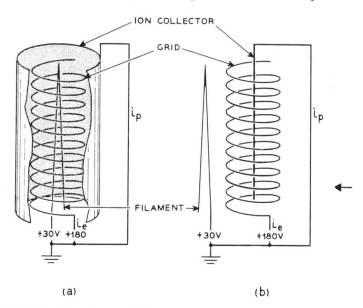

FIG. 15. Triode hot-filament ionization gage geometry: (a) early form; (b) Bayard–Alpert inverted structure.

the grid and the outer cylindrical electrode. These positive ions were collected at the outer electrode, which was held at about -25 volts with respect to the cathode. Such a gage was useful in the range from 10^{-3} to 10^{-8} Torr. The lower limit was determined by a current to the ion collector which was independent of the gas density. This current was a flow of photoelectrons from the ion collector, and was indistinguishable from a flow of positive ions to the collector. The photoelectrons were ejected by low-energy X-rays coming from the grid, produced when electrons from the hot filament struck the grid.

The Bayard–Alpert gage[83] was designed to minimize this photo-current by reducing the area of the ion collector. The geometry shown in Fig. 15(b) is inverted from that of Fig. 15(a), in that the filament is outside the grid, and the ion collector is a thin wire at the center of the grid. Most of the positive ions formed inside the grid are collected at this thin wire, but most of the X-rays coming from the grid miss the ion collector simply because it is so small in area. By this means, the X-ray photocurrent was reduced by a factor of more than 100, and pressure measurements down to 10^{-10} Torr could be made with some accuracy. There is one other important advantage of the inverted structure. Because of the logarithmic potential distribution between the grid and the ion collector, the ionizing electrons retain most of their energy as they pass through the grid volume, except for a small region near the wire in which they fall below an efficient ionizing energy. Thus, about 99 % of the volume within the grid is available for efficient ionization. In the structure of Fig. 15(a), with a potential gradient approximately a constant between the grid and the outer cylinder, the electrons are decelerated to energies inefficient for ionization over an appreciable part of the volume between the grid and the collector.

In commercial versions of the two types of gages, the gage sensitivities are approximately the same, of the order of 20 Torr^{-1} for nitrogen. The sensitivity S is defined by the relation $i_p = Si_eP$, where i_p is the positive ion current, i_e is the electron current to the grid, and P is the pressure.

Three somewhat different versions of the Bayard–Alpert gage are shown in Fig. 16. In the first, the grid is a self-supporting spiral with open ends. The sensitivity of this gage is reduced because an appreciable number of the positive ions can escape from the open ends of the grid volume before striking the ion collector. The grid can be outgassed by passing a current through it, but the outgassing temperature is limited to that at which the grid starts to sag. Moreover, the ion collector wire can be outgassed only by heat radiation from the grid, which does not

[83] R. T. Bayard and D. Alpert, *Rev. Sci. Instr.* 21, 572 (1950).

produce a sufficiently high temperature. For these reasons, this particular design is not recommended for pressures below 10^{-9} Torr. The gage shown in Fig. 16(b) has closed ends on the grid, which increases the gage sensitivity. Both the grid and the ion collector can be heated by electron bombardment. The bulb shape and size were chosen to minimize the heating of the glass during outgassing of the gage. Another design[84]

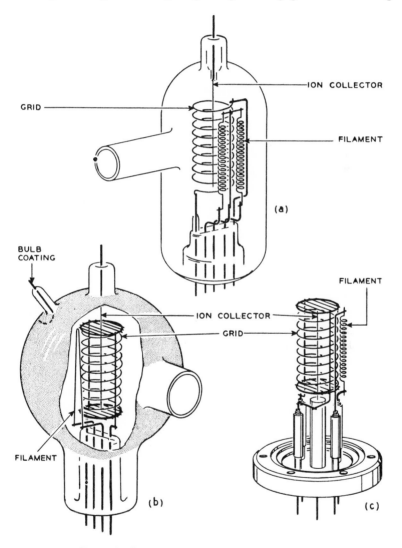

FIG. 16.   Three versions of Bayard–Alpert gage.

[84] W. B. Nottingham, *Natl. Symp. Vacuum Technol., Trans.* 1, 76 (1954).

employs an additional cylindrical grid outside the filament which shields the gage from static charges on the glass walls. With this screen grid at a negative potential, the average electron path length can be increased, thus increasing the gage sensitivity slightly. There is the complication of having to outgas the additional grid. Another way of controlling the static charges on the glass walls is to use a conductive coating on the bulb which can be held at a fixed potential. Except for very careful measurements at low pressures, the extra grid or conductive coating is not essential. Figure 16(c) shows a gage mounted entirely on one flange, so that the gage structure can be placed directly in the space where the pressure is to be measured.

X-ray effects become important in a standard Bayard–Alpert gage at pressures near 10^{-10} Torr. Van Oostrom[85] has described a gage with a collector diameter of only $4\,\mu$ for which he measured an X-ray limit of about 2×10^{-11} Torr. It is necessary to increase the potential between the grid and the ion collector in order to avoid a loss in gage sensitivity as the collector diameter is made smaller. The assembly of this gage is more complicated because the collector is not self-supporting. Schuetze and Stork[86] have concluded that it is possible to reduce the X-ray limit by using a small-diameter wire which is shortened enough to be self-supporting, and increasing the negative collector potential enough to maintain the gage sensitivity.

Another approach to the problem of reducing or eliminating the X-ray photocurrent is the use of one or more extra electrodes to suppress the photoelectron current by driving the electrons back to the collector. The design by Schuemann[87] is the most practical thus far devised, and is shown in Fig. 17. The geometry for the cathode, grid, and ionization region is similar to that in a standard gage. The filament and the shield electrode are at ground potential, the grid at $+150$ volts, the collector plate at -22.5 volts, and the suppressor ring at about -300 volts. The grid and the shield form an electrostatic lens which accelerates the ions to the collector. The shield prevents X-rays from the grid from reaching the suppressor, and also shields the ion drift and collector regions from variations in wall potential. The ion collection efficiency is good, and the gage sensitivity is comparable to that of a standard Bayard–Alpert gage. The suppressor bias voltage may be increased from zero until the photoelectron current has been eliminated, and only the desired positive ion current remains. Thus, the two major components of the collector current may be measured independently. The

[85] A. van Oostrom, *Trans. Natl. Vacuum Symp.* **8**, 443 (1961).

[86] H. J. Schuetze and F. Stork, *Trans. Natl. Vacuum. Symp.* **9**, 431 (1962).

[87] W. C. Schuemann, *Rev. Sci. Instr.* **34**, 700 (1963).

gage has been used to measure pressures as low as 2×10^{-12} Torr, and should ultimately be limited only by electrical current measurement capability. A commercial model is available.[88]

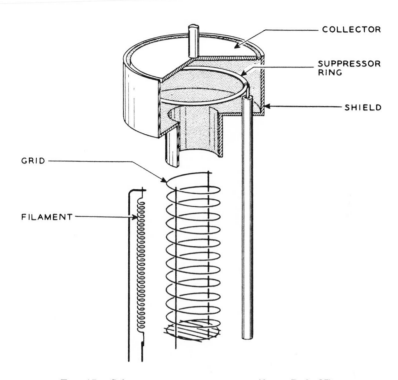

COLLECTOR

SUPPRESSOR RING

SHIELD

GRID

FILAMENT

FIG. 17.   Schuemann suppressor gage (from Ref. 87).

Another method of distinguishing between true ion current and photoelectron current at low pressures has been proposed by Redhead.[89] In this design, a fourth electrode in the form of a modulator wire is placed inside the cylindrical grid of a standard Bayard–Alpert gauge, parallel to the axial ion collector, but located off center near the grid itself. With the modulator at grid potential, V_g, the gage sensitivity is the same as that of the unmodified gage. When the modulator potential, V_m, is equal to that of the ion collector, V_c, a fraction of the ions is diverted to the modulator wire, but the photoelectron current

[88] RCA, Lancaster, Pennsylvania.
[89] P. A. Redhead, *Rev. Sci. Instr.* 31, 343 (1960).

from the ion collector is changed very little. The ion collector currents for the two cases are given by

$$I_1 = i_+ + i_r \qquad \text{when} \quad V_m = V_g$$
$$I_2 = \alpha i_+ + i_r \qquad \text{when} \quad V_m = V_c,$$

where i_+ is the positive ion current, i_r is the photoelectron current from the ion collector, and α is the modulation factor. α may be found from measurements at higher pressures for which $i_+ \gg i_r$. Then

$$i_+ = (I_1 - I_2)/(1 - \alpha)$$
$$i_r = (I_2 - \alpha I_1)/(1 - \alpha).$$

The positive ion current can be modulated by 30–40 %, while the corresponding change in i_r is an order of magnitude smaller.[36] This is because the escape probability of the photoelectrons from the ion collector depends on the potential gradient near the collector. This gradient is large near the collector, and is relatively independent of the modulator potential. This gage has been used extensively in studies of the factors which can affect residual currents.

A different approach to the problem of residual currents is to minimize their effect by making the ionizing efficiency of the electrons much greater. In addition to allowing measurements at lower pressures, this makes possible the use of smaller electron currents and lower filament temperatures, thus minimizing pumping, effects on gas composition, and heating effects. The electron ionizing efficiency can be increased by increasing the average electron path length. One method for increasing the electron path length involves the orbitron geometry described in Section 5.1.1.1. Mourad et al.[90] have described an orbitron ionization gage, shown in Fig. 18, with electron paths of the order of 2500 cm, and an X-ray photocurrent small enough to permit pressure measurements down to at least 5×10^{-11} Torr. The electrodes may be outgassed by electron bombardment if the central wire is used as an emitter. The achievement of long electron paths without use of a magnetic field is an important advantage of this design.

Lafferty[91] has described an ionization gage in which the average electron trajectory can be made very long by the use of confining electric and magnetic fields. The Lafferty design is shown in Fig. 19. The magnetic field of 250 gauss is 2.5 times the cutoff field for the cylindrical magnetron geometry. Electrode potentials are + 300 volts for the

[90] W. G. Mourad, T. Pauly, and R. G. Herb, Rev. Sci. Instr. 35, 661 (1964).
[91] J. M. Lafferty, J. Appl. Phys. 32, 424 (1961).

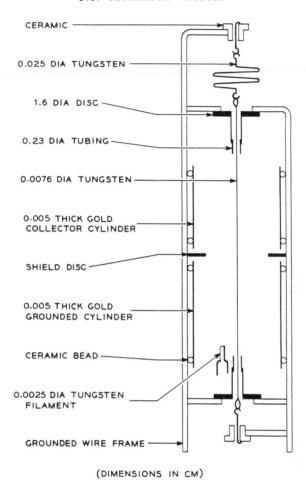

CERAMIC

0.025 DIA TUNGSTEN

1.6 DIA DISC

0.23 DIA TUBING

0.0076 DIA TUNGSTEN

0.005 THICK GOLD
COLLECTOR CYLINDER

SHIELD DISC

0.005 THICK GOLD
GROUNDED CYLINDER

CERAMIC BEAD

0.0025 DIA TUNGSTEN
FILAMENT

GROUNDED WIRE FRAME

(DIMENSIONS IN CM)

FIG. 18. Orbitron ionization gage (from Ref. 90).

anode, -10 volts for the shield, and -45 volts for the ion collector. Very small electron emission currents in the range from 10^{-6} to 10^{-9} amp are used to ensure stable operation. This current cannot be measured directly in normal operation with the magnet in place, and thus the electron emission cannot be directly regulated. At pressures below 10^{-9} Torr, there is little scattering of electrons by gas molecules and the anode current does not depend on pressure. It does depend on electron emission, presumably because of radial velocity components which the electrons acquire by mutual interaction. Thus, the electron emission can be held constant in this region by regulating the anode current. The ion collector current is a linear function of the pressure over the range from 10^{-8}

down to 4×10^{-14} Torr. Lafferty[92] has modified the gage by adding an electrostatic lens to focus the ion current onto the first dynode of an electron multiplier, so that a pressure of 10^{-15} Torr should produce an output current of 10^{-11} amp.

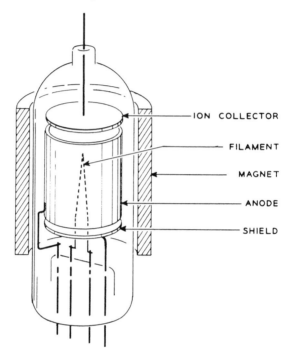

ION COLLECTOR

FILAMENT

MAGNET

ANODE

SHIELD

FIG. 19.   Lafferty hot-filament magnetron gage (from Ref. 91).

5.1.2.1.2. COLD-CATHODE IONIZATION GAGES. The Penning type of ionization gage, which utilizes a cold-cathode discharge in a magnetic field, has been developed for operation in the ultrahigh-vacuum range. This development required the selection of electric and magnetic fields in which the discharge could be maintained down to very low pressures, and the reduction of field emission currents and leakage currents across insulators to sufficiently low levels. Such a gage does not have an X-ray limit, because the electron current which produces the X-rays is proportional to the pressure. It is also free of the undesirable effects associated with a hot filament, including the possibility of filament failure. Some disadvantages of this type of gage are the following: (1) The ion current is not a linear function of pressure except over limited ranges. Therefore, the gage must be calibrated over a wide range of

[92] J. M. Lafferty, *Trans. Natl. Vacuum Symp.* **8**, 460 (1961).

pressure. (2) The pumping speed is rather high and cannot easily be changed. (3) At low pressures, the discharge is difficult to strike unless an auxiliary source of electrons is provided. (4) Oscillations occur in the discharge at all pressures, requiring care to prevent errors in pressure measurement. (5) An external source of heat, such as an oven or an rf heater, is required for adequate outgassing.

A cold-cathode magnetron gage has been described by Redhead,[93] and is shown in Fig. 20. The cylindrical anode is perforated to improve

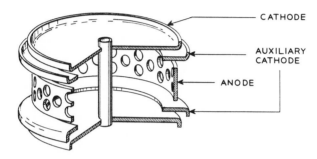

FIG. 20.   Redhead cold-cathode magnetron gage (from Ref. 93).

gas flow through the gage. The ion collector consists of the axial cylinder connected with two end discs. The annular auxiliary cathodes are shaped and polished to reduce field emission from the end discs to a minimum. An anode voltage of 5–6 kv and an axial magnetic field of 1000 gauss are normally used. This gage has a linear relation between ion current and pressure in the range from 10^{-4} to 10^{-10} Torr. It may be used to measure pressures at least as low as 10^{-12} Torr.

An inverted magnetron gage has been described[94] in which the anode is a rod on the axis and the ion collector is a cylinder with partly closed ends. A magnetic field of 2000 gauss is parallel to the axis of the structure, and the anode voltage is 5–6 kv. This gage was calibrated over the range from 10^{-4} to 10^{-12} Torr. The ion current, I, was related to the pressure, p, by the expression $I = bp^n$, where b is a constant and n has a value near 1.10. These gages require a well-stabilized high-voltage supply, and must be shielded from light if pressure measurements below 10^{-10} Torr are to be made.

Two recently developed discharge gages have metal bodies and ceramic-insulated leads so that helium permeation and illumination from the surroundings are excluded. Both use a light-weight magnet which can be supported by the gage itself. The Kreisman[8,95] gage

[93] P. A. Redhead, *Can. J. Phys.* **37**, 1260 (1959).
[94] J. P. Hobson and P. A. Redhead, *Can. J. Phys.* **36**, 271 (1958).
[95] W. S. Kreisman, *Bull. Am. Phys. Soc.* [2] **8**, 143 (1963).

contains a weak radioactive source to ensure positive starting at low pressure, while the triggered discharge gage[96] has a filament which may be heated for an instant to provide a burst of electrons which will initiate the discharge.

5.1.2.1.3. GAGE SENSITIVITY FOR VARIOUS GASES. Tabulations[1,4] of the relative sensitivity of hot-cathode ionization gages for various gases reveal some spread in the values found by different workers. For chemically active gases such as water vapor, hydrogen, and oxygen, observations may depend strongly on such factors as the temperature of the filament, or its carbon content. Vapor pressures of organic materials such as oil pump fluids are quite difficult to measure because of decomposition of the vapor molecules and reactions with gage electrodes which can change the gage sensitivity with time.[1] Nevertheless, it is useful to have a list of approximate values of relative sensitivities. Such a list is given in Table III, based chiefly on the tabulations cited above.[1,4] For precise work, it is necessary to have a gage calibration for each gas under stated operating conditions for the gage. For cold-cathode ionization gages, the same approximate relative values may be used. Reported values usually fall within the spread of values found for hot-cathode gages.[94,96]

TABLE III.   Approximate Relative Sensitivity of Ionization Gages for Various Gases[a]

Gas	Relative sensitivity
He	0.18
Ne	0.25
H_2	0.45
O_2	0.85–1.25
H_2O	0.9
Dry air	0.95
N_2	1.0
CO	1.06
A	1.25
CO_2	1.36
Kr	1.8
Xe	2.7
Hg	3.5

[a] Sensitivity for nitrogen taken as unity.

5.1.2.1.4. PUMPING EFFECTS IN IONIZATION GAGES. From the discussion in Section 5.1.1.1 of ionic and chemical pumping, it is clear that all ionization gages act as pumps to some extent. In early work

[96] J. R. Young and F. P. Hession, *Trans. Natl. Vacuum Symp.* **10**, 234 (1963).

with small glass systems, Alpert[97] reached and maintained pressures near 10^{-10} Torr by utilizing the pumping action of a Bayard–Alpert gage. The atmospheric helium permeating the glass envelope was pumped at a speed of about 10^{-2} liter/sec. In a Bayard–Alpert gage, most of the ion pumping occurs at the envelope. The ion current to the envelope is five to ten times that to the collector. For appreciable pumping of helium, it is necessary to have a film of metal on the glass.[98] Such a film is usually produced by evaporation during outgassing of the grid structure.

The pumping speed for active gases such as N_2, O_2, and H_2 may be appreciably greater because of chemisorption on metal surfaces of the gauge. Hobson[99] measured an initial chemical pumping speed of 2 liters/sec for nitrogen in a Bayard–Alpert gage just after the gage was outgassed. Other workers[100,101] have reported maximum pumping speeds for nitrogen of 0.1 liter/sec or more.

Certain gases are dissociated at a hot filament, and the dissociation products may be chemisorbed or may interact with impurities in the filament to produce new species in the gas phase. It has been shown that pump speeds of the order of 0.1 liter/sec for hydrogen can result from such effects.

The amount of gas which can be pumped by a gage depends on the gas, the ion energy, and the area and material of the pumping surface. As a saturation condition is approached and re-emission becomes increasingly important, the effective pumping speed approaches zero. The time required for this may be quite long, of the order of several months at a pressure of 10^{-9} Torr.

Measurements of the pumping speed of cold-cathode gages yield generally higher values, of the order of 0.1 liter/sec for inert gases, and as high as 2 or 3 liters/sec for O_2 and CO_2.[102,103] Of course, the results depend on the previous treatment of the gage. With a cold-cathode gage, it is not easy to control the pumping speed because the operating parameters must be held within narrow limits. With a hot-filament gage, any effects arising from ionization may be greatly reduced by decreasing the electron emission current to a small value such as 100 μa. Dissociation interactions at the filament can often be eliminated by using a filament which can operate at a lower temperature.

[97] D. Alpert, *J. Appl. Phys.* **24**, 860 (1953).
[98] L. J. Varnerin and J. H. Carmichael, *J. Appl. Phys.* **26**, 782 (1955).
[99] J. P. Hobson, *Vacuum* **11**, 16 (1961).
[100] D. G. Bills and N. P. Carleton, *J. Appl. Phys.* **29**, 692 (1958).
[101] J. R. Young, *J. Appl. Phys.* **27**, 926 (1956).
[102] T. N. Rhodin and L. H. Rovner, *Natl. Symp. Vacuum Technol., Trans.* **7**, 228 (1960).
[103] G. Barnes, J. Gaines, and J. Kees, *Vacuum* **12**, 141 (1962).

5.1.2.1.5. ERRORS IN PRESSURE MEASUREMENT. Possible sources of error in pressure measurement with ionization gages have been discussed by Redhead[104] and Hobson.[105] The most common error is the assumption that the pressure in the gauge is the same as at some other point in the system. This is not true unless the conductance from the gage to the desired point is so large that no significant pressure drop is produced across it by the pumping action or outgassing of the gage.

The gage sensitivity is affected by the bulb potential.[106] This potential is ordinarily determined by secondary emission effects at the glass surface, and may also be affected by high-frequency Barkhausen–Kurtz oscillations occurring in Bayard–Alpert gages[104] which can drive electrons to the glass bulb and make it go more negative. Such variations can be eliminated by putting a conductive coating on the glass wall and holding it at a known potential.

It should be emphasized that the undesired residual current in a hot-filament ionization gage is not a constant in time, and can be changed by appreciable factors in the course of normal usage. The existence of adsorbed gas layers on gage electrodes can change the X-ray production at the grid and the electron yield per ion at the ion collector. Glass decomposition products deposited on filaments may lead to the production of alkali metal ions.[107] When the grid structure is covered by a foreign gas or impurities of some kind, electron bombardment of the grid can release positive ions or neutrals, thus giving a current not related to pressure. It has been observed in some cases that the pressure indicated by a gage apparently drifts up slowly after the electron emission current is reduced from, say, 4 ma to 20 μa.[108] The effect becomes increasingly important at lower pressures. This increase in gauge current is actually not produced by a pressure rise, but rather by electron dissociation and ionization of a gas layer on the grid which is able to form there at very low electron emission currents, but not at higher currents.[109,110] Another striking example is that of oxygen. After oxygen is admitted to a pressure of about 10^{-7} Torr and is again pumped out, the residual current is quite high for an appreciable time thereafter, with a time decay constant varying approximately inversely with the

[104] P. A. Redhead, *Natl. Symp. Vacuum Technol., Trans.* **7**, 108 (1960).

[105] J. P. Hobson and P. A. Redhead, paper presented at *11th Natl. Vacuum Symp., Chicago, 1964.*

[106] G. Carter and J. H. Leck, *Brit. J. Appl. Phys.* **10**, 364 (1959).

[107] D. G. Bills and A. A. Evett, *J. Appl. Phys.* **30**, 564 (1959).

[108] J. W. Ackley, C. F. Lothrop, and W. R. Wheeler, *Trans. Natl. Vacuum Symp.* **9**, 452 (1962).

[109] W. C. Schuemann, J. L. de Segovia, and D. Alpert, *Trans. Natl. Vacuum Symp.* **10**, 223 (1963).

[110] P. A. Redhead, *Vacuum* **13**, 253 (1963).

electron current. With the true pressure in the 10^{-10} Torr range, the gage may indicate a pressure 10 to 100 times larger. This effect is attributed to electron bombardment dissociation of MoO_2 on the grid, yielding a current of O^+ ions. Similar large increases in residual current are observed after water vapor and CO are admitted to a gage and pumped out again. Denison et al.[111] have suggested that impurities such as potassium and sodium from a tungsten filament can deposit on the grid, and there be ionized by electron impact and driven to the ion collector. They ascribe some of the effects observed with oxygen to an increased rate of liberation of impurities from the filament because of chemical etching of the filament in oxygen. These spurious ion currents can be eliminated by keeping the grid clean. The fact that it apparently is not always possible to keep the grid clean at electron emission currents of the order of $10 \mu a$ is one disadvantage in using very low electron emission currents. However, it should be noted that there are cases in which no trouble was experienced in keeping the grid clean at low electron currents.[112]

There are circumstances in which a so-called reverse X-ray photoelectron current can be significant.[113] If the gage envelope potential is the same as the ion collector potential, as is true for a nude gage in a close-fitting metal sleeve, some of the photoelectrons produced at the envelope are able to reach the collector, thus giving a current of sign opposite to that of the "normal" photoelectron current leaving the collector. In a typical case, the X-ray limit of a given nude gage structure can be reduced by a factor of 20 by operating the gage inside a metal sleeve instead of in a truly exposed location. With a glass envelope, the bulb potential is normally close to that of the filament, so that photoelectrons from the walls cannot reach the collector.

In a cold-cathode discharge gage, there are plasma oscillations which cause breaks and instabilities in the gage current vs. pressure characteristic. This difficulty has produced some lack of confidence in the accuracy of these gages at pressures below 10^{-10} Torr. There are reports,[114] however, which state that the Redhead gage characteristic is reproducible down to 10^{-11} Torr, and probably down to 10^{-13} Torr, provided that applied fields are held constant and the gage is clean. Comparison of a Kreisman[95] gage and a Redhead[93] gage on the same

[111] D. R. Denison, H. F. Winters, and E. E. Donaldson, Trans. Natl. Vacuum Symp. 10, 218 (1963).

[112] W. D. Davis, Trans. Natl. Vacuum Symp. 10, 254 (1963).

[113] W. H. Hayward, R. L. Jepsen, and P. A. Redhead, Trans. Natl. Vacuum Symp. 10, 228 (1963).

[114] F. Feakes, F. L. Torney, Jr., and F. J. Brock, Final Report for Contract NASW-625. National Research Corp., Cambridge, Massachusetts, 1964.

system showed good agreement down into the 10^{-12} Torr region.[8] Occasional pressure bursts in one gage increased the reading of the outgassing gage, but did not affect the other gage. Also, after the gage pressure had been increased from the 10^{-12} to the 10^{-10} Torr range by admission of gas, the gage would not read pressures in the 10^{-12} Torr range again without a bakeout of the gage.

5.1.2.1.6. GAGES FOR PRESSURE ABOVE 10^{-4} TORR. There are many occasions when it is desirable to introduce a gas into an ultrahigh-vacuum system to a pressure which is greater than can be measured with a standard Bayard–Alpert gage. Examples are the introduction of a noble gas for sputtering of a surface, or the admission of a gas for gas discharge studies. It is possible to use a standard Bayard–Alpert gage up to a pressure of about 10^{-2} Torr if the grid of the gage has closed ends and if the electron emission current is reduced to 100 μa. Schulz[115] found that the ion current–pressure characteristic is linear under these conditions. At higher pressures, the ion current tends to saturate as the pressure rises. Schulz and Phelps[116] have described gages in which the electron paths are well-defined and insensitive to pressure, all the ions are collected at all pressures, and the sensitivity is relatively small. With such a gauge, a linear ion current vs. pressure characteristic may be obtained over the range from 10^{-5} to 1 Torr. A thoria-coated iridium filament permits operation in active gases such as oxygen at these relatively high pressures.

Thermal conductivity gages have long been used for pressure measurements in the range from 10^{-3} to 1 Torr. Commercial versions of thermocouple and Pirani gages have been developed for which the calibration is unchanged by a high-temperature bakeout. They lack the advantage of a linear characteristic, and they have a limited range, but they also have a negligible effect on gas pressure and composition, in contrast to an ion gage.

For pressures from 0.1 to several hundred Torr, a thin-membrane manometer using a capacity probe to indicate the diaphragm position is very useful. One side of the diaphragm is connected to the ultrahigh-vacuum system, while the other is connected to a source of gas at a variable pressure which can be measured by a manometer. The null position is the capacity reading when both sides are evacuated. An unknown pressure in the vacuum system is determined by introducing a gas on the manometer side until the null reading is restored. The gage may be baked, and the metal diaphragm protects the vacuum side from contamination from the manometer system. Such a gage has been

[115] G. J. Schulz, *J. Appl. Phys.* **28**, 1149 (1957).
[116] G. J. Schulz and A. V. Phelps, *Rev. Sci. Instr.* **28**, 1051 (1957).

described by Alpert *et al*,[117] and commercial versions are available.[118]

5.1.2.2. Partial Pressure Gages. A knowledge of the identity of the various gas species which contribute to the total pressure in a system is often of crucial importance to the correct understanding and interpretation of phenomena under study. At pressures in the ultrahigh-vacuum range, the desorption of molecules from the walls or the interaction of gas molecules with impurity atoms present on walls or electrodes can significantly alter the constitution of the gas phase. Moreover, there may be important variations in residual gas sources and pumping speeds for different processing histories, temperatures, structural materials, and pumping methods.

Various types of mass spectrometers have been developed intensively in recent years, and some progress has been made towards fulfilling the rather exacting requirements for ultrahigh-vacuum use. These may be listed as follows: (1) The sensitivity should be great enough to permit the measurement of partial pressures of 10^{-11} Torr or less. Since the collected ion current in a spectrometer with a hot-filament ionization source seldom exceeds $10^{-4} \times$ (pressure in Torr), a current of 10^{-15} amp must be measured with accuracy and speed for a partial pressure of 10^{-11} Torr. (2) The output signal for a given mass peak should be proportional to the pressure of the corresponding constituent, over a range of six decades in pressure. This condition is satisfied for most instruments for permanent gases at pressures less than 10^{-5} Torr. (3) The resolution should be adequate to allow the measurement of weak signals of one mass in the presence of strong signals of a neighboring mass. Various definitions of resolution are found in the literature. If resolution is defined as the ratio $(M/\Delta M)$, where ΔM is the width of the peak at M measured at half height, a value near 50 is a minimum requirement, and values a factor of ten higher are often needed. (4) It should be possible to view in a short time the entire portion of the mass spectrum which is of interest, so that changes in gas content can be monitored. A scan time of less than 1 second for the whole range is often required. (5) The instrument should be compact and easy to operate. (6) It must withstand bakeout, and the internal electrodes should be capable of thorough outgassing. (7) The cost should be low. At present, the cost of the most suitable instrument is often comparable to the cost of the rest of the system combined. There is little doubt that the high cost has prevented the use of these instruments in experiments where they were sorely needed. Appreciable effort and time are often required for operation of the instrument and interpretation of the spectra. These may be the price of doing a valid experiment.

[117] D. Alpert, C. G. Matland, and A. O. McCoubrey, *Rev. Sci. Instr.* **22**, 370 (1951).

[118] Granville-Phillips Co., Boulder Colorado. MKS Instruments Inc. Burlington, Mass

Most mass spectrometers employ a hot-filament source of electrons which are accelerated to ionize the gas molecules present in the source volume. The ions are accelerated to a given energy and are then separated according to their charge-to-mass ratio by some combination of electric and magnetic fields. This hot-filament source can affect the gas composition by reactions at the hot filament, or by desorption from the electrodes. However, the X-ray limit found in ion gauges is not present, because the ion collector electrode is well-shielded from the source. The phenomenon of electron bombardment ejection of ions from adsorbed gas layers on source electrodes can produce ghost lines in the mass spectrum, because these ions may have an initial energy which is added to the energy imparted by the accelerating electrodes.[105]

Magnetic sector spectrometers have been the most widely used for partial pressure measurement. In such an instrument, the ions of uniform energy travel in a magnetic field which is perpendicular to circular orbits of the ions. The radius of the orbit for a given particle depends on the charge-to-mass ratio of the particle, its energy, and the magnetic field strength. Ordinarily, ions of different charge-to-mass ratio are focused on the ion detector by adjusting the ion energy. It is possible, also, to use an electromagnet and sweep the mass spectrum by varying the magnetic field.

A 180° deflection magnetic sector spectrometer which is quite compact and relatively simple to construct has been described by Goldstone.[119] This spectrometer in a glass envelope can be baked at 450°C, and the entire electrode structure can be outgassed at 1000°C by rf induction heating. The radius of curvature of the ion paths is only 1 cm, in a magnetic field of 3750 gauss from a permanent magnet with a 3-cm pole face diameter. Ion accelerating voltages from a 350-volt supply cover all masses except mass 1. The instrument has a resolution of about 45, and a sensitivity of about 1 Torr^{-1}. With a vibrating reed electrometer able to measure 5×10^{-16} amp and an electron emission current of 25 μa, a partial pressure of 2×10^{-11} Torr can be measured. While the resolution and sensitivity are quite moderate, and there is no possibility of a rapid scan, this partial pressure gauge and its associated electrical equipment are quite simple. A number of commercial spectrometers of similar characteristics are available, some of all metal construction.

Larger spectrometers of greater resolution and sensitivity have been described by Reynolds[120] and Davis and Vanderslice.[121] The former, by using an electron multiplier for the ion detector, was able to measure

[119] L. Goldstone, *Rev. Sci. Instr.* **35**, 1265 (1964).

[120] J. H. Reynolds, *Rev. Sci. Instr.* **27**, 928 (1956).

[121] W. D. Davis and T. A. Vanderslice, *Natl. Symp. Vacuum Technol., Trans.* **7**, 417 (1960).

partial pressures of about 10^{-12} Torr at a total pressure of 5×10^{-10} Torr. The instrument of Davis and Vanderslice employs a 90° sector with a 5-cm radius of curvature, and can resolve adjacent mass peaks up to about mass 140. With an electron multiplier, signals corresponding to a pressure of 10^{-14} Torr can be detected. By using counting techniques, Davis[3] was able to measure a partial pressure of $C^{13}O^{18}$ of 10^{-16} Torr.

The gain in signal resulting from the use of an electron multiplier for the ion detector allows one to decrease the output load resistance to get a short response time. Thus, a fast scan rate may be used, and the mass spectrum can be displayed on an oscilloscope. Sweep rates of 1 msec per atomic mass unit are typical, and rates as high as 1.5 μsec per mass unit have been used successfully.[3]

The omegatron,[122] pulsed-beam time-of-flight analyzer,[123] and various rf mass spectrometers[124] separate the ions of different charge-to-mass ratios by the difference in time required to travel over a given path. Of these, only the omegatron has been widely used for partial pressure measurements. In this instrument, a cylindrical beam of electrons forms a line source of ions on the axis of a volume in which there is a uniform magnetic field parallel to the line source and an rf electric field perpendicular to the source. Ions for which the cyclotron frequency, determined by the quantity $H(e/m)$, is the same as the frequency of the applied rf field are able to gain energy and spiral outwards to reach the ion collector. Ions with other (e/m) values travel in smaller circular paths near the axis of the volume, and cannot reach the detector. The mass spectrum is usually swept by changing the rf frequency.

Alpert and Buritz[125] have described a small, simplified version in a glass envelope, allowing high-temperature outgassing by bakeout and rf heating. In a cubical volume of 2-cm edge, with a magnetic field of 2100 gauss and an rf voltage of 2 volts, a resolution of about 15 was obtained. The rf frequency was swept from 3 Mc to 81 kc to cover the mass range from 1 through 40. The gauge sensitivity was 10 Torr^{-1}, which is comparable to that of a Bayard–Alpert gage. A partial pressure of 10^{-9} Torr could be detected. The characteristics of similar omegatrons have been studied by Dümmler[126] and Zdanuk et al.[127] The adjustments for maximum sensitivity and resolution are rather critical, and very good stability of the rf and magnetic fields is required for reproducible results. Since the geometry of the omegatron makes it difficult to add any

[122] H. Sommer, H. A. Thomas, and J. A. Hipple, *Phys. Rev.* **86**, 697 (1961).

[123] W. C. Wiley and I. H. McLaren, *Rev. Sci. Instr.* **26**, 1150 (1955).

[124] W. H. Bennett, *J. Appl. Phys.* **21**, 143 (1953).

[125] D. Alpert and R. S. Buritz, *J. Appl. Phys.* **25**, 202 (1954).

[126] S. Dümmler, *Vakuum-Tech.* **10**, 131 and 184 (1961).

[127] E. J. Zdanuk, R. Bierig, L. G. Rubin, and S. P. Wolsky, *Vacuum* **10**, 382 (1960).

kind of current multiplier, the lower partial pressure limit capability has been in the 10^{-11} Torr range.

The magnet required for the spectrometers described above can be a serious disadvantage, not only because of the weight and bulk, but because of stray magnetic fields introduced at the experimental apparatus. A mass filter which uses no magnetic field has been described by Paul et al.[128] The quadrupole geometry is shown in Fig. 21. The cylindrical

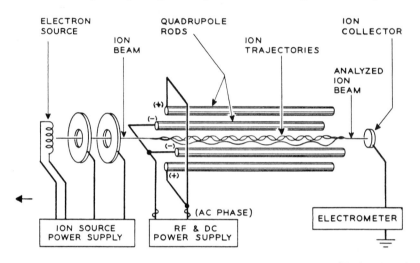

FIG. 21.   Schematic drawing for quadrupole mass spectrometer. (Varian Associates.)

bars are excited with both an rf voltage and a superimposed dc voltage, resulting in a hyperbolic electrical field. Since this field has surfaces between the rods which are always at zero potential, it is possible to produce a part of the field by using only one rod and a 90° V-shaped electrode, which is the so-called monopole geometry.[129] Analysis of the paths of ions injected along the axis of this structure shows that, for specified voltages and rf frequency, ions of only one charge-to-mass ratio have stable orbits and succeed in reaching the ion collector at the far end. Other ions are deflected to the rods. The mass range may be swept by frequency or amplitude modulation of the rf voltage, or by varying both dc and rf voltages. Adequate resolution can be achieved with path lengths of the order of 20 cm. The energies of the injected ions need not be uniform, but may be spread over a rather broad range, typically from 50 to 150 volts. The geometry lends itself easily to the use of open ion sources and current multipliers at the ion collector.

[128] W. Paul, H. P. Reinhard, and U. von Zahn, Z. Physik 152, 143 (1958).
[129] U. von Zahn, Rev. Sci. Instr. 34, 1 (1963).

Hudson[130] has pointed out that the instrument is very flexible in that characteristics can be varied appreciably without making mechanical changes. For example, the resolution may be increased by using a higher frequency or lower ion energy, but the available mass range is thereby decreased. Greater sensitivity can be achieved at the cost of poorer resolution by increasing the ion energy or decreasing the dc/ac voltage ratio. In the monopole spectrometer described by Hudson, the resolution is variable between 40 and 400 by adjustment of the dc/ac ratio. Operation is possible over a mass range from 1 to 300. With an electron multiplier on the ion collector, partial pressures lower than 10^{-13} Torr have been measured, and fast scan rates are possible. At least three commercial versions of this type of instrument have recently become available.

A more limited but very sensitive method of analyzing the gas content of a system at very low pressures has been described by Redhead.[131] It is a refinement of the flash filament technique suggested by Apker[132] and described by Hagstrum[133] and others.[134,135] A tungsten filament is heated at a uniform, relatively slow rate, so that the temperature monotonically increases with time. Pressure transients are observed when temperatures are reached at which chemisorbed gases are driven off from the wire. A correlation of individual pressure peaks with specific gases can be made by using known gases or a mass spectrometer on initial tests. Although the resolution is poor, the sensitivity allows the detection of a partial pressure of 10^{-14} Torr with a 2-minute adsorption time.

A final word should be said about results obtained be various investigators for the residual gas composition in ultrahigh-vacuum systems. Specific results depend on many variable factors such as materials of construction, type of pump used, and processing history. In many cases, the major source of the observed residual gas has been the mass spectrometer itself. A tabulation of results[4] shows that the gases most commonly observed are one or more of a group of seven: H_2, He, CH_4, H_2O, CO, N_2, and CO_2.

5.1.2.3. Gage Effects on Gas Composition. In this section, a brief discussion will be given of the ways in which the operation of a gage or a mass spectrometer may change the composition of the gases in a system. The gage as a source or sink for gas has been adequately discussed. The remedy for the former is an adequate high-temperature

[130] J. B. Hudson, Paper presented at *11th Natl. Vacuum Symp., Chicago, 1964.*

[131] P. A. Redhead, *Natl. Symp. Vacuum Technol., Trans.* 6, 12 (1959).

[132] L. Apker, *Ind. Eng. Chem.* 40, 846 (1948).

[133] H. D. Hagstrum, *Rev. Sci. Instr.* 24, 1122 (1953).

[134] J. A. Becker and C. D. Hartman, *J. Phys. Chem.* 57, 153 (1953).

[135] G. Ehrlich, *J. Phys. Chem.* 60, 1388 (1956).

outgassing of all gage electrodes. The pumping action can be minimized by operating at low electron currents.

There are various interactions by which one gas is converted to another by the operation of a gage. Such interactions are most pronounced when the gas is exposed to an incandescent filament. Gases such as hydrogen, oxygen, water vapor, and some hydrocarbons are dissociated at a hot tungsten filament. The dissociation products are chemically active, and may combine with impurities in the filament or on other metal or glass surfaces to produce new species.

The case of hydrogen has been studied by Hickmott.[39] He found that hydrogen dissociated at a hot tungsten filament operated at temperatures above $1000°K$ in a glass bulb resulted in the production of carbon monoxide, water, and methane. The carbon monoxide pressure increased from the low 10^{-9} to the 10^{-8} Torr range when hydrogen was introduced to a pressure of 1.5×10^{-7} Torr with the tungsten filament at $2000°K$. Becker et al.[136] showed that the production of CO under these circumstances can be greatly reduced by using a filament from which carbon impurities have previously been removed by prolonged heating in oxygen. The conclusion is that the chief source of the carbon must be the impurities in the tungsten filament, while the oxygen and water must come from the glass walls. Water formed at the glass may decompose at the filament to supply the oxygen for combination with carbon impurities. Some CO may be released directly from the glass by the atomic hydrogen. It is known[4] that some CO is usually present on the glass walls of a UHV system, and may be liberated by rubbing one glass surface on another.

The reactions of oxygen at a hot filament have been studied extensively.[102,136-138] CO and CO_2 are formed by interaction of the oxygen with carbon impurities in the filament. Young[138] found similar results for filaments of tungsten, rhenium, and molybdenum. At an oxygen pressure of 10^{-6} Torr and a tungsten filament temperature of $2000°K$, the CO pressure increased from less than 5×10^{-9} Torr to 1.2×10^{-7} Torr and the CO_2 pressure to 6×10^{-8} Torr. Another process occurring at the filament is the pumping of oxygen by the formation of WO_3 which evaporates and deposits on the walls.

It seems fairly certain that the methane which has been observed[39,139] in systems in which hydrogen is present is formed by the interaction of atomic hydrogen with the carbon impurities in various electrodes.

[136] J. A. Becker, E. J. Becker, and R. G. Brandes, *J. Appl. Phys.* **32**, 411 (1961).

[137] J. H. Singleton, Paper presented at *11th Natl. Vacuum Symp., Chicago, 1964.*

[138] J. R. Young, *J. Appl. Phys.* **30**, 1671 (1959).

[139] T. Pauly, R. G. Herb, and R. D. Welton, Paper presented at *11th Natl. Vacuum Symp., Chicago, 1964.*

The carbon impurity content is high enough to account for the observed results.

The chemical reactions at a hot filament which have been described may be reduced by one of three methods.

(1) The temperature of the ion gage filament may be reduced by using a coating with a low work function. Hickmott[39] used a tantalum filament coated with lanthanum boride[140] which gave emission up to 50 μa at 1100°K. This greatly reduced the production of atomic hydrogen at the filament, and led to a reduction of the amount of CO produced in a flow of H_2 by a factor of 17 in comparison with that produced with a hot tungsten filament. Thoria-coated iridium, rhenium, or tungsten[141] are also suitable as low-temperature filaments. An oxide-coated platinum-nickel ribbon filament[142] can give several milliamperes emission at a temperature of 1000°K, and is easily reactivated after exposure to air at room temperature. More work is needed at very low pressures with partial pressure analyzers and gages which can measure residual currents to determine which type of low-temperature filament is most suitable for an ion gauge.

(2) The carbon content of a tungsten wire can be greatly reduced by heating it to a temperature of 2200°K in oxygen at a pressure of 10^{-6} Torr for about 48 hours.[136]

(3) If the hot filament is surrounded by electrodes of metal, such as molybdenum, at which active species such as atomic hydrogen can efficiently recombine, further chemical reactions can be greatly reduced. Hickmott[39] found that the hot filament in his omegatron, which was almost completely surrounded by molybdenum electrodes, caused very little CO production in a H_2 atmosphere in comparison with the hot filament in the ion gage with glass walls.

5.1.3. Ultrahigh-Vacuum Systems

5.1.3.1. Descriptions of Representative Systems. For a worker whose research requires an ultrahigh-vacuum system, it is well to have a basic knowledge of the construction of such systems, whether the system is to be assembled from components or purchased as a custom-built unit. In many respects, of course, the system design is the same as for systems in which higher operating pressures are used. One important difference is the provision for high-temperature outgassing which is required for a UHV system. Compactness of design is very desirable to limit the cost

[140] J. M. Lafferty, *J. Appl. Phys.* **22**, 299 (1951).

[141] O. A. Weinreich and H. Bleecher, *Rev. Sci. Instr.* **23**, 56 (1952).

[142] A modern version of the "combined" oxide-coated filament described by H. D. Arnold, *Phys. Rev.* **16**, 70 (1920).

and weight of the heating equipment. Uniformity of outgassing temperature is also desirable, and may require monitoring of the temperature at many points on large systems. Connecting tubes which pass through an oven wall require special provision for heating to ensure that no one section of the tube remains relatively cold. Any surface which remains appreciably lower in temperature than other parts of the system during bakeout, and which cannot be isolated from the system by a trap or a valve, will in most cases prevent the attainment of ultrahigh vacuum because of residual outgassing.

It is customary to design ovens with sufficient power to reach the desired bakeout temperature in a few hours. The power required to *maintain* this temperature is much less, and a temperature sensor and automatic regulator which will establish an upper limit for the temperature is a wise investment. In cases where one part of the system, such as a trap or a pump, is to be cooled before the rest of the system, separate heaters and controls are required. Bennett[143] has discussed the various factors which enter into oven design.

During a system bakeout, it is important that every filament or electrode in the system be operated at a temperature at least as high as it will be at any subsequent time. Electrodes which are likely sources of gas, such as the grid of an ionization gauge, or electrodes near hot filaments, should be heated to temperatures in the range from 1500 to 2000°C. Electron bombardment heating is the most convenient method. This requires electrical leads and connections which will withstand bakeout temperatures in air. Although it is possible to perform this localized heating when the oven is removed from the system, it is then usually necessary to bake the system again. In glass systems, rf induction heating of electrode structures is often a possibility.

An example of a small glass system is that of Allen and Gobeli,[144] shown in Fig. 22. This has been used for the study of photoemission from surfaces produced by cleavage of single crystals in an ultrahigh vacuum. Successful operation of this system over a period of several years, with frequent changes in the experimental tube, was based on the availability of the services of a skilled glassblower. There are two pump lines coming up through the table top, one for the main experimental tube, and one for a cesium evaporation unit.[145] There is a two-stage glass mercury diffusion pump for each line, backed by a mechanical pump. The trap in each line is of the type shown in Fig. 5(a). The main bakeout oven is suspended from a hoist from the ceiling, and can supply 6 kw of heating power. A small electric oven surrounds each pump line just

[143] A. I. Bennett, Jr., *Vacuum* 3, 43 (1953).

[144] F. G. Allen and G. W. Gobeli, *Phys. Rev.* 127, 150 (1962).

[145] F. G. Allen and G. W. Gobeli, *Rev. Sci. Instr.* 34, 184 (1963).

FIG. 22(a). Photograph of small glass mercury diffusion-pumped system.

beneath the table top, and the traps are baked by substituting another oven for each Dewar. A typical bakeout cycle is as follows. After the pressure has been reduced to 1×10^{-6} Torr or less, the system above the table top is brought up to $425°C$ over a period of 2 hours. The traps are then raised to the same temperature. After an additional 3 hours, the traps are chilled with liquid nitrogen. The gage grids and all filaments are thoroughly outgassed by electron bombardment and ohmic heating, respectively. The pressure is now in the 10^{-6} Torr range.

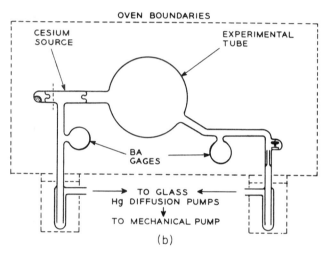

FIG. 22(b). Schematic drawing for system shown in Fig. 22(a).

The Dewars are lowered from the traps for 1- to 2-minute intervals, during which the pressure rises as gas which is weakly bound in the traps is released. Upon subsequent recooling of the traps, the pressure is observed to be lower. This process of degassing the traps is repeated at intervals until no pressure rise is observed in the 10^{-6} Torr range when a trap is warmed for 2 minutes. At this time, approximately 6 hours after the start of the bakeout, the oven is turned off and raised quickly to provide a rapid rate of cooling. No forced draft cooling is used. Within 1 hour, the pressure has fallen below 1×10^{-8} Torr, and reaches 2×10^{-10} Torr within 12 hours or less. The pressure continues to drop slowly for several days to reach an ultimate of 8×10^{-11} Torr. To maintain this pressure, it is necessary to refill the Dewars for the traps only once every 48 hours.

On the main experimental tube, there are seven arms which contain stainless steel bellows for motions through the vacuum wall. The sample crystal may be cleaved, and the cleaved face may be turned to face a quartz window for ultraviolet radiation, or another electrode for contact potential measurement by the Kelvin method, or a cesium vapor source. When work with one target is completed, a clamp may be loosened, the target pushed off the support and dropped to the bottom of the tube, and a new sample moved from a storage tray in a side arm and clamped into position in the target holder. In this way, a total of twenty-four cleavages on eight different samples have been made without opening the tube to air. The good visibility provided by the glass bulb, coated with SnO, is essential for this variety in manipulations. During such manipulations, the pressure usually rises into the 10^{-9} Torr range, but returns again to the 10^{-10} Torr range within 5 to 10 seconds.

The cesium ampoule is added to the system by glassblowing after the 425°C bakeout. The pressure in the cesium source arm is brought down to the 10^{-10} Torr range again after outgassing of the associated glass tubing by torching. In gas adsorption experiments, this cesium source could be replaced by a tube leading to one or more bakeable metal valves on the table top and gas bottles just beneath the table. In this case, only one pump would be required.

An all-metal station of comparable size has been described by Caldwell,[146] and is shown schematically in Fig. 23. The work chamber

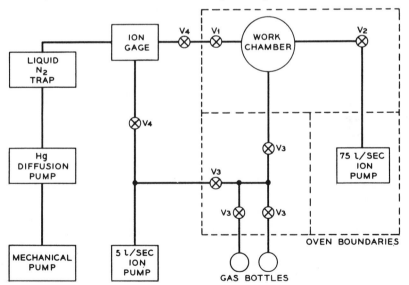

Fig. 23. Schematic drawing of small all-metal ultrahigh-vacuum system with mercury diffusion pump and sputter-ion pump. V_1, V_2, and V_3 are bakeable metal valves with conductances of 32 liters/sec, 118 liters/sec, and 1 liter/sec, respectively. V_4 is a non-bakeable metal valve with a Viton seal and a conductance of 40 liters/sec.

[146] C. W. Caldwell, Jr., Paper presented at *11th Natl. Vacuum Symp.*, *Chicago*, *1964*.

is a low-energy electron diffraction tube, with gun and grid structure, viewing window, sample holder, vacuum gage, evaporator, gas admission line, and pumping line all on demountable metal flanges. The combination of a mercury diffusion pump and a sputter-ion pump is very convenient, since the diffusion pump can be used to handle any large gas loads, while the ion pump can be reserved for convenient maintenance of low pressures over extended time periods. With the valving as shown, the ion pumps need never be exposed to high pressures. The normal procedure for evacuating the system is as follows. The diffusion pump stack alone reduces the pressure to the 10^{-6} Torr range within 30 minutes. All filaments are then outgassed by ohmic heating. Valve V_2 is opened with the 75 liters/sec pump operating, V_1 is closed, and the pressure drops quickly to the 10^{-8} Torr range. The main oven is operated at 300°C for 3 hours, and allowed to cool slowly for 12 hours, yielding a pressure in the 10^{-10} Torr range. With filaments and sample hot, the pressure rises to the mid 10^{-9} Torr range, but gradually decreases over several days to the low 10^{-10} Torr range. This latter period can be shortened considerably by a second bakeout after filaments are outgassed again. If the 75 liters/sec pump should become contaminated, it can be baked out along with the rest of the system, using the diffusion pump for exhaust. With valve V_2, the ion pump may be isolated to any extent desired from the work chamber when gas is admitted to the chamber. The smaller ion pump may be used to evacuate the gas inlet header when the diffusion pump is not operating.

Much larger systems of stainless steel with volumes of 3000 liters or more have been constructed in recent years for space simulation studies. In general, pumps, traps, and valves are scaled up in size along with the volume of the work chamber, and there are no essential differences in procedures because of the large size. For practical reasons, bakeout temperatures are usually limited to 250°C. Heater strips or jackets mounted directly on the metal shell are used in place of ovens. Forced draft air cooling is helpful in reaching low pressures more quickly after a bakeout. Pressures in the 10^{-11} Torr range have been reached in a period of the order of 24–36 hours using either diffusion pumps or a combination of sputter-ion and titanium sublimation pumping. Liquid helium cryopumping has been used to shorten the evacuation time and to produce pressures in the 10^{-12} Torr range in these large systems.

5.1.3.2. Leak Detection. Although the methods used for detecting leaks are much the same for all vacuum systems, a brief review is in order because of the importance of the problem.

If at all possible, each component of a system should be checked as a separate unit with a helium mass spectrometer leak detector. The usual sensitivity of such an instrument allows the detection of a leak of

1×10^{-10} std cc per sec, and it is possible to extend this to about 1×10^{-12} std cc per sec with some commercial instruments. Provision is made on some instruments for the use of other probe gases such as hydrogen, neon, or argon, but helium is usually preferred because it is safe, is present to only 1 part in 200,000 in the atmosphere, and has a high rate of diffusion through leaks because of its small mass.

Once a system has been assembled, it is usually possible to find any leaks with equipment which is normally part of the system. The presence of a leak is ordinarily indicated by a failure to reach or maintain a certain pressure under given conditions. Such a failure may result from other causes, such as the malfunction of a pump or a trap, or outgassing from some component. If various sections of the apparatus can be isolated by closing valves, and the pressure observed as a function of time, it is often possible to determine the nature of the trouble. If there is a hole through the wall, the pressure will increase linearly with time for long periods, because it will approach atmospheric pressure as a limit. If the pressure rise is caused by outgassing, a departure from a linear rise is soon observed, because the pressure limit in this case is the vapor pressure of the contaminant, which is ordinarily much less than 1 atmosphere. During such a test, the pumping action of the gages should be minimized by intermittent operation or the use of low currents.

If a large leak should develop which prevents attaining a pressure low enough for operation of an ionization gage, a Tesla coil may be used to produce a discharge through a glass wall. The color of the discharge is characteristic of the residual gas. If liquids such as alcohol or acetone or a gas such as CO_2 are applied to the leak, there is a marked change in color from the red-violet characteristic of air to a whitish-blue. In an all-metal system, it is frequently possible to insert a length of glass tubing just for this purpose. The connecting line from a diffusion pump to a forepump is an example of an optimum location.

Over the pressure range in which an ionization gage can be operated, the gage itself can be used as a leak detector, because of the differences in its sensitivity for various gases. Helium gas sprayed on a leak through the vacuum wall causes the ion gage reading to go down. Pumps should remain operating during this test. If the ion gage reading is steady before the helium is applied, and if the equilibrium gage current is balanced out with a backing circuit, the sensitivity of this method is comparable to that of a conventional helium mass spectrometer leak detector. Good sensitivity is possible also with liquids such as acetone, which may cause the gage reading to go up as hydrocarbon vapors reach the gage, or down as the hole is temporarily plugged. For very small leaks, it is often difficult to know whether or not the leak remains plugged by the liquid, and further attempts to pinpoint the leak location are hindered. Helium gas usually gives more clear-cut results.

Systems equipped with a sputter-ion pumps also have a built-in leak detector, because the pump has different speeds for different gases, and the equilibrium discharge current changes when a probe gas is applied to a leak. Of the common gases, helium and oxygen produce the greatest change in pump current. The current increases when helium is applied, and decreases when oxygen is applied. With a circuit to balance out the equilibrium current and amplify small changes in current, a sensitivity comparable to that of a helium mass spectrometer-type detector is achieved. Advantages are the absence of a hot filament and refrigerants and the possibility of using the detector at any time during a processing cycle that a steady current can be obtained.

Finally, a partial pressure analyzer can serve as a versatile and sensitive leak detector, which is one more good reason to incorporate such a device into an ultrahigh-vacuum system.

5.2. Methods of Gas Purification*

5.2.1. Introduction

Many experimentalists in atomic physics have encountered problems associated with residual impurities in gases. Chemical and atomic interactions in the gas phase have cross sections as large as those for near-resonant excitation transfer ($\sim 10^{-13}$ to 10^{-16} cm^2) and electron spin exchange (10^{-14} to 10^{-15} cm^2), whereas the processes of interest are often many orders of magnitude smaller in effective cross section. This range often leads to requirements of ultrapure gases (here 1 ppm or less) at least as regards "active" impurities. This level of purity may be maintained by initial careful outgassing of the system, or by continuous purification.

Since there are no general references for gas purification in the literature, it is useful to describe some general methods and to present a few examples of special applications. The impurity limits specified by commercial suppliers are typically several parts in 10^5 for noble gases and several parts in 10^3 for others. Most of the effects utilized for purification fall into the broad categories of mechanical properties, selective adsorption, electrical cleanup, chemical reactions, and gettering techniques.

---

* Chapter 5.2 is by R. M. Mobley.

5.2.2. Mechanical Properties

Included in this category are thermal diffusion, distillation, condensation, and a special technique in which the superfluid property of helium below the lambda point is exploited. Thermal diffusion[1,2] is the most practical laboratory technique presently in use for the separation of isotopes. It can be used in the separation of binary mixtures, but the method is inconvenient.

The complementary processes of condensation and distillation[3] are widely used. Condensable vapors may be removed by cold traps at liquid nitrogen temperatures. Sanderson[4] gives some criteria for the design of effective fractional condensation traps. Fractional distillation is used by manufacturers in the reduction of air, and deuterium-free hydrogen is available by this method. We pass over this broad field except to mention an elegant technique reported by Keulemans[5] for the distillation of uncondensable vapors from CO_2. The method can be adapted for other gases shipped in the liquid phase. The cylinder is purified *in situ* by attaching a pressure column to the gas and liquid outlets. CO_2 and other vapors proceed up the column via the gas outlet by the opening of a needle valve above the column. CO_2 is recondensed

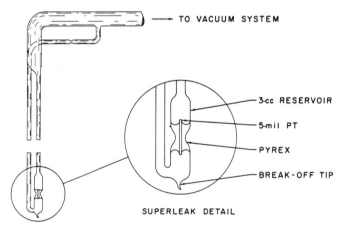

TO VACUUM SYSTEM

3-cc RESERVOIR

5-mil PT

PYREX

BREAK-OFF TIP

SUPERLEAK DETAIL

FIG. 1.   Glass system used to obtain ultrapure helium with a superleak.

[1] R. C. Jones and W. H. Furry, *Rev. Mod. Phys.* **18**, 150 (1946).

[2] K. E. Grew and T. L. Ibbs, "Thermal Diffusion in Gases." Cambridge Univ. Press, London and New York, 1952.

[3] A. B. Burg, *J. Am. Chem. Soc.* **56**, 499–501 (1934).

[4] R. T. Sanderson, "Vacuum Manipulation of Volatile Compounds," pp. 86–93. Wiley, New York, 1948.

[5] A. I. M. Keulemans, "Gas Chromatography," 2nd ed., p. 227. Reinhold, New York, 1959.

in an ice-cooled trap and is returned to the liquid outlet of the cylinder and other vapors escape. The CO_2 loss is a few per cent.

Biondi[6] has reported attaining purities of one part in 10^{10} for helium using a superleak. A detail of his apparatus is shown in Fig. 1. The superleak consists of a 0.125 mm platinum wire sealed in a Pyrex capillary. Superfluid helium is able to penetrate the leak at 0.2 cc/min. In operation, the apparatus is evacuated and degassed via the two lines shown. The lower line is sealed off and the system is immersed in a liquid helium bath which is pumped below the lambda point. The break-off tip is then broken by an attached wire, and liquid He enters the lower chamber, allowing the superfluid component to leak into the 3-cc reservoir.

5.2.3. Selective Adsorption

The process of physical adsorption provides convenient methods of purification at moderate to high pressures. Adsorption is often limited to a monolayer of adsorbate, but this amounts to a considerable amount of gas even for smooth surfaces. The number of molecules in one monolayer in an area of 1 cm² for several gases are listed in Table I. Adsorption has been widely studied.[7,8] There are many different conditions as to the surface characteristics of the adsorbent, the sticking

TABLE I.   Amount of Adsorbed Gas per Monolayer for Various Molecules[a]

Gas	No. of molecules per monolayer per cm²	Equivalent volume at STP (cm³)
H_2	15.22×10^{14}	5.67×10^{-5}
He	24.16×10^{14}	8.99×10^{-5}
Ar	8.54×10^{14}	3.18×10^{-5}
N_2	8.10×10^{14}	3.02×10^{-5}
O_2	8.71×10^{14}	3.24×10^{-5}
CO	8.07×10^{14}	3.00×10^{-5}
CO_2	5.34×10^{14}	1.99×10^{-5}
CH_4	5.23×10^{14}	1.95×10^{-5}
NH_3	4.56×10^{14}	1.70×10^{-5}
H_2O	5.27×10^{14}	1.96×10^{-5}

[a] From Dushman,[7] p. 381.

[6] M. A. Biondi, *Rev. Sci. Instr.* **22**, 535 (1951).

[7] S. Dushman, *in* "Scientific Foundations of Vacuum Technique" (J. M. Lafferty, ed., revised ed.). Wiley, New York, 1962.

[8] A. R. Miller, "The Adsorption of Gases on Solids." Cambridge Univ. Press, London and New York, 1949.

probabilities of the adsorbate, and the density of the adsorbate. The following statements are generally true:

(1) Adsorption is due to van der Waals forces acting between the gas molecule and the lattice atoms.

(2) The vapor and adsorbate reach equilibrium at a given temperature, pressure, and volume of adsorbed gas.

(3) The amount of adsorbed gas is greater at lower temperatures, indicating that energy is released in the process.

(4) Gases with high boiling points are more easily adsorbed than gases with low boiling points.

(5) Physical adsorption is a reversible process with respect to changes in temperature and pressure.

The fact that adsorption is not specific in its action in most cases is a drawback. However, the ability to purify large amounts of gas at high pressures is a great advantage. Almost any solid adsorbs after being properly outgassed. Property (4) allows selective adsorption to be used by passing over the absorbent several times to adsorb the less volatile gases. Materials commonly used include charcoal, silica gels, silicates, and powdered metals.

Activated charcoal has a greatly enhanced effective surface area due to the formation during treatment of micropores (comparable to molecular size) in an amorphous carbon base. The surface area may reach as high as 2500 m^2/gm.[9] With reference to the equivalent volumes per monolayer of Table I, this would allow adsorption of 750 cm^3 of N$_2$ at STP if a monolayer is formed. This saturation value can be approached at liquid air temperatures for adsorption by charcoal as indicated by the data in Table II,[10] in which it was found that 103 cm^3 of N$_2$ was adsorbed per gram. With further reference to Table II, it is seen that liquid air-

TABLE II. Adsorption by Charcoal at Liquid Air Temperatures[a]

Gas	Temp. (°C)	P (mm Hg)	Equiv. vol. (STP) adsorbed per gram (cm^3)
He	−195.5	27.0	0.21
Neon	−195.5	30.5	6.18
N$_2$	−182.5	33.2	103.00
H$_2$	−195.5	20.6	56.00

[a] From Claude via Dushman, reference 7, p. 453.

[9] Dushman, reference 7, p. 437.
[10] G. Claude, Compt. rend. 158, 861 (1914).

cooled charcoal is an effective purifier for neon and helium; and it can also be used to remove neon from helium.

The techniques of gas chromatography[11-13] are useful for the purification of gases, although their most important use is in the analysis of gas mixtures. Separation of gases is accomplished by passing the sample through a column of solid or liquid material with a transport gas. The molecules are adsorbed and subsequently traverse the material, with the various components passing through at well-defined times. Some column materials are alumina, silica gel, charcoal, and certain silicates. The latter include artificially prepared zeolites[14] called molecular sieves. The ones most commonly used are marketed by the Linde Co. and are sodium aluminum silicate (types 4A and 13X) and calcium aluminum silicate (type 5A). These materials apparently occlude only those molecules that correspond to the pore size, and are the only column packing materials that separate O_2 and N_2.[15] It is also found that they are effective in separating argon and O_2.[16]

Some application of gas chromatography to gas purification has been made. Glueckauf and Kitt[17] reported the preparation of pure deuterium using a column of palladium black on asbestos at room temperature. Molecular sieve material has been used at $-183°C$ to purify argon. Jones and Milton[18] used a dehydrated sodium aluminum silicate and found that O_2 and argon were adsorbed in a ratio of 15 to 1. Studies using many different column materials and gas mixtures are reported in the literature.[19]

5.2.4. Electrical Cleanup

In high-vacuum devices, residual gases are often removed by hot-cathode and cold-cathode ion pumping,[20] in which ionized atoms are

---

[11] Keulemans, reference 5.

[12] P. G. Jeffery and P. J. Kipping, "Gas Analysis by Gas Chromatography." MacMillan, New York, 1964.

[13] R. R. W. Scott, ed., "Gas Chromatography." Butterworth, London and Washington, 1960.

[14] R. M. Barrer, *Disc. Faraday Soc.* **7**, 135 (1949).

[15] Jeffery, reference 12, p. 30.

[16] G. S. Vizard and A. Wynne, *Chem. Ind.* No. 6, 196–197 (1959).

[17] E. Glueckauf and G. P. Kitt, *in* "Vapor Phase Chromatography," (D. H. Desty, ed.). Butterworth, London and Washington, D. C. (1957) (Proceedings of the London Symposium on Vapor Phase Chromatography, May/June 1956).

[18] R. A. Jones and R. M. Milton, *Chem. Abst.* **52**, 2474 (1958).

[19] For a large number of references for separation of particular gas mixtures, see "Gas Chromatography Abstracts 1958–1959," C. E. H. Knapman, ed. Butterworth, Washington D. C. and London, 1960.

[20] D. Alpert, Production and measurement of ultrahigh vacuums, *in* "Handbuch der Physik," Vol. XII. Springer, Berlin, 1958.

driven into filaments or other metal elements. In electrical discharges without electrodes inert molecules can be activated[21] by excitation and will then react with the vessel walls. These methods are nonspecific and moreover operate only at low pressure so that they are of limited use for gas purification. The presence of an ionizing beam can enhance gettering action, which will be discussed below.

One electrical method capable of widespread application is catephoretic segregation in a glow discharge.[22] In a glow discharge at 1–20 mm pressure gases are separated by the migration of the more easily ionized gas to the cathode region of the discharge tube. The segregation is caused by the fact that, although all gases are ionized by the electron beam, the ionization is transferred to the more easily ionized gas by charge exchange. The per cent of segregation depends on the initial impurity level, but is quite complete for small concentrations of impurity.

Riesz and Dieke[23] describe a system for the removal of neon from helium. The arrangement is shown in Fig. 2. Neon is found to con-

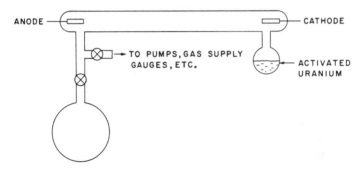

FIG. 2.   Arrangement for catephoretic segregation of noble gas mixtures in a glow discharge.

centrate at the cathode in a time characteristic of the storage bulb size (2 hr.). Spectroscopic observations of the helium and neon lines (at 5047 and 6402 Å, respectively) along the length of the tube indicate that at the anode end the neon concentration is about 10^{-4} of that at the cathode, which is presumably true for the entire storage bulb region. It is further observed that the neon is slowly (several days) removed by ion pumping and activation reaction in the cathode region. The authors also studied Ne–A, A–Kr, and Kr–Xe mixtures with similar results.

[21] G. Carter, *Vacuum* **9**, 190 (1960).
[22] L. B. Loeb, *J. Appl. Phys.* **29**, 1369 (1958).
[23] R. Riesz and G. H. Dieke, *J. Appl. Phys.* **25**, 196 (1954).

5.2.5. Chemical Reactions

This category embodies the full range of chemical laboratory technique and it is impossible to review it effectively here. Moreover, the techniques are used in preparation of the gases and do not usually provide ultrapure (1 ppm) gases. Dehydrating filters are effective to this level. Some manufacturers have complete lines of catalytic conversion purifiers for noble gases and the common hydrocarbon and industrial gases. As an example, Englehard Industries, Inc., specifies less than one part per million impurity for either O_2 or H_2 (if one is willing to allow 0.1 % impurity of the other) in a process converting these gases to water. These devices are particularly useful for purifying large amounts of gas at high pressures.

5.2.6. Use of Getters[24,25]

The requirement of low residual contaminants in filament lamps and vacuum electron devices has led to wide application of gettering techniques.[26] In this method, a solid gettering material, usually a metal, is used to trap and retain gases through absorption into the lattice or chemical reaction. The latter can be separated into chemisorption (bonding with unsaturated surface atoms or with valence bands of the metal) and the formation of true reaction products such as oxides, nitrides, and hydrides. The distinction between physical adsorption and chemisorption, although not always discontinuous, is illustrated by the potential curve in Fig. 3,[27] in which it is seen that irreversibility with respect to changes in temperature and pressure and the presence of an activation energy are the important distinctions. Trapnell[28] has examined the chemisorption properties of some twenty metal films. He found that a definite order of affinity of several gases was common to all metal surfaces (in order of increasing affinity, this was N_2, H_2, CO, C_2H_4, C_2H_2, and O_2). Thus O_2 is chemisorbed by all metals except Au, and N_2 is the least active. The relative affinities for these surface reactions are markedly different from those with the metal in molecular form.

Flash getters, in which a film of the metal is deposited on a surface by vaporization in a vacuum or inert atmosphere, are easy to use and very effective for cleanup of noble gases. This method can be used at room temperatures where chemisorption can take place (the activation energy as shown in Fig. 3 is low) as well as physical adsorption.

[24] Dushman, reference 9.

[25] R. W. Roberts and T. A. Vanderslice, "Ultrahigh Vacuum and its Applications." Prentice-Hall, Englewood Cliffs, New Jersey, 1963.

[26] W. Espe, M. Kroll, and M. P. Wilder, *Electronics* **23**, 80 (1950).

[27] A. B. Huang, *J. Vac. Sci. Tech.* **2**, 6 (1965).

[28] B. M. W. Trapnell, *Proc. Roy. Soc. (London)* **A218**, 566 (1953).

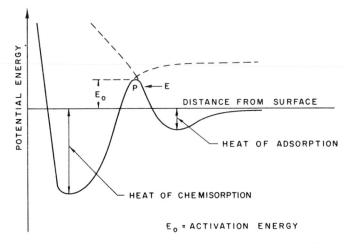

FIG. 3. Potential energy of molecule at a surface illustrating adsorption and chemisorption.

In Fig. 4 is shown a schematic drawing of a convenient system used for purifying argon. The metal-clad barium wire is flashed in a vacuum. Argon is admitted to the experimental system through the gettering vessel at 2 atm pressure and is continuously purified by diffusion to the getter film. If the valve is closed, experimental measurements[29] indicate that the impurity level rises to several parts per thousand in 2 days due to outgassing of metal parts. The open system has run for weeks with no perceptible drift. An estimate of the effectiveness of barium getters was made by Bennett[30] in an experiment requiring

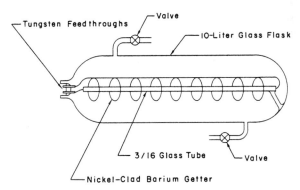

FIG. 4. Glass system for flashing barium getter wire. The wire is led through the glass tube and draped back along the tube.

[29] D. Theriot, Yale University (private communication).
[30] W. R. Bennett, Jr., *Ann. Phys.* **18**, 367 (1962).

ultrapure noble gases. Cels *et al.*[31] have reviewed the properties of modern barium getters.

Wagener and Marth[32] have measured residual pressures evolved above different types of flash getterers in a high-vacuum system. The partial pressures measured with an omegatron are shown in Table III.

TABLE III. Residual Pressures above Flashed Getters in a High-Vacuum System Measured with an Omegatron[a]

			Per cent impurity				
Type of getter	P (mm Hg)	Ar	H_2O	CH_4	CO	He	H_2
Ba (KIC)	6.7×10^{-9}	—	40	30	20	—	10
Ba (nonmagnetic)	5.6×10^{-9}	—	5	55	20	—	20
Ti	6.0×10^{-9}	—	30	50	10	—	10
Ta	1.2×10^{-8}	75	7	10	—	4	4
Mo	4.9×10^{-9}	—	30	25	25	10	10

[a] From Wagener and Marth.[32]

The measurements were made 1 day after close-off from the pumping system and flashing of the getter. They note that methane is relatively inert to any getter (indeed it is often evolved in gettered systems)[33] and that the large amount of argon gas above tantalum is probably due to the use of argon in the manufacture of tantalum.

Bulk getters are commonly used at elevated temperatures to clean large amounts of gas. The dominant mechanism is absorption by solution of the gas in the metal, which requires operating temperatures of 400–1500°C. Noble gases do not dissolve in metals, but can be gettered in ion pumps by ionization and injection into the metal surface.

Common bulk getters used include titanium,[34,35] thorium, tantalum, zirconium, molybdenum,[36] uranium, and calcium. Hafnium has been found to be ineffective.[37]

[31] R. Cels, C. W. Reash, and J. S. Wagener, *in* "Transaction of the Eighth Vacuum Symposium and the Second International Congress" (Luther E. Preuss, ed.), Vol. 1, p. 220. Pergamon Press, Oxford, 1962.

[32] J. S. Wagener and P. T. Marth, *J. Appl. Phys.* **28**, 1027 (1957).

[33] D. Lichtman, *J. Vac. Sci. Tech.* **1**, 23 (1964).

[34] V. L. Stout and M. D. Gibbons, *J. Appl. Phys.* **26**, 1488 (1955).

[35] J. Morrison, *in* "Sixth Symposium on Vacuum Technology, Transactions" (C. R. Meissner, ed.), p. 291. Pergamon Press, Oxford, 1960.

[36] H. E. Farnsworth, R. E. Schlier, T. H. George, and R. M. Burger, *J. Appl. Phys.* **29**, 1150 (1958).

[37] P. della Porta, G. Piziano, S. Origlio, and F. Ricca, see Ref. 31, p. 229.

Following is a description of a system designed to maintain the purity of argon at 50 atm to a few ppm. The argon was circulated continuously over a bed of heated titanium using a magnetically driven piston with a flow rate of 20 liters per hour. Figure 5[38] shows gettering rates obtained

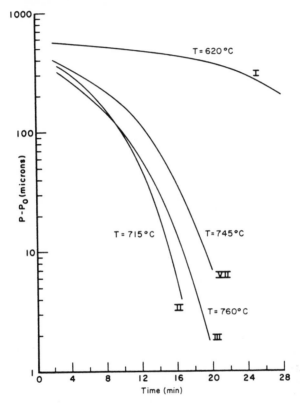

FIG. 5. Data showing dependence of gettering rate on temperature and amount of gas admitted with a system using bulk titanium.

by admitting air at atmospheric pressure into a small chamber connected to the purification system. The numerals indicate the number of times 60 cm³ of air at atmospheric pressure was admitted to the system. The pressure leveled off at values consistent with the fraction of noble gases present in the atmosphere. The dependence of the gettering rate on the temperature and the total amount of air gettered is seen. Subsequent experimental measurement indicated that the 1–4 ppm oxygen impurity present in reagent grade argon was effectively removed.

Palladium is used in a different way for the purification of hydrogen.

[38] W. E. Cleland, Yale University Thesis (1964), unpublished.

Hydrogen is strongly dissolved in heated Pd, and has a high rate of diffusion[39] through the metal, which can thus be used as a filter for hydrogen. Young[40] has shown that hydrogen passed through Pd and a Pd–Ag alloy at 6000°C is pure to a few parts in 10^{10}. He also used this effect to measure the impurity partial pressure in a sample of reagent grade hydrogen simply by letting the hydrogen diffuse out of the sample volume. The method is commonly used to purify large amounts of hydrogen. Other gas-solid systems with usable diffusion rates are tabulated by Jossem.[41]

5.2.7. Analysis of Samples

It is often possible to test the efficacy of a purification system without recourse to analysis of the gas by measuring the effect of adding controlled amounts of impurities. The analysis of ultra pure gases is quite difficult. Some devices are available for measuring specific impurity content to 1 ppm. Flame ionization detectors and nondispersive infrared detectors are used to measure total hydrocarbon content. Oxygen can be monitored to 1 ppm by several devices. The techniques of gas chromatography are especially useful. It is noted that mass spectrometers are limited at this range of impurity level by the background gas.

[39] P. A. Silberg and C. H. Bachman, 1954 Vacuum Symposium Transactions, p. 52. Committee on Vacuum Techniques, Inc., Boston, Massachusetts, 1955.

[40] J. R. Young, *Rev. Sci. Instr.* **34**, 891 (1963).

[41] E. L. Jossem, *Rev. Sci. Instr.* **11**, 164 (1940).

AUTHOR INDEX

Numbers in parentheses are footnote numbers. They are inserted to indicate that the reference to an author's work is cited with a footnote number and his name does not appear on that page.

L

M

SUBJECT INDEX

A

Adiabatic fast passage, in atomic beam, 246
Adsorption, selective
  amount, 320
  characteristics, 321
  materials, 321-322
Alkali beams, 167-168
Analysis of spectra, 90-96
  complex spectra, 92
  Edlén formula, 94
  effect of degree of ionization, 91-92
  use of computer, 94
Angstrom, 50
Annihilation radiation, wavelength, 14
Anomalous magnetic moment
  of electron, 30, 35, 40-41
  of positron, 43
Argon purification, 327
Asymmetry, polarization, 233
Atomic angular momentum, 109-112
Atomic beam detector
  electron ejection, 133, 165-166
  electron multiplier, 168
  photomultiplier, 141, 143
  Stern-Pirani, 164
  surface ionization, 168
Atomic beam resonance, 154-170, 192-198
  apparatus, 154-170
  hyperfine structure measurement
    of H, 163-166
    of He, 166-167
    of other atoms, 167-170
  measurement of atomic g factor, 192-198
Atomic trajectories, 239-240
Auger process, 133
Avogadro's number, 3-4

B

Bakeout procedures, vacuum, 289-290
Basel convention, 233
Bearing materials in vacuum, 287-288
Bohr magneton, 107
Boltzmann equation, 223

Breit-Rabi formula, 115, 119, 196, 236
  corrections, 119
Buffer gas, 172, 182, 186

C

Catalytic conversion gas purifiers, 324
Catephoretic segregation (noble gases), 323
Ceramics, 272
Charge exchange, 252-254
Charge on molecule, 9
Chemisorption, 324
Chronotron, vernier, 221
Collision light, 139, 141, 146-147
Comparators, 93
Compton scattering, 12
Condensation (vapors), 319
Configuration interaction, 109
  core polarization, 109
Cyclotron resonance of electron, 18-22

D

Density matrix, 227-229, 242-245
  diagonalization, 228, 243
Depolarization
  of atoms, of ions, 249-250, 252-253
  of radiation, 146, 176, 179-183
Dirac electron, 23, 31
Dispersion, angular and linear, 66-67
Distillation (gases), 319
Doppler broadening, 61, 121, 123, 183
Double resonance, technique, 176, 181, 188, 206-208

E

Effective magnetic moment of atom, 236
  variation of, 236
Einstein probability coefficients, 215-216
Electric dipole moment, limit
  of Cs atom, 44-46
  of electron
    measurement, by atomic beam, 44-46
    by (g-2) experiment, 43-44